Practical Guide for **Sporting** & **Working dogs**

Dominique GRANDJEAN
Nathalie MOQUET
Sandrine PAWLOWIEZ
Anne-Karen TOURTEBATTE
Franck CACCIANI
Hélène BACQUÉ

UMES
unité de médecine de l'élevage et du sport

ANiWA
PUBLISHING

ROYAL CANIN

WITH SPECIAL THANKS TO

Marie-Pierre Ellie (Ellitrad Translations), for the scope of the work she and her team accomplished, and for her passion toward the subject.

David Kronfeld, for being simply... the best;

Fabrice Ressier, Marina Lepiller, and Vanessa Fuks, for the doctoral theses that were so useful in writing this work;

Henri Lagarde, Jean-Yves Berger, Bernardo Galittelli, Renaud Sergheraert, and many, many others for their trust in the Breeding and Sports Medicine Unit and their constant, open relationship;

Jean-Yves Moraillon, for believing in the Breeding and Sports Medicine Unit even before it came to be;

Jerome Gautier (Canine Center Terres d'Avallon), for his help and kindness, and for his knowledge in the area of canine education;

Rosita, Audrey, and Quentin for their understanding (again!);

Lea, the spunky little sled dog with whom I fell completely in love during a long race.

Dominique Grandjean, DMV, Ph.D. , HDR

Art Director: Guy Rolland
Coordination: Béatrice Fortamps
Project editor (Prepress): Diffomédia / Paris
Illustrations : Agnès Pezon
Cover photo: German Sheperd/Collection Royal Canin

Translation & rewriting & adpatation : Cabinet Ellitrad /Trish Moalla, Julie Plovnick, Isabelle Riener

PREFACE

One person in ten thousand has the innate power to improve the lives of all. This revelation, which was dramatized by Ayn Rand, brings to mind one veterinarian who has improved the lives of tens of thousands of dogs used for hard work and stress—racers, stunters, haulers, herders, hunters, diggers, gunners, guides, guards, sentinels, sniffers, trackers, and rescuers. All of these dogs are likely to benefit from a better understanding of behavior, nutrition, exercise physiology, stress pathology, environmental adaptation, welfare (fitting the dog by selection to its environment and work, or vice versa), and veterinary care. The one man who has practical experience and conducted research on all of these topics is a vigorous professor at Alfort in France. That Dominique Grandjean has run the extra mile to write this engaging and refreshing book is a telling glimpse of his innate power and generosity.

The final moments in this book deal with ethical and regulatory issues of our times. Here our author has cast aside the often hidden agendas of past conflicts and focussed our attention on what is good for the dogs. Perhaps that should be Dominique's by-line, "What is good for dogs?"

DAVID KRONFELD
THE PAUL MELLON DISTINGUISHED PROFESSOR OF AGRICULTURE
AND PROFESSOR OF VETERINARY MEDICINE,
VIRGINIA POLYTECHNIC INSTITUTE AND STATE UNIVERSITY,
BLACKSBURG, VIRGINIA

SUMMARY

INTRODUCTION

Dogs have been Man's companions for 4000 years, helping us accomplish our daily tasks, then gradually contributing to our quality of life, then in the 1800s becoming an integral part of our leisure time and activities. Over time, Man has become more and more involved in the dog's life, too, working to select, raise, train, and feed the animal in the best ways possible—and not simply so it will survive longer at his side, but out of the simple desire that the dog live a better life.

Dogs' roles have changed and valuable new roles have developed, not the least of which is the rescue dog. Many human lives have been spared because of the courage and abilities of search and rescue dogs: lost people, victims trapped under rubble or snow, or those struggling for their lives in dangerous water. Dogs are also law enforcers in the fight against terrorism, drugs, and crime, as well as talented "detectives" in the identification of flammable products.

In work as in pleasure, humans tend to compare the elements of their lives to those of the people around them. We have even created regulations and competitions in which to rate our dogs, gradually turning pets into professional athletes as a variety of canine sports came to life: Field Trial, Pulka, Ring, herding, dog sledding, Coursing, and Schutzhund, just to name a few. Some may even reach Olympic status one day, as was the case in 1932 (when humans and dogs competed together, though it was more logical in the case of the pulka and dog sledding…). Other demonstrations represent a special way of educating children and dogs through games (if you need convincing on this one, simply attend an agility competition!). Finally, through the use of herding dogs, we can again appreciate some of the grand old treasures Mother Nature has provided us.

Canine sports are growing throughout the world, as are the notoriety of each of the disciplines and the professionalism involved in each. The best example of the widespread appreciation of canine sports is the spectacular show, presented for the first time in 1990 to 50,000 spectators in the POPB, an indoor sports arena in Paris-Bercy, France (Royal Canin trophies for Sporting and Working dogs).

Faced with the great diversity of canine sports involving several million dogs throughout the world each weekend, it seems to us that the time has come to provide dog lovers with this book, the fruit of several years of hands-on experience and scientific research devoted specifically to Sporting dogs.
In addition to a brief but necessary presentation of all Sporting and Working dog disciplines, this book is intended to bring together current veterinary and scientific knowledge in the areas of preparation and pathology as they relate to Sporting dogs.

The authors of this work are veterinarians in the Breeding and Sports Medicine Unit at the National Veterinary School in Alfort, France, which was created in 1996 with the goal of establishing a permanent technical center for veterinarians, breeders, and handlers by developing clinical and scientific research programs for canine sports medicine.

A knowledge of the various different physiological bases governing the brief, but intense effort of the racing Greyhound as compared to the endurance required of a sled dog, as well as the body mechanics that control the relationships of such opposing qualities as force, resistance, endurance, speed, and the psyche allow us to better define appropriate training, nutrition, and genetic selection for a given Sporting or Working dog. Such types of effort can lead to specific health problems that a veterinarian must be able to treat without compromising the dog's future performance. The handler's goal is, of course, to prevent such problems as best as he can. Unfortunately, knowledge can also be a source of deceit in people, such as in the case of performance enhancing drugs, which are detrimental to the animal.

Since medicine for Sporting and Working dogs can only be developed and practiced through an active presence in the field, we hope that this work will convince owners, handlers, and veterinarians to learn more about each other and work together in the areas of education, prevention, treatment, and research. While the education of and behavioral approach to leisure dogs and Working dogs remains the privilege of the canine specialist who spends his days with dogs, it seems to us, whether bureaucrats proponents of scientism like it or not, that this new approach of canine sports medicine is earning its own place and the respect and trust of handlers—at their sides in the field. We hope such a stance is acceptable to the reader…

Finally, the Breeding and Sports Medicine Unit would like to express its sincere appreciation to the Royal Canin company, and especially to its Research Center in Saint Nolff, for its constant scientific collaboration and long-standing partnership, without which none of this would have been possible.

This book is dedicated to a friend and a Master, Professor Mark Bloomberg, a great promoter of canine sports medicine at the University of Florida in Gainesville, who was taken far too early from those who love him still.

PROFESSOR DOMINIQUE GRANDJEAN
DVM, PH.D., HDR
DIRECTOR OF THE BREEDING AND SPORTS MEDICINE UNIT
NATIONAL VETERINARY SCHOOL OF ALFORT (FRANCE)

FOREWORD

Since 1968 Royal Canin has been demonstrating its commitment to owners and breeders of Sporting and Working dogs throughout the world by providing them with high-energy foods that are specifically adapted to effort, endurance, and extreme climatic conditions and by offering training and technical advice to help them succeed in their activities.

As a partner of the Breeding and Sports Medicine Unit at the National Veterinary School in Alfort, France, Royal Canin continues to fulfill its role in the world of Sporting and Working dogs by sharing knowledge and training.

This book is the continuation of the first book already published in this collection *The Practical Guide for Dog Breeding* (1997).

The Practical Guide for Sporting and Working Dogs brings together as much information as possible to meet the expectations of dog lovers, trainers, breeders, teachers, practicing veterinarians, and students.

We would like to express our sincere appreciation to everyone who has participated in the creation, production, and illustration of this book.

RENAUD SERGHERAERT
DIRECTOR OF RESEARCH AND DEVELOPMENT
ROYAL CANIN GROUP

UTILITY DOGS

From man's best friend, dogs have become not only man's helpmate but also a vital part of numerous search and rescue interventions. The 3rd millennium will be the millennium of the "rescue dog."

2

DRUG DOGS

Many dogs are used in the war against drugs because of their excellent sense of smell. Soft and hard drugs are legally produced throughout the world, but their sale is strictly illegal.
These substances may be easily hidden, but are quickly detected by an experienced dog despite tactics used by traffickers (pepper, hermetically sealed containers, etc.).

Brief History

Dogs were first used to search for drugs in Israel. During the Vietnam war, the military police used dogs to reduce illegal drug trafficking.

In France, the national police starting using anti-drug dogs in 1965. Ten years later, the first dogs were trained for this purpose by the Gendarmerie in Gramat and fifteen years after their initial use, customs also began using the dogs to search for drugs.

In 1970, the United States and France implemented procedures to facilitate searches and preventive actions. The problem remains international trafficking. Indeed, in March 1972, the United Nations could only issue recommendations without attacking the "national sovereignty" of producing countries, which can therefore continue their activities.

The Dog's Roles

The dog's main role is of course to detect hidden drugs. The place at which the animal intervenes may vary. Dogs are brought on site to search for drugs (apartments, hangars, etc.), into means of transportation (cars, trucks, trains, etc.), and even check people for drugs on their persons.

The conditions of intervention sometimes mean that a handler needs to search a person who may become aggressive if stopped for a search. The second role of the dog is then to master anyone who refuses search, under its handler's control.

Drugs are sometimes hidden quite ingeniously...better never where a well-trained dog can't find them (here behind the head rest on a train bench)

The Concept of a Dog Team

The team cannot function separately. The handler guides his dog toward items that the dog would not ordinarily search of its own volition (bathrooms, carpeting in cars, etc.). Certain types of training also teach the dog to search in a very systematic way, leaving very little to the animal's own choice of where to search.

The dog is always controlled by its handler. It is always on a leash when in public, and always released when in an enclosed area.

The goal of training a drug dog is to motivate the animal toward the smells of different drugs. Most countries have this type of training for dogs. It consists of motivating a dog with a specific object, then replacing the object with different drugs as the dog progresses. These "toys" are hidden while the dog watches, then while the animal is not looking to develop search behavior. While training the dog, the handler learns to recognize different reactions in the dog (tail wagging, ears held erect, etc.) to better interpret its reactions in the field. The dog indicates the presence of drugs by barking or scratching the ground in front of the drugs' location.

Summary of Primary Narcotics

	Narcotic	Odor	Country of Origin
Family Opiate	Opium	Noxious, characteristic	Turkey, Afghanistan, Iran, India, Laos, Thailand, Cambodia
	Morphine		Turkey, Afghanistan, Iran, India, Laos, Thailand, Cambodia
	Heroin	Vinegar	Turkey, Afghanistan, Iran, India Laos, Thailand, Cambodia
Cocaine		Mixture of glue and acid	Grown: Bolivia, Peru, Processed: Colombia, Chili
Cannabis		Fragrant, characteristic	Afghanistan, Colombia, Congo, Indonesia, Lebanon, Morocco, Mexico, Nepal, Turkey
LSD		Odorless (for humans)	Manufactured: United States, Germany, France, Great Britain
Ecstasy			United States
Mescaline			
Fenciclidine (Angel Dust)			
Psilocybine (mushrooms)			Mexico, France...
Benzodiazepine and barbiturates			Manufactured
Meprobamate			Manufactured
Amphetamines			Manufactured
Glues, solvents, etc.			Manufactured

Note: It is sometimes said that drug dogs are actually "drugged" to increase their sensitivity to the drugs in question. This is absolutely false, and for several reasons:

– dogs also suffer withdrawal symptoms, which make them more aggressive and less able to concentrate on their work, which would make for a disorganized and dangerous search for the people around the dog.
–The dog would not be able to make several searches in a row because it would have satisfied its drug needs.
– The dog would not be able to detect all drugs since it would have to be administered all of the various drugs on the market.
– Drugs destroy certain nerve cells, especially olfactory cells.
– Finally, it would be really expensive to support the animal's habit!!

Choice of Dogs

The ideal drug dog loves to play, is dynamic, and medium-sized, which allows it to search everywhere and to climb or jump over obstacles if necessary. It needs to have good endurance since it may be asked to perform several searches on the same day. Belgian Malinois are often chosen because they are smaller and more lively than German Shepherds.

Prized for their keen sense of smell, dogs are essential team members of anti-drug organizations throughout the world today.

IN SEARCH OF EXPLOSIVES

Thanks to its keen sense of smell, a dog can detect the presence of various explosives used today.

Brief History

It is extremely important for dogs to "carefully" mark explosives to avoid triggering them.

Dogs were first used to search for explosives in February 1959 in Algeria under the command of General Constantine in the southeast zone. This area is crossed from North to South by 200 km (125 miles) of railways. During 1958, 54 bombing attempts were made to this railway. The 40 that were successful in damaging it cause problems for traffic during several days. The explosives in question were 80 mm and 105 mm shells and butane bottles fill with 35 to 40 kg (78 to 88 lb.) of TNT. The lighting system was crude, and the delayed triggers were set using an ordinary alarm clock. The attempts made by the National Liberation Front to disrupt railway traffic of Saharan petroleum were essentially stopped by the discovery of three such bombs. The dogs went along the tracks before the convoy and indicated all suspicious odors. The best results came from tracking dogs that were able to follow the trails to the explosives.

An increase in attempts perpetrated by anarchists or terrorists has called for more intense training of personnel and greater technical methods.

Since the 1970s, Israel has been using dogs to detect letter bombs.

On May 1, 1971, the New York Police Bomb Squad got its first two dogs. Over the next two years, they discovered 21 bombs.

Similarly, in 1977-1978 in Germany, such dogs were used by the Palatinate police to discover weapons and explosives hidden by terrorists.

In France, the Gendarmerie started in 1979, but only when terrorism struck did the specialty actually begin to develop. After the bombing at the synagogue on the rue Copernic in Paris on October 3, 1980 in which 12 people were wounded and 4 people killed, Paris police created two dog teams to search for explosives.

The Dog's Role

Dogs are perfectly integrated into today's war against terrorism, adding their own special abilities to existing systems to prevent explosions.

Dog round out security teams in a variety of strategic locations: airports, road stations, train stations, etc. Its role is to check travelers' bags in the baggage hold (the dog works before the bags are put in the hold) or in the cabin (the dog is in contact with travelers and checks isolated bags).

The way in which the dogs and the leader are trained is very similar to that of drug dogs and their handlers; the only thing that changes is the object being sought. The dog does indicate the presence of explosives in a different way, however: Any type of explosive could detonate upon the slightest contact with the dog, so the dog is taught to mark its location by sitting (if the explosive is located above the dog), or by lying down (if it is on the ground or buried). The dog must then be calm as it works in order not to pass the explosives and trigger them.

The dogs used are very rarely in the public and are therefore never called upon to overcome an individual during a search.

Such dogs are used in many countries to search for explosives, especially where terrorist attacks are likely to occur: United States, France, Great Britain, Northern Ireland, etc.

Explosive materials used to train dogs to search for explosives.

Products	Composition
Dynamite	40% nitroester
Plastrite (PF)	87% pentrite + 9.75% oil + 3.25% gum
Tolite	100% tolite
Nitrate, Fuel	Ammonium nitrate + TNT
Ammonal	Aluminum nitrate + TNT
Formex	89% pentrite + 11% natural rubber binder
Hexolite	60% hexogen + 40% tolite
Octocire	95% hexogen + 5% wax
Tetryl	00% tetryl + 1% graphite

SEARCHING FOR VICTIMS BURIED IN RUBBLE

The olfactory abilities of Working dogs are ever more valued the world over in the area of civilian safety, especially during explosions, collapses, earthquakes, and landslides. Depending on the type of accident and the location of the (sometimes unconscious) victims that rescue services are presented with, it may be necessary to use special biological detection methods that are now well-known for their success: Search and Rescue dog teams.

Brief History

A dog's sense of smell and its ability to discover human presence have long been recognized. In The Odyssey, Homer describes how Ulysses' faithful dog Argos was the first to recognize its master after his long voyage. Though this ability was first used for somewhat negative ends (for example, using dogs during the Middle Ages to find escaped serfs), men, especially the military, discovered early on the animal's capacities for detecting the presence of human beings (sentinel dogs). More recently, dogs' abilities to find people have been used in rescue services.

During the first World War, teams of search dogs were first organized by the allied armies to find wounded survivors. During this time, war dogs underwent quite a transformation, since apart from their sentinel duties, these animals had been called upon to do a variety dangerous tasks: carry letters, deliver messages, telegraph wire, ammunition, and medical supplies from one point on the front to another. Dogs searched for wounded survivors in collapsed trenches or areas that were difficult for men to enter. In this respect they were the precursors of today's search and rescue dogs.

In Great Britain during the blitzkrieg in the second World War, dogs were first used to find victims buried in rubble. As early as 1954, training centers for rescue dog teams were created in the United States, Germany, and Switzerland. Swiss dogs proved their exceptional abilities during the earthquake in Frioul, Italy in 1976. Twelve dogs found 42 survivors and 510 bodies were recovered. In 1977 in Romania, 10 dogs helped find 57 survivors and 97 bodies.

The first French dogs were used in 1980 in El Asnam, Algeria (10 survivors and 500 bodies were found). At the same time, American teams were responding to the catastrophe caused by the eruption of Mount Saint Helen.

Today, rescue dogs are used to find victims buried in rubble during earthquakes all over the world (Iran, Mexico, Armenia, Colombia, California, etc.) or during building explosions in urban areas (such as Oklahoma City disaster in 1995, and on a weekly basis in large cities throughout the world).

The Dog's Roles

The role of the search and rescue dog is not limited to earthquakes, landslides, typhoons, or volcanic eruptions. They may intervene in the event of a collapsed building, after a fire, after work area or mine caves in, after a gas-related explosion or one caused by terrorism, or even during train or airline disasters. Unfortunately there are many instances in which we need their help.

Capson-type geographic tools (that are able to detect very small noises, such as a heartbeat) are also used to locate survivors, but unlike dogs, their use requires total silence, which is rarely the case during excavation operations. A correctly trained dog can work on any terrain, in dark underground areas, in conjunction with rescue workers, and regardless of noisy machines (cranes, jackhammers, bulldozers). Also, the Capson does not detect casualties, whereas the dog not only locates them, but also indicates live victims differently from casualties, which speeds up the rescue-excavation team's intervention. Professionals unanimously agree that dogs are indispensable partners during rescue efforts in rubble.

The Concept of a Dog Rescue Team

As with any job that pairs humans and dogs, a very close bond is needed between the master and the animal. The handler must know his dog perfectly, know how to read it as it moves through the rubble, and constantly be watching for the slightest reaction. In the same way, the dog must have complete trust in its handler in order to go wherever asked regardless of how difficult the terrain may be.

Such a relationship requires a lot of preparation. After basic training in obedience, agility, etc., and a period of getting to know each other, the work is directed toward actual searches. In this field, techniques vary depending on schools and countries. In general, the handler will count on the dog's devotion to him and its enthusiasm toward a particular toy (a ball or chew toy). The handler, then another person, and finally several people hide with the dog's toy, which is what motivates the animal to find them. When the dog finds the "buried" people, it indicates the victim by barking and scratching the ground. The toy's appeal develops the intensity and accuracy with which the dog marks the location. These are essential qualities in good search and rescue dogs working in rubble.

Once the animal is able to detect several victims that have been hidden without its knowledge, the dog and its handler will be certified according to the procedures set up in the country in question. handler and dog are then listed on a national level as a professional or charitable civil or military search and rescue team capable of working in rubble.

Choice of Dogs

The dogs used to work in rubble must have an excellent sense of smell, a calm and sociable disposition, be balanced and full of energy and enthusiasm for the game. Sociability towards humans as well as toward other dogs is essential for these animals since they will have to work in heavily populated areas.

The most common breeds used are shepherds, especially Belgian and German Shepherds. The small Pyrenees, Doberman, Beauceron, and Labrador have also proven themselves in rescue work in rubble.

Rescue dogs have already proven their worth many times over in the huge number of human lives they have saved throughout the world. They are truly indispensable members of rescue teams in types of disasters where victims are buried. The area is constantly being developed and many countries have officially integrated rescue dogs into varies systems for civilian safety.

AVALANCHE SEARCH AND RESCUE DOGS

The frequency of avalanches in cold seasons endangers people's lives every day. The winter of 1998-99 was a tragic example of the massive alpine phenomenon. Because of their highly developed sense of smell, dogs are a valuable tool in search and rescue teams.

Brief History

The first public mountain rescue teams were created in 1772 upon the initiative of the magistrate of Savoie, Pia. They were organized at the end of that century and proved very effective from the period of 1887-1892. Only during the second world war did avalanche rescue dog appear as we know it today.

In 1050 on the Italian border of Switzerland, the Grand Saint Bernard Hospice was created to provide safety for travelers. The arrival of the Saint Bernard dog took place around 1660, its mission being to protect the hospice. Around 1750 the dogs were used to guide travelers crossing the passage. They learned to recognize the way in snow and fog and were able to find travelers lost in the storm.

Considered the precursors for avalanche search and rescue dogs, these Saint Bernards used their senses of direction and smell, but could only find avalanche victims that were not buried too deeply and helped them at least temporarily with the famous little barrels they wore around their necks.

The first avalanche search and rescue dogs seem to have appeared with a bit of trivia in Switzerland before the second world war: A young boy was swept away by an avalanche while his dog was watching. The dog saved his life by pinpointing where the child was buried and digging until he found him. After this event, the Swiss Army began training the dogs. At the end of the war, the Swiss Alpine Club took over. Several mountainous countries also created teams of humans and dogs to perform search and rescue in avalanche situations.

Rescue dogs from Mt. Saint Bernard, from the Petit Journal, February 5, 1933

As a result, in March of 1970 after the Val d'Isere catastrophe in which 39 people were killed, French authorities developed the use of mountain dogs. Since then, the number of dogs has increased each year in response to the recklessness of off-trail skiers and hikers who risk their lives—as do the rescue team members working to save them. Stories about victims buried in avalanches are often heard on the news, but rarely are those about the rescuers who risked their lives to help them.

The Dog's Role

Scratching is the primary way a dog marks an object or person.

Search and rescue in avalanche situations is one of the rare disciplines of rescue, with rubble, in which the dogs' help is needed immediately. Their keen sense of smell, speed, and tenacity make them invaluable in the task at hand. Search and rescue dogs are part of a team of sounders and diggers. The teams work simultaneously, but the dogs' work takes priority in the field.

The dogs are invaluable because of how quickly they work. The time factor is clearly essential in mountain rescues and the faster the avalanche is searched, the better the chances are that the rescuers will find the buried people alive. The dog's role is important in this respect: Doing equal (or even more) work, the dogs explore the ground much faster. A careful search of the area using sound waves by 20 trackers takes 20 hours to get 100% results, whereas a dog can work 2 hours in an area of about 2.5 acres and achieve the same results.

Transmitter-receivers are more and more used by rescuers. The only necessary condition for their use is that the person buried in the avalanche also have one! And several different brands are available, each with its own frequency. Before entering the mountains, each person should inform local rescuers of the brand of his transmitter.

The Concept of Human and Dog Rescue Teams

Since they spend a lot of time in this rough territory, handlers are also men who are used to the constraints of live in the high mountains and who have perfectly mastered skiing on all kinds of terrain.

As for the team made up of humans and dogs, the bond created between the dog and its handler is essential. The dog must have complete trust in its handler to work in the avalanche and during difficult transportation (by helicopter, for example) and the handler must know his dog perfectly in order to interpret even its smallest reaction.

The learning curve is gradual, but varies depending on the technique used. The two difficulties encountered by the dog during a mission are taught first: travelling on difficult terrain and finding a person the dog does not know. The dog must first find its handler whom it saw hide nearby, progressing within a trench being dug between the dog and its master's hiding place. Training continues and progresses so that the dog is able to move around in the aftermath of a large avalanche and detect the presence of a person it does not know.

Choosing the Dogs

Two breeds of dogs are primarily used: The Belgian Malinois and the German Shepherd. These are in fact the two breeds of dogs used in all rescue disciplines and they have definitely earned their keep. They are the right size and weight to move around in the snow

Summary of fatal avalanches since 1995.

Season	Country	Number of Fatal Avalanches	Number of Fatalities
1995 - 1996	Canada	2	4
	United States	22	31
	France	1	1
	Nepal	2	3
	Pakistan	1	30
	Slovenia	1	1
	Switzerland	1	3
	Ukraine	1	4
	Total	**31**	**77**
1996-1997	Afghanistan	1	100
	Armenia	1	3
	Austria	1	4
	Canada	13	15
	United States	13	19
	France	3	10
	Georgia	1	1
	India	1	1
	Italy	2	3
	Norway	1	2
	New Zealand	2	3
	Pakistan	2	8
	Peru	1	2
	Russia	2	3
	Switzerland	3	12
	Turkey	1	6
	Total	**48**	**192**
1997-1998	Argentina	1	3
	Canada	12	21
	United States	25	27
	France	3	18
	India	3	40
	Iran	2	35
	Japan	1	1
	Nepal	2	4
	Norway	1	2
	Tajikistan	2	57
	Turkey	1	12
	Total	**53**	**220**
1998-1999	Austria	3	40
	Canada	6	15
	Scotland	2	5
	United States	12	26
	France	8	25
	India	1	23
	Italy	2	5
	Iran	1	4
	Nepal	2	7
	Pakistan	1	12
	Romania	1	2
	Russia	2	8
	Switzerland	4	16
	Total	45	188
	Total 95-99	**177**	**677**

Dogs must remain calm with the trackers, even during a helicopter lift.

and they have a constant will to work. Their coats are thick and short or medium-long and do not hold the snow the way a long-haired dog would. It is also interesting to see how easily the dogs adapt to their new living conditions: in a few days their coat has gotten thicker with the noticeable development of an undercoat and the hair in the inter-digital spaces is more resilient and forms "snowshoes" to increase the surface area of their paws, the skin on the pads of their feet hardens and becomes more resistant to the snow and salt on the roads. Only the dogs' eyes must be protected against the ultra-violent rays. During training and prolonged periods in the sun, handlers use a protective eye lotion against their harmful effects, such as conjunctivitis.

Using avalanche search and rescue dogs is an invaluable tool against the ticking clock. As a result, a large number of these dogs are found in high-risk areas where they are part of mountain rescue teams.

TRACKING DOGS

Concentration and a keen sense of smell are the primary qualities asked of a tracking dog during a search for a missing person.

Brief History

For several centuries, man has used dogs as trackers. Humans are often the game being tracked. This use of dogs is closely linked to the military, who often used dogs to locate the enemy.

For several decades now, tracking dogs have been more and more used to find people that are reported by their friends and family to authorities or rescue services as being missing or lost.

The Dogs Roles

The dog works in the same way regardless of whether he is looking for a criminal or a missing person, not making a distinction between friend and foe.

The goal of the search is three-fold:
– to indicate the direction taken
– to find the person
– to find objects lost along the trail or nearby

The start of the trail, which provides the smell being sought, can come in several different forms:
– an object belonging to the person being sought
– clues in the area where the person was seen for the last time (footprints, etc.)
– looking for the start of the trail when it is impossible to indicate which person the dog is to look for. The dog should begin searching left and right to find the start of the trail.

The Concept of a Dog Team

Even if the dog is working alone, a handler needs to be present for several reasons:
– only the dog's handler is able to understand the dog's actions, whether they be positive (when the dog gets closer to the person being tracked, for example) or negative, when the dog is lost (if a dog is upset by losing the trail, it may refuse to continue)
– if a dog is having difficulty proceeding, its handler may help it (climbing over fences or crossing rivers, for example)

The team work involved in training a tracking dog is in teaching a dog to use its sense of smell to follow a trail and in training the handler to understand the dog's actions.

Choosing a Tracking Dog

Until Saint Louis (1214-1270), French kings used Saint Huberts, which are excellent running dogs. This breed, known as the Bloodhound, is still used today in the United States.
Today, many countries have decided to emphasize other breeds (primarily Herding breeds such as the German Shepherd and Belgian Shepherds) that have qualities that running breeds do not necessarily share:

– extreme capacities for concentration, in order not to become distracted by other smells
– dynamic workers
– resistance and endurance, because trails may sometimes be very long. It is often necessary to have several dogs on a trail so that some can rest.
Many people have been found thanks to the extraordinary sense of smell and tenacity that tracking dogs have. If the dogs don't actually find the person, they have been responsible for finding the person because of their discovery of objects belonging to the person along way or even finding the initial direction in which the trail began.

Trails must be entered very carefully.

TRUFFLE-HUNTING DOGS

Though truffles have been hunted for several centuries, dogs have only been the animal used to find them for the last 70 years. It is difficult to tell when they were first used to hunt for truffles. It was probably around the beginning of the 19th century, but was mentioned earlier. In 1776, Vigi first used dogs to help find truffles. In 1828, the Dictionary of Natural Science (Dictionnaire des Sciences naturelles) by professors from the Jardin du Roy mentions using dogs to hunt for truffles though pigs were more common. The pig was first replaced by the dog around 1830 when a farmer trained a dog for the first time by taking him truffle hunting with the sow. It is also hard to say why man first preferred pigs to dogs for this task. Perhaps because pigs instinctively dig for truffles and dogs must be trained to do so. Nevertheless, there are many advantages to using dogs in truffle hunting: They are not naturally inclined to eat the truffles they find; they tire much more slowly, and are easier to transport on truffières.

There is no breed of truffle-hunting dogs

Dogs are not used in every country in truffle hunting. Apart from France, Italy is one of the only other countries to train dogs for this purpose. Other truffle producers such as Spain and New Zealand prefer to use pigs or other animals.

No particular breed is used more than others in truffle hunting. Some advise against using running breeds because they are likely to lead the truffle hunter astray while tracking game instead of truffles. There is no specific truffle-hunting breed of dogs, but certain ones seem better at the task than others, such as the Poodle, the Fox Terrier, the German Shepherd, and the Dachshund.

A truffle-hunting dog must have a keen sense of smell, and be calm, obedient, and sociable. It must not destroy the truffles it finds or be distracted by its environment if other animals or people are present. It must have good endurance since a real hunt, which takes place in winter, can last 5 or 6 hours, sometimes on frozen ground.

The most essential quality in the dog is cooperation with its handler, with whom it forms a permanent team.

When hunting for truffles, a good dog adopts a certain attitude that we do not find in any other type of use, even when searching for explosives. A dog released in an area that should have truffles proceeds slowly, sniffing from right to left, turning around, stopping, backtracking, etc. Suddenly it drops its nose to the ground, inhales deeply, strikes the ground with its paw, and again breathes in the dimethylsulfure molecules characteristic of truffles. Then it scratches the ground with both front paws, keeping its nose down. Its shoulders are down, its back bowed and hind legs drawn under the body. The dog positions its body the same way a wolf does in cold weather when it discovers a field mouse hole. The handler must never allow his dog to dig all the way to the truffle. He must stop the search before the dog's nails reach it (they are generally buried 3 to 20 cm [1 to 8 inch.] down in the soil).

The master may then use a toy to distract and reward the dog for his work, at least in the beginning. If the dog is too impulsive, he may also use obedience exercises. This way the dog begins to associate "sit" or "down" with the sudden end to the search.

Training may begin very early, around 5 or 6 months of age in conjunction with obedience training.

At first the dog becomes accustomed to coming when its handler calls and sitting at his feet. The handler/dog team can go into the field where the handler will hide small pieces of cheese under an obstacle. He give the dog the command to find the cheese, then after having repeated the command, leads the dog to the hiding place, continuing to repeat the command. The dog's sense of smell will quickly help it to find the cheese, whose smell resembles that of a truffle. This exercise may last ten minutes or so and can be repeated a few hours later, twice a day.

The handler does the exercise again the following days without giving up, getting angry, or rushing the dog. Soon the puppy will understand the phrase "Find it" and will start to look for the hidden cheese. It will naturally push aside the obstacle in its way in order to get the cheese in the same way it will point out truffles at the end of its training.

Next, the dog must become familiar with truffles. The master does the same exercise before, but this time hides a truffle—one that is ripe and very fragrant—beside the cheese. The dog looks for the cheese without thinking about the truffle. The truffle's smell gradually becomes associated with the idea of finding a reward. It generally takes about a week for this new reflex to be developed.

Then the pieces of cheese are placed in a bag that the handler keeps with him. The truffles are hidden under obstacles, but never in the same places. The handler tells the dog to find it and when the dog strikes the obstacle with its paw, the handler takes the truffle, has the dog smell it, and gives the dog a treat.

The exercise should be made more difficult by burying the truffles deeper and deeper, but very gradually and being careful to bury them farther in advance as they get buried deeper.

It takes about three weeks to train an average dog. Some dogs are particularly talented and can be trained in a few days. Nevertheless, training should be gradual in order not to rush the dog. The handler should take care not to discourage the dog. He must also show the dog his enthusiasm since the dog is working simply to make his handler happy.

DIFFERENT TYPES OF SEARCH DOGS

Other than "traditional" search disciplines, new initiatives are being developed throughout the world to capitalize on dogs' keen detection abilities.

Searching for Minerals

In 1962, dogs were used for the first time in Finland to detect minerals. They were used in prospecting on sulfuric rocks. This initiative was later used in Sweden, the USSR, and Canada.

In other countries, dogs have been used to search for nickel and copper deposits, though these are more difficult to locate than the strong odor of sulfuric rocks.

The method of training also involves games and is similar to the training methods in searching for drugs or explosives, but in Eastern and Scandinavian countries, they say a good dog can detect a deposit up to 15 meters deep (50 ft.). When can we start training dogs to search for gold and diamonds?

Using a dog to detect flammable substances after arson.

Searching for Hydrocarbons

This specialization is found in North America and is starting to develop in Europe. Dogs are trained with different hydrocarbons and intervene after incidents of arson to detect the products used by the criminals. They may also be used to prevent forest fires in areas at risk. The animals mark the location by scratching and the flammable products are then removed as a preventive action toward forest fires, or samples are taken from the area where the dog scratches in the event of a fire.

The main difficulties for the dog are working in areas where crowds of people have been and in difficult olfactory conditions: A fire destroys certain odors, but also gives off several others that can sometimes be toxic and are always bothersome and smoky.

Criminal Investigation Police Dogs

For several years, the Czechoslovakian police has used special units in identifying criminals. Using olfactory clues left at the scene of a crime (clothes, personal objects, etc.), the dog picks the person out of a group by his smell. This type of "positive identification" is considered proof in a courtroom.

Detecting Food Products

Dogs are used to detect food products in American and Australian international airports. It is against the law to bring meat products (sausage, meat cuts, etc.) or plant products (fruits, vegetables, etc.) into these countries.

These dogs, generally beagles (such as in the "Beagle Brigade" in the US) are trained to run the opposite way down the conveyor belts carrying arriving bags as they come out of the planes to detect food. Training is actually quite easy, since a dog's primary motivation is looking for food!

MILITARY DOGS

Because of their exceptional abilities, dogs make up an integral part of military organizations in virtually all countries.

The History of Dogs in the Army

SOLDIERS DOGS

As early as the 13th century BC, dogs participated as soldiers in wars fought by men. These strong animals were effective weapons again the enemy, who fell under their terrible bites. This breed of dog was similar to the Tibetan Bulldog we know today, but it was even bigger with a height at the withers reaching 75 to 80 cm (29 _ to 31 _ inches) [today these dogs measure 70 cm (27 _ inches) at the withers]. These dogs came from Asia and were even more ferocious than the Pharaohs' hunting hounds. They became very popular in Egypt and Greece and ultimately reached the Roman Empire after Greece was conquered. At the same time, the Gauls, Celts, and Germans developed a breed derived from the Great Dane. During the first century BC, famous dog fights were held between warring Roman and Gaul dogs.

The way in which these dogs were trained was simple: Their role was to exterminate the enemy armies, men and horses included. Over the course of the centuries, humans have created for them armors covered with sharpened points or blades, studded collars and even leather coats covered with a flammable substance. These were used to transform the dogs into veritable killing machines that sent the horses and foot soldiers running frightened or cruelly injured. They disappeared in the 19th century with the development of firearms.

SENTINEL DOGS

The keen sense of smell and predilection toward defending and guarding their master made dogs an obvious choice for sentinels around many forts, citadels, and fortified cities. Plutarque recounted the exploits of his dog Soter: Corinth is protected by a garrison, with 50 dogs sleeping on the beach. One evening, enemy armies disembarked. The soldiers had celebrated the night before and were not keeping watch as they should have been. The dogs went to battle the army, but were greatly outnumbered. 49 of the dogs were killed. Only one, Soter, managed to escape and sound a warning with his barks. The Corinthians then gathered their weapons and were able to fend off their assailants. To reward the dog for its courage, he was given a collar that read "For Soter, Defender and Savior of Corinth." This type of dog was especially common in the Middle Ages to defend great sites such as the Mont Saint Michel in Paris or the fortified city of Saint Malo where, since 1155, 24 English Bulldogs were released onto the shore each evening to protect the boats from pirates. This type of surveillance came to an end in 1770 when a young officer walking along the beach was devoured.

TRACKING DOGS

Many dogs have been trained to follow the trail left by a person. In America during the invasion of Indian territories by Columbus, dogs were trained to find and kill Indians.

Thousands of Indians in La Vega were chased away by only 150 foot soldiers, 30 horsemen, and about 20 dogs. Later, Spaniards in South America used dogs to chase slaves that escaped from plantations. They were trained by showing them black mannequins filled with blood and guts. The dogs became excited by the smell and quickly made the connection between the slaves and these mannequins that were given to them in the fields. Escaped slaves had little chance of surviving when they were found.

In the war between France and Algeria, dogs helped locate enemy troops that manage to break down security systems. This was the case with Gamin, a German Shepherd from the military kennel of Beni-Messous. This dog was so ferocious when it arrived in Algeria that no one could approach it. A final attempt was made by the soldier Gilbert Godefroid who made a remarkable change in the animal. Early in the morning of March 29, 1958, Godefroid suddenly awoke. A troop of approximately 200 men broke through the electric fences at the Tunisian border. Gamin and his handler were dispatched by helicopter and quickly began searching, followed by the men of the 1st Foreign Regiment of Parachutists. The trail was fresh and easily found and when Godefroid released his dog, a stream of automatic weapon fire fatally wounded the soldier. Also wounded, Gamin charged and ripped the shooter's throat out. The dog then crawled back to his handler and lay down beside him to protect him. It took six men and a tent tarp to control the dog. Gamin was taken back to camp and survived, but no one was ever able to approach or command the animal again. The military commanders decided to let the dog retire peacefully to the central kennel in Gramat where according to the orders from the Ministry he should "be attentively cared for until his death." Some say that Gamin died of heartache, two weeks after arriving in the kennel. His ashes are kept at the National Center of Cynophillic Instruction in Gramat and a monument was erected in his honor.

Americans used tracking dogs in Vietnam. In this type of guerrilla warfare, dogs were trained to silently follow soldiers to discover the withdrawal zones and camps of the Vietcong.

Relay Dogs

Keeping up-to-date with detachments and communicating with other points on the front line is essential for carrying out military plans of attack or defense. Before telecommunications were invented, dogs were widely used as messengers.

In ancient times, dogs swallowed messages and were sacrificed upon their arrival so the important documents could be retrieved. This practice was quickly ended however, not because of how atrocious the act was, but because of the extreme costs involved…

In the 18th century, Frederic II the Great again used the method to ensure correspondence among the armies of the Kingdom of Prussia. These dogs were highly regarded during the Seven Years War and led to a new line of message and relay dogs.

From the war of 1914-1918, courier or messenger dogs were developed. Their selection was fairly strict: They had to be between 40 and 70 cm (15 3/4 and 27 1/2 inches)at the withers with a neutral coat, in perfect health, with excellent sight, hearing, and smell, and be calm, intelligent, and obedient. According to the military manual, these dogs had to be between 2 and 5 years old to have reached their potential. They also had to be strong enough to resist difficult climates, food and water deprivation, and fatigue. Their role was fundamental: They

linked points that were several kilometers apart in atmospheric conditions that were often difficult. It has been reported that messenger
dogs could run 5 km (about 3 miles) in 12 minutes during bombing.
Ironically, the dogs were visibly carrying messages that could be easily decoded by enemy troops. The method still proved to be a good one
since messenger dogs were rarely captured.

HARNESSED DOGS AND DOGS USED TO CARRY LOADS

Dogs can carry up to 7 kg (15 lb.) of weight. As a result, they were
widely used during different conflicts to carry ammunition, supplies,
even weapons to the front lines. German dogs captured during the war
of 1914-1918 were carrying small machine guns. Two types of dogs were
developed to carry loads during the war: telegraph dogs and pigeon dogs.
Telegraph dogs carried a spool of telephone wire that unrolled across a
dangerous route through trenches, gunfire, barbed wire, etc. to re-establish communications that had been cut due to fighting. Pigeon dogs
were trained to carry homing pigeons to out-posts.

Using harnessed dog teams dates back to 1911 when the Belgians
harnessed powerful dogs to machine guns on wheels. The dogs were
considered preferable to horses because of their greater endurance and
excellent mobility, following men in the underbrush. Dogs were also
harnessed to carts with provisions, stretchers carrying the wounded,
and even used as veritable sled dogs by the Germans on the eastern
front. Because of the debate that developed around a dog's ability to
pull anything on wheels, only the Belgian, German (for a short period), and Russian armies actually used this type of dog.

PATROLLING DOGS

Since dogs have a highly developed instinct as guards, patrol dogs
soon became common. Used to flush out enemies hidden in groves
and other thickets, dogs served to help prevent ambushes and alert
their handlers to the presence of enemy troops. These dogs were also
used to guard and escort prisoners. Few dogs' names are remembered
for posterity, but they nonetheless helped many patrols flush out the
enemy and find their way.

MEDICAL DOGS

The first dogs used to hunt for the wounded were trained by the
Egyptians. Once a battle was over, the dogs were released into the battle field to find wounded survivors, whom they pointed out to their
handlers and licked.

Medical dogs reappeared next in the 20th century. Trained to find
wounded survivors, they indicated the survivors' presence by bringing
back an object that belonged to them: a soldier's helmet, for example,
was a sign for rescuers who followed the dogs to the victims. The dogs'
role was fundamental since the wounded could only be brought back

at night, and the dogs' sense of direction was of great use. The first medical dog society was created in 1885 by a Belgian named Van de Putte, followed by a German society created by an animal painter named Bungartz. France began using medical dogs in 1908.

Several stories recount the exploits of such dogs. Let us note, for example, the account of a soldier from Mans who was wounded on November 2, 1915, "I had been hit by a shell in the arm, a bullet in the jaw, and a sword had sliced off part of my scalp. I was half-buried in the dead bodies of several of my friends when I felt a smooth touch on my forehead. A medical dog was licking my face. Despite my serious injuries, I was able to sit up a bit. I knew that medical dogs were trained to take injured soldiers' helmets back to camp, but I had lost mine. The dog hesitated and I said, "Go, boy, go get help." He understood and took off for the camp. He was so persistent, barking and pulling on their coats that he got the attention of two stretcher-bearers. They followed as he led them to me and saved my life."

Dangerous Missions

Dogs are sometimes used in difficult situations and special conditions.

During the war between France and Indochina, the terrain and vegetation caused a lot of problems for the operations led by French troops. During the first months of the campaign, it was discovered how dangerous it was for parachutists to be dropped into enemy territory. Only dogs were able to speed up the soldiers' tedious searches. On September 5 and 6, 1949, an attempt was made to have a group of dogs parachuted at the jump school in Meucon. The main difficulties encountered in teaching the dogs to jump involved getting the dog out of the plane and the landing. Lighter than a human, the dog took much longer to reach the ground and landed far away from its handler, which greatly slows down the operation. Using a smaller chute solved the problem and from that point on the dog landed at the same time and in the same place as its handler.

Medical dogs. Illustrated supplement from the Petit Journal, April 18, 1915.

Other dogs have unfortunately left their mark on history. The Russian general Panfilon conceived of the idea to train dogs to hunt for food under tanks during the onset of German armies. Left without food for one or two days before an attack, the dogs had a mine strapped to their backs and were sent off "in search of food." Such extremely cruel practices nevertheless had a significant impact on the German troops.

Current Uses of Military Dogs

GUARD DOGS

Dogs are used to protect military installations in a variety of ways: attached to a fixed post or a trolley or loose in an enclosure or a hallway.

In a fixed post: The dog is attached with a chain that is less than 4 meters long (13 feet) in a narrow passageway necessary to access a given area or in the surveillance of hallways or entrances.

To a trolley: The dog may be attached with a leash to a cable at ground level or in the air (no more than 2.5 meters [8 feet]) that is less than 25-30 meters long (80 to 98 feet). A dog that is tied up will bark more readily than one that is loose and as a result will sooner alert its handler to the presence of others.

In an enclosure: The dog may be located inside or outside an installation, surrounded by a simple fence in an area less than 2,500 square meters (26,800 square feet).

In a hallway: The dog moves about a hallway formed by a double enclosure that is 2 meters (6 1/2 feet) high and 2.5 meters (8 feet) apart. It should not be longer than 100 meters (330 feet).

The advantage of a loose dog is in its intervention in a large area. The main complication encountered is that it is hard for the dog to monitor all aspects of a large area at once.

There are two main objectives for a guard dog:
– it should bark and alert its handler to the presence of a person who is trying to pass or enter an area to which access is prohibited, while intercepting the person.
– upon command, it should intercept a person who does not respond to warnings or find a person who is camouflaged.
The presence of a handler is mandatory to:
– interpret the dog's reactions, immediately intervene at the first sign of warning and to warn intervention teams
– stop the dog's attack
– send the dog to intercept or look for individuals

RECONNAISSANCE DOGS

When a dog and its handler find themselves as the first to explore an unknown area, their goal is to detect enemy presence.

There are different uses depending on the terrain and the group's overall mission.

Stationary mission: Without moving, the dog must be able to detect any movement by the enemy

Dynamic mission: there are several types of dynamic missions:
– reconnaissance along an axis: The dog and its handler move ahead of a group an operate in a specific direction. Upon the handler's command, the dog is free to search along the sides of the axis at varying distances from the group depending on the terrain. It is therefore able to detect

an enemy presence up to a distance of about 50 meters (165 feet).
– reconnaissance of a particular point: The dog is sent with or without its handler to gather information about a specific area less than 50 meters (165 feet) away if it is alone.
– reconnaissance of an area: The dog searches ahead of a group on either side of the axis in an area of about 50 meters (165 feet). Several dog teams may intervene depending on the type of area, which is divided into parallel lines.

Special missions:
– reinforcements in surrounding the enemy: Because of their speed and biting attacks, dogs can intercept fleeing enemies, especially on dense, rough ground.
– reduction of underground sites: Dogs can pinpoint the presence of individuals or equipment camouflaged in caves and underground rooms.
– detection of various equipment.

The role of the dog team ends once the enemy has been located and the alert given. The dogs only engage in combat if they or their handlers are attacked.

SURVEILLANCE AND OBSERVATION

The dog plays a role of stationary detection toward a moving enemy. Used in observation posts or in reconnaissance for protecting a bivouac or an operational PC, dogs are able to detect the presence of a person at 300-400 meters (980-1,300 feet).

TRACKING

Tracking consists of searching for one or more individuals on the run. The goal is three-fold:
– to find the individuals
– to find any objects or equipment lost or hidden along the trail or nearby
– to indicate the direction taken by the individuals.

Starting a trail may be done in several ways:
– using clues left accidentally by the individuals on the run (a shoe or piece of torn clothing, for example)
– presumed clues in the area where the enemy has been noted (footprints, etc.)
– looking for the start of the trail when it is impossible to indicate to the dog which individual should be tracked. The dog should begin searching to the left and right to find the beginning of the trail.

COMPANION DOGS

Dog teams reinforce security measures in military bases where the mission is to search a given area following an itinerary known by the dog and its handler. This mission is often accomplished in circles. The dog may either be on a leash or free to move around. It should alert its handler to any unknown presence and neutralize the individual if he tries to flee.

One particular mission, combing, is performed when an individual is suspected to be present. The area may then be divided into several sections and covered by several dogs.

MINE-DETECTING DOGS

Mine-detecting dogs are currently used for two types of missions. The dog must:
– Indicate the presence of mines by sitting. Lying down, which would more precisely indicate the position of the mine, is dangerous for the dog because the animal tends to move forward to lie down, rather than move backward to sit.
– Indicate the presence of mines by moving away. A group of soldiers can then approach using the dog's footsteps, leaving the mines intact.

In any case, the dog is kept on a leash with a harness that allows it freedom of movement. It must also proceed in a straight line, constantly keeping its nose to the ground during its search.

The dogs are taught two possible ways of proceeding:
– The handler walks behind the dog
– The handler walks on the road while the dog proceeds laterally on the terrain to be searched.

ATTACK DOGS

These are primarily used against unpredictable or deranged individuals that are holed up in their homes or against individuals holding hostages. They avoid the dangers posed by a weapon being used in the presence of a third party.

The dog is selected for its physical, athletic, and psychological qualities (even-tempered, brave), and keen senses. Dogs often work in pairs during missions, which requires precise training.

PEACE-KEEPING DOGS

These dogs are used to control crowds and to ensure that demonstrations and protests proceed peacefully. They may or may not be muzzled.

Different countries use peace-keeping dogs today:
– in Germany, anti-demonstration brigades use Rottweillers
– In the United States, dogs were used for a long time to control Black demonstrations, though today they are not used as much. In some states, such as California, a state law prohibits any attack in which a dog bites. The dog will then be muzzled.

In August, 1988, dogs were used by Czechoslovakian anti-riot services during demonstrations commemorating the Prague Spring of 1968.

Attack dogs can be released 2 meters (6 1/2 feet) from the ground during interventions.

SOCIAL USES FOR DOGS

Dogs have performed various functions and participated in such diverse activities as war, meat production, and sled pulling in polar regions for a long, long time. The Roman Empire was the pioneer in dog breeder, and even referred to as the "land of a thousand dogs." The various types of dogs were primarily used to guard farms and herds and to hunt.

But a dog's usefulness doesn't stop there: The dog's role evolved toward that of a constant companion, completely devoted to its master and ready to defend him at all costs. It was primarily during the Renaissance that the dog developed this role of "pet."

Social and economic upheaval caused by changes in our society over the last decades have profoundly affected the relationships between humans and dogs. Massive urbanization, development of mechanical transportation, and significant changes to social and economic structures have caused greater isolation in people. Dogs and other pets have entered into new relationships with people, and are sometimes necessary to balance their place in society.

Dogs are not only around people for the affection they provide, but they are also "used" to satisfy other needs. In this way, dogs become an integral part of the quality of our daily lives, serve as therapists, assistants to the handicapped, and can even help criminals re-enter society.

Dogs as a Symbol of the Quality of Life

Capacity for interaction with others and social skills are the primary criteria by which the "minimal" quality of life is judged. Dogs allow people to meet these two criteria. They are a constant presence, a means of protection and defense, sometimes even a surrogate partner (after divorce or the death of a loved one, for example), and they bring their masters out of a lonely situation, help them regain their self-esteem and self-confidence.

Dogs also contribute to people's well-being through their very presence and the unexpected situations they create. They influence our physiological and psychological health by reducing day-to-day stress. Petting an animal, particularly your own, significantly reduces blood pressure, skin temperature, and heart rate. It also brings an instant calming feeling. A researcher at Cambridge University has shown that, compared to people who do not have dogs, dog owners experience a significant drop in minor health problems (roughly 50%) during the first months after acquiring a dog.

The benefits of the human/dog relationship begin with childhood. A study carried out in Germany on more than 300 families (with more than 500 children among them) with dogs provided significant figures: 90% of parents questioned felt that the dog played a "teaching" role and held an essential place in the child's quality of life. 80% of the children considered their dog as first and foremost a friend and confidante. The animal therefore serves to socialize the child by helping him through different stages of life and by stimulating learning and awareness of the child's own abilities. The dog helps the child develop independence by teaching him obedience, self-control, and pain, concepts that are essential for his development. Through his responsibility for the dog, an adolescent can find a meaning for his life, feeling that the animal is counting on him.

Dogs as a Factor for Social Stability and Reintegration of Young People

According to Konrad Lorenz, animals help manage incompatible impulses with life and society. Dogs represent a sense of belonging to a community and serve as a sort of "social lubricant."

A recent study done in Germany shows that through their affectionate support, dogs allow people to avoid certain risks in large cities and metropolises. Young people with dogs differ in many ways from young people without dogs: They are more satisfied with their lives and their work; they try to succeed more in school and work; they have positive relationships with people older than them, and demonstrate a need for security, understanding, and tenderness. The study reveals that alcohol consumption, intensity of conflicts with parents, and lack of self-confidence are greater in young people who do not have dogs. Young people also see dogs as a way to deal with other risk factors in large cities: loneliness, crime, lack of responsibility and communication.

The way dogs give completely of themselves and are so extremely loyal appear to be stabilizing factors for young people in particularly versatile and changing environments. The young person must take responsibility for the animal and a daily routine is established, thereby giving him a sense of choice and control. The dog becomes a non-threatening support for the person's aggressive impulses. The dog can reduce tensions within the family unit and facilitate communication between people in difficult situations.

Despite everything, relationships between young people and dogs are not exempt from problems: Aggression, unplanned puppies, dog fights, etc. The dog itself can sometimes be the cause and expression of its own social difficulties. Basing their approach on the idea that the young (and not so young) are always ready to learn more about their pets, special teams use dogs in the field as a pretext to approach marginal populations with the goal of reducing urban violence.

Many countries are already using dogs as mediators to re-integrating young people into society. The first experiments were held in "problem" areas and detention centers in the United States and France. Each time, organizers were surprised by the special attention young delinquents gave to the animals, communicating much more successfully with them than with others in their group. When the animals were given to the young people, they soon felt responsible for the animal—for another life. Through contact with the animal or after the animal had been introduced to the institution, some learned to communicate effectively, to love, and to respect others.

Dogs in Therapeutic Roles

Stress and health problems are not perceived in the same way by dog owners and people who do not have dogs. Psychosomatic symptoms, such as nervousness, stomach aches or migraines, heart or cardiovascular problems, insomnia, etc. are less frequent in people with dogs!

In addition to the beneficial role dogs play in preventing health problems for the people around them, they are also actually used in therapy for a variety of reasons:
– sensorial and physical stimulation
– memory stimulation
– greater communication among therapy patients, personnel, and families
– constant motivation to break away from the routine

Dogs are being used more and more to help combat loneliness for people suffering from senility. During their hospitalization, patients must overcome the separation from their family and friends and also deal with a disruption of their normal routine. In addition to physical pain, simply being dropped into a new environment and feeling more dependent than usual can weaken patients psychologically. Data gathered in English-speaking geriatric institutions has show that most patients in contact with dogs felt less alone, appeared happier, and accepted treatment more willingly.

A study carried out in the United States showed that the presence of a dog around patients suffering from Alzheimer's disease had an

"awakening" effect and triggered reactions that allowed them to increase their efforts at socialization (smiles, looks, compliments, warm welcomes, forward movement toward others, physical contact, etc.).

Observations have also shown that autistic children are able to establish close relationships with animals, showing a closeness that they rarely do with the people around them. Certain patients seek a dog as a companion, to give or receive comfort, or to have someone to trust in a way that they never have had with family members.

Several studies have established the advantages of pets (especially dogs) for a person's well-being, emotional growth, and quality of life.

Seven international conferences on the interactions between people and animals have been held in London (1977), Philadelphia (1980), Vienna (1983), Boston (1986), Monaco (1992), and Geneva (1995). In 1992, the drive to bring together all of the national associations into one federation led to the creation of IAHAIO (International Association of Human Animal Interaction Organizations). The 8th International Conference on human/animal relationships was held in Prague in September 1998 and centered on the theme "Animals in Society, Yesterday, Today, and Tomorrow."

Crossing
a pedestrian area.

DOG FOR THE HANDICAPPED

SEEING-EYE DOGS

A constant companion for the blind, seeing-eye dogs have existed since the 1930s when the first training centers were opened in Great Britain.

One third of the breeds used are German Shepherds; the rest are Golden Retrievers and Labradors, again chosen because of their obedience and abilities to learn. The puppies come from a special breeder, since puppies from traditional breeders do not have all of the necessary qualities. Breeders were developed specifically with seeing-eye dogs in mind and often provide the dogs for seeing-eye dog schools. These centers of study work on the genetic selection of the dogs, trying to suppress character flaws or bone and joint malformations (such as hip dysplasia). The puppies are placed in breeding families after weaning, then distributed amount different schools. The females return to the center regularly to give birth since in most cases they ensure the continued reproduction of the line.

Training takes four months, spread out over several periods, during which the dog first learns obedience. This consists of simple exercises during which the dog must hold specific positions, fetch objects, become accustomed to wearing its harness, and walk correctly beside its master. This stage lasts a week and is taught exclusively by the instructor. Then comes the stage during which the dog learns to avoid all types of obstacles and to warn its master. This is the most crucial stage of learning. The instructor will intervene in this respect for the first month. The dog is then turned over to a blind person who must get used to the dog and become accustomed to being led through various courses. A very close bond develops between the person and the dog since they live in constant contact with each other. The instructor is their common bond and must also "train" the blind person to use the dog.

After four months in the seeing-eye dog school, the master/dog pair is ready to face daily life together for the first time and for many years to come. The animal's role as the "eyes" of the blind person is truly essential. It allows the person to return to a more active social life and to have a job that is compatible with his handicap. Having a seeing-eye dog is an invaluable step towards independence for a blind person.

Such associations continue to develop around the world in order to provide as many handicapped and vision-impaired people as possible with ever more well-trained dogs.

DOGS TO ASSIST THE HANDICAPPED

It hasn't been very long that dogs have been trained to help physically handicapped people re-enter society.

These dogs belong to two different breeds: The Labrador and the Golden Retriever. They are even-tempered, docile and quick to learn commands. Training is done in two stages. The first involves introducing the puppy to a family, in much the same was as for a seeing-eye dog. Then the dog is trained inside an association to respond to about fifty different commands.

The role of the "host family" is essential and conditions the dog for the actual training stage. From the age of three months, puppies are "pre-trained" or socialized as the family teaches them obedience. Every three weeks, the dogs and their temporary masters come together in a center for follow-up on their training, advice, and even corrective training for character flaws that would prevent future work in assisting the handicapped. After this "pre-training" stage, which lasts until the dog is 18 months old, the dog is trained to help a person with limited mobility. During this period, which generally lasts about six months, the dog lives in the center full time and meets its future master there during the last two weeks of its training. At this point, masters and dogs are paired off based on their respective needs and abilities. Training takes place on a daily basis and a monitor looks after the dog for about half an hour each day. After 2 years, about a third of the dogs must be retrained for physical reasons (hip problems, for example) or behavioral reasons (the dog must be sociable, calm, and obedient). The main goal is to establish a working harmony between master and dog. They must have a mutual understanding and the person must be able to use the dog well. To do this, candidates who want to adopt dogs to assist them participate in a fairly demanding two-week training period during which they learn to take care of the dog and how to give it commands. Complete training for the dog costs about 10,000 _ (approx. 10,000 $), which limits the number of trainees and especially the number of dogs being trained.

At the end of the training period, the dogs are able to respond to about fifty different commands such as: picking up an object that has been dropped, bring objects (telephone), open and close doors, turn lights on and off, help move chairs into areas that are difficult to access, etc.

Dogs that assist the handicapped can indeed accomplish numerous tasks for their masters, making a human assistant unnecessary. They also play an important therapeutic role for people, particularly children, who suffer from illnesses that can cause them to be physically or emotionally withdrawn from society. In addition to the tasks for which they have been trained, there are many ways in which does stimulate handicapped children. Kids are truly comforted by their dog companions, which in turn allows them to open up more to people and to trust those around them. Children accomplish movements they never would have dreamed possible. Dogs push them to go "beyond their limitations." Research has been done on this therapeutic phenomena, especially as it relates to autism, an illness for which the cause is unknown and for which there is currently no treatment.

These dogs also break down perceived social barriers in public, making it easier for some people to strike up a conversation with a handicapped person.

DOGS FOR THE DEAF OR HEARING IMPAIRED

Being deaf or hearing impaired can prove such a significant handicap that it quickly leads to isolation from society. Dogs can quite successfully be used to make life easier in such situations.

There are several centers for such dogs throughout the world, for example in the United States, England, and Holland. The Soho Foundation was formed in Herpen, near Nimegues, Holland in 1984 and is in charge of purchasing and training dogs for people who are handicapped or hearing impaired. The Soho Foundation works in conjunction with England where most of the dogs are purchased. The breeds used are primarily Golden Retrievers, but there are also Welsh Corgis and Bearded Collies.

At eight weeks old, the dogs are placed in Dutch families, preferably those with children, where there receive a basic education and adapt to a wide variety of environments (city life, the supermarket, the woods, etc.) until they turn one year old. They then return to the Foundation and really begin to learn their actual functions. They will need to learn more than 70 oral commands and 20 gestures. It should also be noted that a deaf or hearing impaired person's voice is quite different in intonation and diction from that of a hearing person. This requires additional effort and adaptation.

The dog's training consists of learning to react to certain noises and to alert its master, such as: jumping on the bed when the alarm goes off, tugging on the master's pant leg when someone is at the door, or carefully taking the master's hand to alert him of an unexpected guest.

The dog will also certainly serve as a companion to its master, making him feel less isolated from society.

Hunting dogs

Despite the controversy surrounding it, hunting is a sport practiced and loved by many and it involves millions of dogs around the world. It is a sport for the dog as well as for the master in that it requires excellent physical condition, strength of character, determination, and observation in addition to a good hunting dog's keen sense of smell.

Pointers and Retrievers

These dogs are primarily used in hunting feathered game (pheasants, woodcocks, partridges, etc.). They have a special hunting technique that allows them to feel at ease in the open, with slight cover, or in the middle of the woods. These hunting dogs are first asked to detect game that may be hidden in inaccessible places. To do so, the dogs must search the area in loops. The master first sends the dog to the right, then the left. Once game has been detected, the dog points, striking a position that is characteristic of these breeds and remains completely still. The hunter then flushes out the game and shoots. During this, the dog must remain completely still. Finally, the hunter gives the command and the dog retrieves the game.

For certain breeds where the relationship is not perfect, two dogs may be used: one to point and one to retrieve the shot game.

Retrievers are different from pointers in that they explore an area in very large loops, sometimes up to 100 meters (330 feet). The hunting technique remains the same.

Water Dogs

These dogs are used in marshy areas or around ponds. Their role consists of retrieving shot game that has fallen in the water and is therefore inaccessible to the hunter. Here, certain intrinsic qualities of the dog are important, such as a love of the water and of retrieving. Again, the game is generally fowl, and most often duck.

Blood Dogs

These special types of dogs look for an animal that has been more or less seriously injured by following its trail of blood. Any breed can be a blood dog, but the wire-haired Dachshund and the Bloodhound are particularly talented in the area.

The dogs must not be sent immediately after an animal has been wounded and care should be taken not to disturb the clues (hair, blood, etc.), which could make the dogs' job more difficult. The exact location of the animal when it was shot should be noted, the location of the first clue, the direction in which the animal fled, and then the dog leader should be called in.

Tracking wounded animals in this way is often successful for the hunter and also shortens their suffering.

Hunting

The original form of chasse à courre hunting is French, but it is also practiced in England and North America. This type of hunting is divided into two categories: large game hunting in which the Hunt is performed on horseback, and small game hunting which is practiced on foot, behind the dogs. In both cases, it is the dogs that actually hunt and give chase. No guns are allowed.

The expression chasse à courre appeared for the first time in the Hunting Treaty of Yauville. Prior to that, we spoke of chasse à force or French-style hunting. The hunt itself was very short and the animal, out of breath, was overtaken by the hounds before it could devise a clever defense. The Hunt, however, is only practiced with running dogs. The dogs follow the scent left by the animal but never actually see it while they are hunting (or very rarely).The command of Marolles marks the birth of the Hunt at the end of the 12th century. Philippe Auguste (1180-1223) was the first hunting king. The first rules of the Hunt were established under Louis IX. It was during this time period that hunting colors originated. Under Louis XV, two

Beginning of a hunt with two sounders.

works make reference: that of Leverrier de la conterie (the school of hunting with running dogs) and the Hunting Treaty of Yauville. The Hunt then had written rules, which remain in place even today.

Large Game Hunting

The domestication of the horse allowed men to hunt fast animals. Large game hunting is the art of taking an animal using only dogs and horses that have been trained, bred, and selected for the task, as well as guiding them and helping them whenever possible. This type of hunting is practiced on large or fast animals in France: stags, deer, wild boars, and wolves.

The number of dogs making up the team (running dogs) may reach 100 in larger hunts. These dogs are different from tracking dogs, which are leashed and controlled by a handler to search for and locate the animal before it is overtaken.

Before the beginning of the hunt, the area where the animal spends the night should be located and isolated without flushing out the animal or causing it to flee. Its age is determined, as are its sex and strength based on its attitude, its feet and the damages it causes to vegetation. Then the running dogs track the animal until it surrenders. Once the dogs have been released, the hunters sound the start of the meet and the start of the hunt. The participants are then invited to follow the pack and the game.

Whatever the hunt, the horns always announce which animal is being chased, which way it is going, if it enters the water, or if it changes forests. The main difficulty is to maintain the path of the game, which varies according to the atmospheric conditions (the path is often not found because of hot weather or rain), and also according to the animal. An animal at the start of the hunt leaves a much stronger trail than an animal after an hour and a half of hunting.

From the beginning of the pursuit, the animal will use certain tricks to try and escape its pursuers:

Changing: The animal crosses a region where other animals of the same species live, which can cause confusion in the pack and send it chasing a different animal.

Crossing a stream, river, or pond: The animal crosses water to try and conceal its trail. The dogs then try to pick up the location where the animal left the water.

The animal has such a head start on the pack that its smell disappears.

Double paths: These are intended to slow down the dogs. The animal being pursued backtracks and then takes another direction after 100 meters or so (330 feet).

If, at the end of the day, the dogs have not given up on the game and the game is exhausted, the hunters sound the "kill," sealing the animal's fate. Often the game turns around to face them and to try one last time to escape. In this case, the "kill on foot" is sounded. The animal is quickly taken with a knife or dagger, at which time the "hallali par terre" is sounded. The best cuts are given to friends and the lesser cuts are gathered and given to the dogs. The "quarry" is then sounded.

Fanfare plays and the team leader cuts the front right foot from the animal and gives it to the person he has chosen to honor for his role in the hunt. The "honneurs du pied" is then sounded.

Finally, the hunt is closed with the "Saint Hubert," "l'adieu des maitres," "l'adieu des piqueurs," and the "bonsoir."

In reality only one hunt in three or four ends in the death of the animal because the animal often gets away by changing forests and by leaving the perimeter of the hunt.

History of Hunting Horns

Horns allow communication during the hunt by using very specific melodies depending on the situation, and also to guide the dogs in the pack that are particularly sensitive to sounds.

The current form of the horn only appeared around 1680 in the time of Louis XIV. Before this period, the hunter used a horn. The Marquis de Dampierre, inspired by the fanfare of the Court, composed virtually all of the current hunting repertory. Around the time of the first Empire the hunting horn started to become popular. In 1817, Pernet created a hunting horn with three and a half turns, .55 meter (21 _ inches) in diameter, then .37 meter (15 _ inches) in diameter, which corresponds to the hunting horn used today. This instrument has therefore been around for 290 years, 140 in its current form.

About the Animal Hunted

Hunting stag requires precise knowledge of the terrain (several trips per week to learn it are sometimes necessary) in order to foresee all of the possible ways the animal may flee. Nevertheless its path is marked and remains fairly constant throughout the hunt, unlike the deer and the rabbit. Well-fed dogs with good endurance are best in this type of hunt to push the stag beyond these speeds. A well-hunted stag can be taken in two and a half hours, but if it uses several tricks, the hunt may last more than five hours.

Wild boars are much harder to track because they are particularly erratic and mistrustful. They also have an excellent sense of smell. The boar's main defense is its speed and endurance. Once it has taken off, the wild boar tends to run straight ahead, drawing on its speed and endurance. Even if the boar's path is greater than the deer, the dogs can gain ground if the pack does not stay tightly together. In general, six or seven hours are needed to catch a wild boar. Once it is caught, the boar turns to face the dogs and the hunters must act quickly and carefully to take the animal before it kills or injures the best dogs in the pack.

Small Game Hunting

This is a chasse à courre for rabbits, badgers, or fox. The hunters are on foot behind the dogs, which form a smaller pack than in large game hunting.

The first rabbit hunts are recounted in the Art of Hunting by Xenophon, four centuries before Jesus Christ. He describes a hunt that takes place the same way they do today, except ending in nets.

The hunting technique is the same as for large game hunting. The main difference lies in the fact that the path is much less marked and the range of tricks used by the game is greater. The rabbit belongs to the group of animals that can retain their odor in times of stress, which makes the hunt even more difficult for the dogs. It can also hide in many more places because of its smaller size: herds of cows or pigs, farmyards, drains, burrows, trees, etc.

The Pack

For a pack to be good, the dogs should all be the same size, shape, and color. Most importantly, they should work at the same speed and with the same endurance. Each breed has its own way of hunting and mixing breeds in a pack necessarily affects its quality. One exception to this rule is in hunting wild boar, where Fox Terriers can be useful in flushing out the game because of their particularly aggressive character.

Running dogs are not trained, but rather are seasoned on the path of one or more animals. An animal is considered a seasoned participant once it has participated in a few quarries and has gotten a taste for the hunted animal's flesh and the smell it leaves along the path. The dog then tries to hunt like the others and remains on the path.

Teams

Whether it is large or small, the hunt requires a team. This refers to the equipment and personnel involved in the Hunt, such as the handlers (those who take care of the dogs), the piqueurs (those that guide the dogs), the horses, the dogs, the cars, etc. This group has the right to hunt on a certain area of land and to hunt certain animals.

In France, for example, there are approximately 300 teams in a Hunt: 100 for rabbits, 60 for deer, about 70 for foxes, 40 for stags, and about 15 for wild boar.

This represents about 12,000 dogs per pack. They are regularly replaced by about 20% per year and breeding is primarily done by the teams themselves.

We shall not go into the media debate concerning the Hunt or ordinary hunting, but shall simply note that the physical condition of the dogs is an important element in a successful hunt. Hunting dogs are Working dogs, sometimes even Sporting dogs, require optimal preparation, and present specific veterinary concerns.

WATER RESCUE DOGS

Though water rescues are recognized as a very valuable service, there is currently no school to train dogs in water rescue situations. Only national federations provide team training. All master/dog pairs work for free, devoting their energy and free time to saving human lives in water-related accidents.
Training centers in France have, nevertheless, created a water rescue certificate (which is not yet officially recognized) that would allow a program to be officially created.

The Newfoundland and Its Natural Calling

In such an activity, the dogs must first have no fear of the water, be large and strong enough to pull significant weight, and be resistant to cold and humidity.

Despite its love of the water and fearless nature, the Labrador is not terrible effective over long distances or with heavy loads. The Newfoundland, however, is widely known as a water dog and is much more effective in water rescue situations. This breed has extreme pulling power because of its impressive jaws and musculature (towing a boat of several register tons), its resistance to cold which allows the dog to work regardless of weather conditions, its extremely calm yet tenacious nature, and finally an ability to recognize danger even in circumstances that are completely different from those in which it was trained.

History of the Breed

The Newfoundland's origins are still uncertain. This large breed appears to have descended from the Tibetan Mastiff after it arrived from Asia to North America and the island of Newfoundland. These dogs were used to retrieve fishermen's nets and also on land to pull loads.

In 1001, the Viking Leif Ericson landed on this island with these black and white striped bear dogs. The crossing of these two breeds led to a solidly built breed that was as comfortable in the water as it was on land.

After 5 centuries of evolution in virtual isolation, the breed we know today as the Newfoundland was first discovered by European fishermen arriving on the island of Newfoundland. This breed is extremely gentle and exceptionally brave and was very popular when introduced to Europe. In the 19th century it was used to rebuild the population of rescue dogs in the Saint Bernard hospice.

Its love of people and its natural tendency toward rescue have made the Newfoundland an exceptional water and mountain rescue dog. In 1919, a single Newfoundland is said to have saved 20 people from drowning, which won the dog a medal and widespread recognition.

Fetching an object.

Fetching the master or an unknown person.

Different Uses

In the field of water rescue, the master is first and foremost the rescuer. The dog essentially serves to tow the victim once he has been reached.

A SINGLE DOG

Certain situations do not require intervention by the master, for example towing a person or an object, pulling a boat in shallow water (when the motor cannot be used) or to carrying a rope during floods.

Saving a victim without the master's help is actually just an exercise used during demonstrations or rescue dog competitions for sport.

MASTER AND DOG

The pair remains indispensable in some cases, such as when the victim fights his rescuers. Here, the master controls the victim, while the dog tows them to safety.

Their teamwork is also needed in retrieving a drifting boat; the master goes aboard to take care of the victims while the dog tows, and also during zone searches where the dog follows divers' bubbles while pulling a dinghy.

AREAS OF ACTIVITY
Sea

The dog may act in directly or as back-up for the rescuers upon request by the official rescue services or to ensure safety in rocky areas. Beaches with large waves should be avoided.

River

The Newfoundland may act directly or as a back-up for rescuers already in place or in the rapid intervention of an accident (branches). Nevertheless, we would avoid areas near a lock reservoir when the dog is alone.

Lakes

The dog may respond on sight or when called to ensure safety in tourist areas with its master (primarily in high tourist season). We would avoid areas with hydroelectric dams.

During Flooding

In this case, the dogs are used as a back-up to rescue services already in place, to tow equipment, bring food, or pull evacuation boats.

Currently only two countries have intervention teams in real situations. France has about ten and Italy has a few less. The dogs sometimes go to aid victims, but more often to tow equipment. Over the past few years, the teams have been widely used during floods.

It is possible to see the progress made in such dogs during demonstrations or competitions organized by Federations in sporting situations. The program is completely different since no life is in danger. The dog's own abilities are highlighted, which is different from actual interventions in which the dog serves as tool, albeit an indispensable one.

Titles Awarded

In the United States, working titles are granted to dogs based on their performance:

Water Dog (WD) for juniors

Water Rescue Dog (WRD) for seniors

These two titles are awarded after a series of life saving and water rescue demonstrations.

Draft Dog (DD) for dogs that have passed the tests for maneuvering and boats of all types

Team Draft Dog (TDD) for groups of 2 or more dogs that have completed the same tests as mentioned above.

In its role as water rescue dog, the Newfoundland returns to its initial uses of towing an object on land or in the water (for example, the fishermen's nets.)

Fetching the master or an unknown person (at sea).

With the development of water sports such as surfing and windsurfing, water rescue dogs and their masters may be seem working on English, French, American, and Italian beaches. Demonstrations are also organized in all of these countries to further appreciate the bravery and willpower of these animals and their masters.

HERDING COMPETITIONS

It isn't a rare occurrence these days to see a shepherd and his dog lead a herd to pasture. We also note a new appreciation for this role in dog lovers.

Shepherd dog's working abilities and level of training can be evaluated in a special herding competition. The goal of these tests is to place the human/dog team in conditions that are as close as possible to natural working conditions. Such competitions in Europe only involve dogs that work with sheep, whereas in the United States there are also competitions for dogs working with bovine herds. Demonstrations may also be found with dogs who have been trained on other types of animals such as geese and pigs.

These competitions are divided into two groups: the "inter-breed" division, which is open to all shepherd dogs and those reserved for Border Collies.

While a dog is asked to show a lot of initiative under natural herding conditions, perfect obedience in prescribed exercises is required in the competitions.

Breeds

Not all shepherds use pure breeds because a simple crossbreed can easily accomplish the task of guarding a herd. Nevertheless, depending on the region and the country, certain breeds are recognized as more competent to guard livestock because of their natural qualities.

The Beauce Shepherd: Large, powerful dog with a short coat. The Beauce Shepherd works in contact with the herd and can stand up to the sheep. It is slower and therefore less precise than a smaller shepherd dog, but much more calm. This is primarily a field dog used to guard a herd in an open area.

The Brie Shepherd: Also a large dog, but with a long, rough coat (often considered a handicap). It is rather fast, calm, and generally works at a distance from the herd.

The Picardie Shepherd: Energetic, medium-sized dog with medium-length wiry coat. Like the Beauce Shepherd, this is a field dog, calm and very agile.

The Pyrenees Shepherd: Small, light dog that is lively and has great endurance. Medium-length, wiry coat. It is perfect for guarding and manipulating herds on rugged terrain. Very fast and also readily barks while working.

The Border Collie: Medium-sized dog with long or short coat. The

Border Collie works at a distance from the herd, moves quickly and stays unusually low to the ground (a trait specific to this breed), while constantly maintaining the flock. Some people believe the Border Collie actually hypnotizes the sheep. While excellent at bringing the herd together and ideal in manipulating the animals into a fenced-in area, this breed is rarely used in large fields.

Each breed has its own advantages and disadvantages. A shepherd should nevertheless choose a dog that he likes, and not base his decision on breed or training.

The Border Collie is the most used breed of shepherd dog in the world. It can be found in competitions in France, the United States, England, and Australia.

It has been used with flocks of sheep in the United Kingdom since before the Industrial Revolution, where wool made up a substantial portion of the economy. Any time shepherds got together it was an opportunity to compare dogs, but the first official competition took place on October 9, 1873 in Balla, Wales.

The Border Collie arrived in the United States after the Civil War when the Americans were forming large herds of sheep and cows. They called upon English shepherds and their dogs to watch over the herds.

Every year since, an international competition of herding dogs has been organized by the international federation bringing together all countries using these dogs.

Inter-breed Competitions

These primarily take place in France, where there are many breeds of herding dogs.

Competitions with sheep began with the French Shepherd Dog Club in 1896. In 1961, the Ovine Federation and the Central Canine Society came together to set up official regulations for competitions and rules for working certificates and working championship certificates.

The Course

The obstacles are placed rather far apart and are organized as follows: The dog must go and get sheep from a pen, then bring them through one or more passages, crossing a road and encountering a passing car, and finally lead them alongside a field that is off-limits. This represents the majority of situations encountered by a breeder to lead his herd between two pastures or to the fold.

The course is spread out over about 400 meters (1,300 feet) [200-600 meters (655-1,970 feet)]. The herds contain 120 to 150 animals. Each obstacle counts a certain number of points and a judge evaluates the way in which it is passed.

Participants

All breeds are authorized to compete, but the dogs must be at least one year old, and if possible be registered in the genealogical book. Only professional shepherds or sheep breeders are accepted.

For dogs that are not yet one year old, there may be a performance at the end of the competition if the sheep are in a condition to continue.

Certain competitors may compete with two dogs working simultaneously, but will in this case be in a separate division.

In these competitions, any dog that abandons the task at all will be eliminated. The dog's work is actually quite extraordinary because the animal is asked to work with unknown animals in an unknown area. Since the dog is not allowed to use its own initiative in competition, it must perfectly obey its master. In order to succeed, the animal must be in good physical condition and have had intensive training.

Competitions Reserved for Border Collies

These competitions are found all over the world and may vary slightly depending on the country. Nonetheless, the courses and obstacles remain essentially the same.

In 1873 the first shepherd competition was held in Wales. It was far more successful than anticipated and other competitions were subsequently organized outside of Wales from 1876 on. In 1906 the first international competition was held in Scotland, then others became more common in countries that had imported the Border Collie.

THE COURSE

Three types of tests are possible:

Isolating a sheep

One dog working with a flock of sheep:

Five sheep are placed several meters away from the shepherd. The dog must run toward the flock and stop behind to take control. Then, upon command, it must lead the sheep in a straight line through two barriers. After a tight turn, the sheep must pass two sets of barriers forming a triangle, then stop in a sorting ring. Then, the dog must separate two pre-determined sheep and lead the entire group into a pen.

The dog is allotted 15 minutes to accomplish the exercise. In this instance, the dog works at a distance from a small herd of animals, which poses additional difficulties.

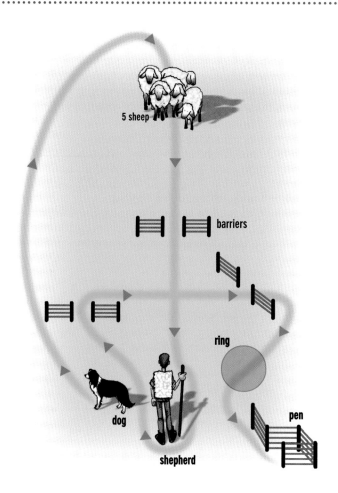

5 sheep

barriers

ring

pen

dog

shepherd

Dog working a
group of sheep

Right turn

One dog working with two flocks of sheep:

Each flock contains ten sheep. The first exercise consists of leading a flock, then abandoning it to go and get the second flock. The dog then brings the two flocks together and brings them to the shepherd. Last of all, it leads the entire herd in a triangle and finishes as in the previous test.

Working with two dogs:

The single flock contains six sheep. Each dog is to one side of the flock and must remain on that side throughout the test. The dogs are not allowed to cross or switch sides. Once they arrive in the sorting ring, the dogs divide the animals into two equal flocks, then each must lead its flock into a pen.

Working with two dogs

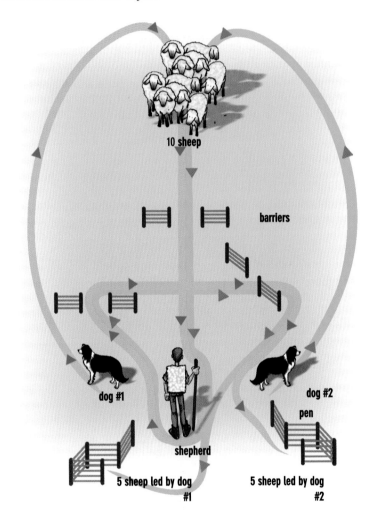

PARTICIPANTS

This competition is open to all Border Collies registered in the genealogical book. The leader must also be the owner of the dog or dogs.

SPORTING DOGS

W hether small, medium, or large, any dog can find a sport just his size. In just a few years, canine sports have not only been fully organized, but also—especially now—virtually all have attained a worldwide level.

Hound racing

Hound racing is a real "industry" in the greatest economic sense of the word in English-speaking countries (Great Britain, United States, Australia, etc.), while only slowly gaining in popularity in Continental Europe. Though, particularly on the Old Continent, all breeds of hounds are allowed to participate in these competitions, it is clearly the Greyhound that has single-handedly ensured the development of this athletic discipline because of extreme popularity with the fans.

Brief History

Since the dawn of time, the Greyhound has been synonymous with speed and remains the oldest pure breed of dog known. After several years of research, Xavier Prziedziecki has traced the first Greyhounds back to the 6000 B.C! Rock engravings suggest that dogs exactly resembling the breed existed some 8000 years before our time in obscure parts of Egypt and Arabia. This original Arabic hound was both a Hunting and a Sporting dog and was greatly admired by its owners, who even allowed the dog to share their tent and travel on camel-back with them. Upon discovering the Greyhound, the Persians made it the only animal authorized to accompany its master to the After World. The Tartars imported it to Russia and crossed it with a local breed, creating the Barzoi. The same phenomenon occurred through the intermediary of Syrian tribes, who brought the Greyhound to Afghanistan and bred the Afghan hound. According to some writers, the word "Greyhound" comes from their popularity with the ancient Greeks ("Greek hounds"). Whatever the case may be, Athenians were extremely fond of the breed and are responsible for the current purity of the breed.

During the Roman Empire, hound races chasing after natural game were organized. A Greco-Roman historian, Arrien, noted the racing regulations during the first century BC in a "Treaty on Hunting."

Then, the Greyhound slowly migrated across Europe to Germany, France, and England with Gaelic and Celtic cults.

This initial activity continued from the Middle Ages to our own time and the increasing difficulty in finding natural hunting areas and game gradually led to the organization of events chasing rabbits, then lures, and more and more these events took place in artificial fields. The first dog racing stadiums were built at the end of the nineteenth century.

The first racing club was organized in 1776 by the Count of Oxford in England under the name "Swaffham Coursing Society." Founded in 1825, the Altcar Society led to the creation of the renowned

"Waterloo Cup" trophy. Finally, in 1858, the National Coursing Club was founded in England and became the supreme authority on races in that country.

Hound races have continued to develop, especially in English-speaking countries (England, Ireland, Australia, New Zealand, United States) and in some Mediterranean countries (Spain, Italy, Morocco).

The first official race in the Americas took place in 1886 in Cheyenne Bottoms, Kansas. The American Coursing Board was created in 1906 and became the all-powerful National Greyhound Association in 1945.

In France, the first Parisian races took place in 1928 and led to the inauguration of the famous Courbevoie Stadium in 1936, which closed in 1951 after years of success.

In non-English-speaking Europe, hound races have survived thanks to a handful of fans. Their efforts brought about renewed interest in the sport in the late 1970s and ended up right behind their neighbors on the other side of the English Channel. But how many years behind they were…

Example of a program for presenting participants in a Greyhound race such as those used in the United States

Competitions

In Australia in 1926, a mechanical rabbit was used for the first time. It later became a lure and nowadays is generally shaped like a giant bone. As a result, dog racing stadiums were built and the gradual confidentiality of outdoor or "coursing" competitions grew. Coursing competitions only use mechanical lures today.

During a race, six or eight hounds are placed in starting boxes and released to chase an artificial lure that is controlled by a man on a 480 meter site (US: 5/16 mile) that looks just like a typical sports track (two straight lines and two semi-circular curves). The lure is pulled by a wire rolled onto a motorized coil or more often by a remote controlled cart moving on a rail.

Depending on the country, there are two main types of competitions:
– those organized by authorized clubs of the national canine organizations dependent on the International Cynological Federation, whose goal is to improve the working characteristics

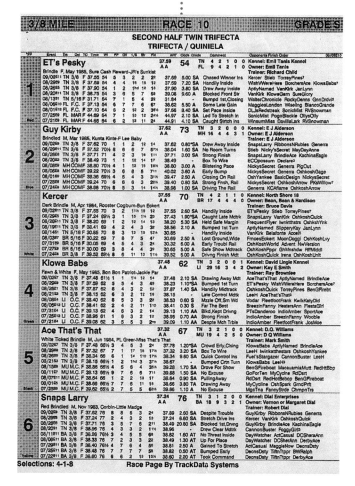

of recognized breeds. The owner of the winning dog receives a cup and betting is not allowed.The best hounds may participate in international tests organized by the UICL (Union International de clubs de Lévriers- International Union of Hound Clubs), which brings together such countries as Germany, Switzerland, Austria, Hungary, Belgium, the Netherlands, and France.

– those for which betting is authorized, whether they are governed as actual private industries like in the United States, or organized by racing societies within a federation, like with horses.

In this world of competition, about ten races take place in the afternoon or the evening and are designed so that all of the hounds have a chance to win, which allows hounds from all categories of speed to participate well.

In Great Britain, Australia, the United States, and Spain, hound races have another dimension. They are completely professional and only involve one breed: the Greyhound. For example, each year in Great Britain there are nearly 20,000 Greyhounds born and more than 60 million race spectators attend events, which puts the sport in second place for the country, behind cricket and ahead of soccer! In the United States, hound races are ranked fifth in sporting event attendance with nearly 40 million spectators. Betting brings in several billion dollars to the budgets of 19 states and charitable organizations receive more than 1.5 million dollars per year from hound races.

The largest individual sum won by a hound in a race was by Ben G. Speedboat in Seabrock (Championship Race), with $125,000, whereas the record of cumulative winnings over a racing career is held by Hompsun Rowdy with $279,000.

Racing Greyhounds

Evolution of the Sport

The large English-speaking societies that govern professional hound races (either closely or loosely) are trying to gain more and more ground on the European continent with the opening of the markets and harmonization of legislations. Such a development would be highly profitable in creating direct and indirect jobs and in developing the breeding of racing hounds. In the meantime, the federations from different countries on the continent have developed relations and created the CGRC (Continental Greyhound Racing Confederation) in 1991. Its goal is to manage the growth of the sport, which—we may as well say it—will likely only profit the Greyhound to the detriment of the other breeds. It is therefore very likely that we will move toward a greater development of Greyhound racing, primarily toward professional operation and shows, while an international structure under the control of the ICF will remain in charge of the competitions of other breeds (Whippet, Barzoi, Afghan, Sloughi, Saluki, Maggyar, etc.).

Let us note, however, that the most "natural" race in coursing certainly continues to exist in the form of chasing a visible lure. This type is different from coursing and "carreras de campas" in that the last two types of tests remain very similar to hunting. The hounds chase a live rabbit, which is prohibited by legislation in most countries. During a lure race, one or two hounds "hunt" a lure that they can see, which is pulled in such a way as to simulate a fast natural chase with sharp turns imitating a real rabbit's movement. Judges observe the dogs' work.

Hound racing is a canine sport that is highly developed in some large countries and that is currently being developed in others. It is both a show and an opportunity for gamblers to try their luck. Its impact on the media and the economy in English-speaking countries has made it a major sport and we will likely see its explosion in Continental Europe over the next few years.

Example of the annual budget of a private dog racing stadium in Australia
(Sandown Greyhound Racing Club, 1993)

Receipts	Sales ($)	Net Profits ($)
Bets taken before the event	25,000,000.00	1,420,000.00
Bets taken during the event	10,000,000.00	334,000.00
Bets taken by bookmakers	11,000,000.00	93,000.00
Total	46,000,000.00	1,847,000.00
Number of racing events	53	

Average performances by breed for racing Greyhounds running a distance of 480 meters.

Race	Average Time (s)
Greyhound	28.5-29
Hungarian Greyhound	29.5-30
Sloughi	32-33
Saluki	33.5-34
Whippet	34-34.5
Borzoi	36-36.5
Azbakh	36.5-37
Deerhound	36.5-37
Afgha	39.5-40

Dog SLEDDING AND SKI PULKA

Dog sledding has only been recognized as a discipline since the beginning of the 20th century. In fact while the Gold Rush was going full swing in Alaska, groups of dogsledders formed and wanted to compare their teams' strength and speed. That's about all it took for the sport to be created...

The First Races in Alaska

The competition was quite lively among dog sled teams and gold seekers and ultimately led to the "Nome Kennel Club," which was founded in 1907 in Nome (in North-West Alaska). Its purpose was simple: for "official" races to be run smoothly by providing the necessary material organization and establishing strict rules.

One year later, Albert Fink, a lawyer from Nome set up the regulations for the very first official competition called the All Alaska Sweepstakes:

– all leaders must be members of the Nome Kennel Club.

– all dogs must be registered with the club.

– the leader can have as many dogs as he wants, but all dogs that start the race must be brought to the finish line, either harnessed in the team, or on the sled.

– the dogs shall be identified and marked at the starting line in order to avoid substitution during the race.

– if two teams become too close together during the race (one right behind the other), the team that has been caught must immediately yield the way by stopping and waiting a certain amount of time before continuing the race.

In accordance with the rules, the "mushers" (or team leaders, from the French marche, which means to walk or to go forth) began the race from Nome to Candle and back to Nome, which is approximately 408 miles (650 kilometers). Five days later, the first teams arrived in Nome and a sporting legend had been born.

On this trail of ice fields, high mountains, frozen rivers, tundra, forests, glaciers, etc., a young Norwegian immigrant named Leonhard Seppala became the greatest name in dog sledding. With his team of Siberian Huskies, Leonhard Seppala would win the All Alaska Sweepstakes in 1915, 1916, and 1917.

One of his competitors, beaten and discouraged would later write, "This man is superhuman. He passed me every day of the race and I wasn't dawdling. It didn't even look like he was driving his dogs, but I have never seen dogs pull so hard. Something was going on between him and his dogs that I will never be able to explain, something supernatural, some kind of hypnotism…".

Siberian Huskies

Between 1908 and 1915, dog teams evolved. The first huskies were imported from Siberia and with John "Iron Man" Johnson as a musher, a new record was set in 1910 (74 hours, 14 minutes, and 37 seconds). In 1911, Allan Scotty Allan won the race with a team of Alaskan mixes (hybrid of Malamutes and Setters) in approximately 80 hours during a terrible blizzard. Another big name in the beginning sport of dog sledding, Scotty Allan ran 8 sweepstakes and won 3 of them, took second place three times, and third place two times.

As for Leonhard Seppala… what can we say? This extraordinary man brought respect to the sport and his best lead dog, Togo, is known by mushers all over the world. He won many races and in New England met a young veterinary student named Roland Lombard. Another great name, "Doc" Lombard continued to run with his dogs and thanks to him, dog sledding in North America grew in leaps and bounds. To this day, he has won more Anchorage World Championship titles than anyone else. He was also the first president of the International Sled Dog Racing Association in North America (ISDRA). Finally, among all of these names making up the history and veritable essence of this marvelous sport, we must mention George Attla, an Athabascan Indian from Huslia, Alaska. George Attla won every race in existence and his book Everything I Know About Training and Racing Sled Dogs is the musher's Bible. A wonderful, but little-known film called Spirit of the Wind tells the story of this extraordinarily brave Indian: George Attla experienced all of his adventures with only one good leg; he had lost the use of the other one in a childhood disease.

Evolution of the Sport

NORTH AMERICA

Since the beginning of the 20th century, races have grown in number in the United States and Canada, leaving their Alaskan birthplace. A second birthplace of races appeared in New England, with the foundation of the New England Sled Dog Club in 1924. In 1932, the Olympic Games of Lake Placid allowed Dog Sledding as a demonstration sport, which was an instant success with the large group of spectators present.

Alaskan Huskies

The second world war definitely slowed progress in the development of competitions, but they later returned even stronger thanks to the increased number of clubs. The Sierra Nevada Dog Drivers should be mentioned because their leader Robert Levorsen was president of the ISDRA from 1971 to 1974. 1971 is also an important year because it was then that the governor of the state of Alaska officially declared dog sledding as a "national sport."

Today it is hard to count the number of competitions taking place each winter in North America. The largest are as follows:
– **Fur Rendez-Vous World Championship** (Anchorage, Alaska)
– **World Championship Sled Dog Derby** (Laconia, New Hampshire)
– **World Championship Dog Derby** (Las pas, Manitoba)
– **Open North American Championship** (Fairbanks, Alaska)
– **Surdough Rendez-Vous** (Whitehorse, Yukon Territory)

All of these races are yearly events attended by tens of thousands of spectators. The races are run in three legs of 25 to 70 km depending on the category (number of dogs), on Friday, Saturday, and Sunday, partially or completely in the snow-covered streets of the cities. But the sport has also changed with the development of very long races, the most famous being:
– **The Iditarod**, the "Last Great Race on Earth," the longest (1,049 miles in theory, but actually more than 1,800 kilometers!), the hardest, the most famous because of its prestigious history since it was started in 1973.
– **The Yukon Quest**, which follows the Yukon River from Whitehorse, Canada to Fairbanks, Alaska for nearly 1,300 kilometers (2,090 miles).
– **The Beargrease Sled Dog Marathon**, which takes place over 800 kilometers (1,290 miles) in Minnesota
– **The Montana Race to the Sky** or **the Labrador 800**.

More and more sophisticated sleds

Finally, a new course has appeared more recently (1996), based on the European model of long distance races in stages (created with the Alpirod in 1988), the International Rocky Mountain Stage Stop Sled Dog Race, which takes place in January in Wyoming. This 12-stage competition with night rests or bivouacs and in which certain dogs may be left to rest during certain stages, is without a doubt the type of competition that is most likely to be developed because of its way of respecting the dogs and more effective prevention by veterinary teams, unlike what happens in a long distance race with check points.

As a result other legends were born, other great names appeared such as Joe Redington, Sr., "Father of the Iditarod," "Doc" Lombard, the veterinarian, Eddy Streeper (multiple champion in the world of speed), Rick Swenson (six time winner of the Iditarod), Libbie Riddles (first woman to win the Iditarod in 1985, elected athlete of the year in the United States) and Suzan Butcher (four-time winner of the Iditarod). Alaskan resident and French doctor Jacques Philip is listed among these names because of his numerous victories in stage races and because he and his famous dog Byron also led a team of dogs at an altitude of more than 6,000 meters (1,830 feet) on top of Mount McKinley!
All of these great competitors remain in the hearts of today's mushers.

SOUTH AMERICA

Dog sledding has only recently appeared in South America, but the first official competition on snow was held in Ushuaia in Tierra del Fuego, Argentina in 1993, which also included some Chilean trails shows great promise for further development in the region.

SCANDINAVIA

If there is a birthplace for dog sledding, it is Scandinavia (Norway, Sweden, Finland) where the most popular discipline was originally not dog sledding, but rather the pulka, a sport that brings together cross country skiing and sledding. The skier is attached by a cord to his team of one to three dogs pulling a small ballasted vessel. In this discipline, which is directly derived from ancient hunting methods, the Scandinavians prefer to use hunting dogs (Braques, Pointers, Setters) since they are:
- faster in shorter distances (7 to 15 km) (11 to 24 miles)
- better psychologically adapted to solitary efforts
This "other" use of hunting dogs entails other precautions, which may sometimes seem comical, but are useful to protect the short-haired dogs from the cold:
- wearing a coat before and after the course
- individual blankets for dogs during bivouacs

Pulkaist in action

The Scandinavians have organized official competitions for nearly 70 years, since the pulka is one of the major sports in Norway and Sweden. In 1994, the Olympic Games in Lillehammer included the official organization of an international speed competition as part of the games' cultural program. It was 600 kilometers (965 miles) long (the Femundlopet) and started while medals were awarded in the Olympics closing ceremony, which allowed the whole world to witness the first steps of an arctic expedition in which the teams would travel to Nagano, Japan, the site of the next Olympic Games.

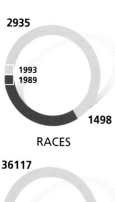
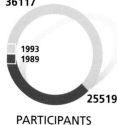
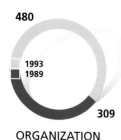
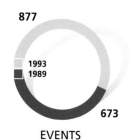
Laponia is the site of two annual international competitions. One is based on the Alaskan Iditarod and is nearly 1,000 km (1,600 miles) long and the other, the Scandream, is run in stages, totaling about 700 km (1,130 miles).

NON-NORTHERN EUROPE

The Swiss Club of Nordic Dogs, founded in 1959 upon the initiative of Dr. Thomas Althans and the judge Paul Nicoud, established its mission as promoting the breeding and development of Nordic dogs breeds. This being the case, it seemed inevitable that it be in charge of the organization of dog sledding races and in 1965 the first Swiss "training camp" was held. It was the first opportunity for dogsledders to actually discover the sport as it is practiced in North America.

A winter course circuit was soon established in Switzerland (Lenk, Saint-Cergue, Saignelegier, Sils-Saint Moritz, etc.) and in Germany (Todtmoos, Bernau, etc.), which later spread to France in 1979 (the Schluct). From that point on, courses continued to be created and the number of dog teams increased steadily. Organizations were established in each country: the Trail Club of Europe in 1973, then a group of European federations under the authority of the ESDRA (the European Sled Dog Racing Association) in 1983. This last organization currently oversees all of the national organizations and is also responsible for the annual organization of European championships (the first ones took place in 1984 in Saint Moritz, Switzerland). These are now divided into two separate categories: speed (300 dog teams participate in 5 different categories) and medium distance (approximately 60 dog teams).

In 1988 the largest European race was created and continued until 1996: the Alpirod-Royal Canin, a competition in stages that took place over 12 days and nearly 1,000 kilometers (1,600 miles). For the first time in Europe, the best Alaskan dog teams participated in a race crossing the Alps into Italy, France, Germany, Switzerland, and Austria... and won the first three competitions (Joe Runyan, Kathy Swenson, Roxy Wright). Starting in 1992, Frenchman Jacques Philip won the competition three years in a row, then Norwegian Roger Leegard and his team of "greysters" closed this important chapter in the history of the sport.

Since the disappearance of the Alpirod, two new courses with stages have been created using part of the original trail: the Alpentrail in the Tyrol and the Alpirush in the Vercors.

Finally, 1990 marked a turning point with the organization of the first world speed championships in Saint-Moritz, bringing together the elite of the world of pulka and dog sledding under the authority of the newly founded International Federation for Sled Dog Sports (IFSS).

INTERNATIONAL ORGANIZATIONS

International Federation for Sled Dog Sport (IFSS)
Founded in 1989 as the logical result of the world development of

dog sledding and ski pulka, the IFSS is responsible for establishing the racing regulations and their evolution, for managing the sport on an international level, for organizing biannual world championships and relationships with the International Olympic Committee since it is already a member of the General Association of International Sporting Federations. The IFSS brings together 45 national federations on five continents (there are competitions in South Africa) and publishes a report every four years that provides information about the growth and evolution of this sport that effects some 100,000 dog teams throughout the world.

International Sled Dog Veterinary Medical Association (ISDVMA)

The ISDVMA appeared in relation to the IFSS and aims at bringing together veterinarians involved in dog sled medicine in an organization that allows them to improve and perfect their specializations. It therefore helps to provide dog breeders and trainers with veterinarians that are more interested, qualified, and up-to-date with the scientific and technical changes in the field of canine sports medicine. The ISDVMA organizes an international congress every two years and publishes several brochures and documents dedicated to sled dog biology and medicine, while establishing research protocols to improve dog lovers' knowledge and dogs' well-being.

Racing Sled Dogs

Brief History

More than 4,000 years ago, nomadic tribes of the North of Lake Baikal in central Siberia were the first to harness their dogs to a sled. Over the centuries, using harnessed dogs became the dominate means of transportation for Siberian tribes such as the Chuchkis or the Samoyedes. These people considered their dogs as companions, protectors, hunters, guardians of herds of reindeer, and pulling dogs. The Chuchkis were in fact the first to really develop sledding techniques. In

Member structures of the IFSS
(International Federation for Sled Dog Sport)

Country	Organizations	Members	Events	Races	Teams
Austria	9	600	12	66	1,151
Belgium	3	250	6	24	480
Czech Rep.	1	480	10	28	345
Denmark	2	130	16	75	460
England	7	550	16	52	1,084
Finland	26	1,000	14	37	464
France	60	1,600	15	69	1,744
Germany	5	2,400	48	284	3,161
Hungary	1	30	2	2	20
Ireland	1	3	0	0	3
Italy	5	400	30	137	2,390
Luxemburg	1	20	1	6	44
Holland	5	200	6	30	481
Norway	80	800	90	193	1,966
Scotland	4	120	6	24	381
Spain	5	250	4	26	220
Andorra	1	5	1	2	4
Wales	3	25	5	13	178
Sweden	56	5,000	89	289	3,977
Switzerland	3	175	9	49	671
Ukraine	1	5	1	1	5
Russia	3	80	4	8	70
Slovenia	1	30	1	3	25
United States	122	11,500	330	1,097	10,525
Canada	63	6200	122	321	4591
Japan	7	345	7	47	1329
Australia	4	200	15	22	152
New Zealand	5	127	11	49	336
South Africa	1	100	10	10	82
Argentina	1	27	1	1	18
Chili	1	13	1	1	8

a recent work published by the FOND Association (Friends of Nordic Dogs), Robert Crane, a Russian teacher who loves Siberian Huskies, writes that the combination of intense climatic variations and the presence of other hostile tribes had forced the Chuchkis to base their economy on the rapid means of transportation afforded by the sled dogs, which allowed them to cover long distances on the uneven ground of the tundra and ice fields.

In approximately 1800 BC, Eskimo tribes populated the Alaskan shores of the Arctic Ocean. There is evidence that these men also used sleds with harnesses of three or four dogs. When the Norwegian explorer Fridtjof Nansen saw North American Eskimos 37 centuries later, what he described was surely quite similar to these original teams. The first written accounts of sled dogs by subarctic people appear in Arabic literature from the 10th century, in accounts of Marco Polo in the 13th century, and in those of Franscesco da Vollo in the 16th century.

Originally the "Nordic" dog was a sight hunter, most likely a descendent of domesticated dogs that had migrated from latitudes further south with tribes of hunters many generations earlier. The dogs that survived in the harsh Siberian climate were large, with very thick coats, resembling a wolf. They are the distant ancestors of today's Nordic breeds. Their ears were short, to reduce heat loss, held erect to hear as well as possible, and covered in fine hair as thermal insulation.

The first mushers were explorers, hunters, or trappers who traveled in these frozen deserted areas. They soon realized that there was no better means of transportation. The most popular of these groups was certainly the Canadian Mounted Police and the postal services of the Hudson Bay Company. A Chippewa Indian from Minnesota, John Beargrease was in charge of transporting the mail on the north shore of Lake Superior. One of the great American races is named after him today.

Postal services in Alaska have long used harnessed dogs to link Seward to Nome (more than 2,200 kilometers of trail), since mail is delivered to prospectors and their gold is brought back to "the city" by the same form of transportation. In 1963, the United States Postal Service paid homage to their last leader, Chester Noongwook from Savoonga on St. Lawrence Island in the Bering Sea. The last official patrol of the Royal Canadian Mounted Police took place in 1969 and was 750 kilometers (1,200 miles) roundtrip between Old Crow and Fort Macpherson.

Evolution of the Dogs

The geographic isolation of peoples such as the Chuchkis, the Koryaks, the Samoyedes and small tribes of the Kamtchatka Peninsula explains how little sled dogs have evolved since the appearance of greater means of communication. At first, "genetic" selection was of the most primitive dogs. Only the smartest lead dogs and strongest males were kept for breeding. The other males were crudely castrated and no other types of dogs or breeds were introduced into these original lines before the end of the 19th century.

The Siberian Husky comes from the Kamtchatka Peninsula and is a very ancient "breed" developed then maintained by the Chuchkis over the course of centuries as a sled dog. These animals were first imported from Siberia to Alaska by a Russian fur trader in 1909 with the clear goal of participating in the second All Alaska Sweepstakes. The breed was then selected for work before, unfortunately, being selected for standards of beauty to become the breed we know today.

The Alaskan Malamute is a more rustic dog, taking its name from the Inuit people that bred it, the Mahlemutes. A pull dog in the etymological sense of the term, the Malamute is rarely found participating in dog sled races today, if only in circuits reserved for pure breed dogs, because of their relative slowness in racing. The same is true of the Greenlander, whose origin is apparent in its name. Though smaller than the Malamute, it is also rarely seen in competition. The Samoyed, which comes from the tribe of the same name in northwestern Siberia is clearly the most efficient of sled dogs, even if its immaculate white double coat also makes it a dog of rare beauty.

Spectators attending their first dog sled race will be surprised at the variety of dogs participating in these competitions: the classic Nordic breeds mentioned above may compete with teams of Braques, Pointers, Greysters (a Norwegian cross-breed mixing a dominate Pointer with a bit of Greyhound), and especially Alaskan Huskies, the most efficient breed that makes up roughly 80% of the world's population of sled dogs.

Though the Alaskan Husky is not recognized as a pure breed by the International Cynological Federation, it is a true breed in the biological sense of the term, an initial mix of Arctic and Indian dogs.

The breed was developed and selected over the last 40 years with the sole purpose of racing. Infusions of Greyhound, Braque, or Pointer blood had little success in first and second generations. The population of Alaskan Huskies is now well established and we are witnessing the development of racing lines specializing in speed, medium- or long-distance. Other hybrids exist and are sometimes encountered in races, such as the Targhee Hound (crossing the Staghound and the Irish Setter) or the Quebec Hound (primarily from the original dogs of Indian populations in the province of Quebec).

Morphometry by performance rank for dogs participating in the Iditarod
(Rooks, 1994) (in cm: 1 cm = 0.3937 inch)

Final Rank	Height	Height of the Forelegs	Length of the Hind legs	Shoulder of Back	Extension of the Forelegs	Thoracic Perimeter
1-5	61.5	60.5	35.7	8.0	63.1	63.0
6-10	59.6	58.3	35.7	7.7	61.1	63.8
11-15	61.5	59.4	34.9	8.3	62.2	65.4
16-20	57.9	57.5	34.6	8.0	59.9	62.7
Mid rank	58.2	56.3	35.3	8.4	59.9	67.3
End rank	56.2	55.1	34.4	8.1	58.6	65.9

Optimal Conformation of the Racing Sled Dog

Until recently, the optimal morphometry of the racing sled dog was essentially the fruit of the musher's practical experience. The first serious morphometrical studies on dogs participating in international level competitions were only done in 1989. With systematic measurements on several hundred dogs over a period of 8 years, Gilchrist created a bank of conformation data regarding the efficiency of the dog's skeleton in relation to its racing abilities. The first element he took into account was the dog's overall balance. In the ideal dog, the scapula, pelvis, humerus, and femur must be the same length. The length, taken in its average value, was called the constant (c) and became the point of reference for all of the other parameters considered. From that point on, information regarding optimal conformation has been provided as a percentage of the reference constant (c):
– the height of the shoulders must approach 200% of c.
– the distance between the elbow and the ground must be approximately 160%.
– the distance from the tarsus to the ground must be approximately 90% of c.

Gilchrist also considered the following elements important:
– the length of the dog must be greater than its height at the withers by approximately 10%.
– the angle of the scapula must vary between 32 and 34 degrees and the angle of the pelvis must be as close as possible to 30 degrees

The results allow us to correlate certain morphometric data with the overall biomechanical potential of a dog, particularly in terms of lesser energy loss in effort, allowing the line of the dog's back to remain practically horizontal during movement.

More recently, Fuhrer demonstrated that a complete morphodynamic study of a dog can be done using cinematographical information during exertion on a treadmill, though no new information was provided in addition to those mentioned previously.

Finally, in 1994 Rooks presented the results of his statistical studies carried out in collaboration with the ISDVMA on dog teams participating in the Iditarod. The efficiency of the skeleton is of primary importance in the way that the dog supports the biomechanical stress caused by high racing speeds maintained over long distances.

The dogs with the best conformations run longer

Different categories of pulka and dog sled races

Type	Category	Number of Dogs per heat	Distance (km)
Speed	S.W. (women's pulka)	1-4	7
	S.M. (men's pulka)	1-4	12
	C	£ 4	7
	B	4-6	15
	A	6-8	20
	O	> 8	25
Mid Distance	Limited	£ 6	30
	Open	≥ 6	40
Course by Stages		≥ 12	60-120
Long Distance		≥ 16	1,000-2,000

and are subjected to fewer traumatic disorders. In this study, the reference constant was still the average value of the four bone segments (the scapula, pelvis, humerus, and femur) and are sought after in as equal a length as possible. Marked differences in the length of these bones causes biomechanical stress on the joints and orthopedic problems.

Balance is obtained by comparing the measurements of the tibia/fibula pair and the radius/ulna pair. If the length of these bone segments is uneven, the dog will run in a way that resembles of a cow, which ultimately results in pain and muscle inflammation. The vertical distance from the point of the elbow to the ground will be longer than the value of the constant.

These statistics also lead to the fact that dogs in the most competitive teams are taller and longer than other competitors on average. The flexion and range of movement of the joints are also fundamental points in a good conformation in sled dogs. A large range of articular movement generates less work and therefore less muscle fatigue over the kilometers. In contrast, limbs that are too stiff will soon lead to problems with tendons and joints.

Granted, there remains lots of research to be done on the field of Sporting dog biomechanics in general, but it is reassuring to see that an interest in the dynamic behavior of different morphologies, which should lead to more efficient and robust dogs in the future where orthopedic disorders are concerned.

Dog sledding and ski pulka have become separate sports in which men and women compete with an equal chance of winning, especially by equally sharing the effort provided by their dogs. Let's hope we see more of the current international development and the integration of children into different competitions, which is a perfect way of learning to respect animals and nature.

Average speeds reached during competition
1 km = 1.609 mile

Type of Race	Speed (km/h)
Speed	30-32
Mid Distance	24-28
Long Distance	14-18

Team in action

RING COMPETITIONS

Ring competitions are very developed in France and Belgium (though their regulations are different). The French Ring is a new discipline in the United States and has a promising future. Ring competitions consist of a series of training tests in which the dog expresses its natural abilities in the fields of jumping obstacles, obedience, and fighting. These tests allow the fundamental qualities of athleticism, dynamism, capacity for obedience, stability of character, and courage to be selected from herding and guarding breeds. To this end, their results appear on pedigrees and serve to inform breeders on the use of the best male dogs to improve the character quality of the breeding.

List of breeds authorized to compete in Ring tests

Group 1

German Shepherd
Kelpie
Beauceron Shepherd
Belgian Shepherds
Brie Shepherd
Picard Shepherd
Pyrenees Shepherd
Scottish Collie
Bearded Collie
Border Collie
Dutch Shepherd
Nizziny
Australian Bouvier
Bouvier des Ardennes
Bouvier des Flandres

Group 2

Doberman
Hovawart
Tibetan Bulldog
Sharpei
Rottweiler
Argentine Bulldog
Boxer
Standard Schnauzer
Giant Schnauzer

Group 3

Airedale Terrier
American Staffordshire
  Terrier
English Bull Terrier
Staffordshire Bull
  Terrier
Black Russian Terrier

Organizing the Competitions

Ring competitions are organized on closed fields that measure 2,500 square meters (26,900 square feet) and are often club fields.
The French Championship is well known and is often held in a stadium to allow the spectators (who are often quite numerous) to sit in the stands.
The best dogs meet during the French Championship after having participated in regional selection competitions. The dogs that reach this level are categorized in two different ways:
– French Championship based on their performance on the day in question
– French Cup, based on cumulative results from the selection competitions and the Championship

THE BREEDS INVOLVED:

Virtually all breeds in the first and second group (herding and guarding dogs) are subjected to work and present sufficient size.
A complete list of breeds authorized to compete may be found in the appendix.

THE DIFFERENT EXERCISES:

Ring Exercises are divided into 3 categories:
Jumping: The dog must jump 3 types of obstacles (high jump, climb a fence, and long jump). The size of the obstacles varies depending on the dog's level.
Obedience: This is a group of exercises in which the dog must pay attention to its handler. During changes of exercises requiring the pair

List of exercises by level of competition in the Ring
(according to S. Migliano)

Exercise	Brevet		Ring I		Ring II		Ring III	
Jumps			Hurdle (1 m)	12	Hurdle (1.10 m)	16	Hurdle (1.20 m)	20
					Long Jump (3.50 m)	12	Long Jump (4.50 m)	20
					Palisade (2 m)	10	Palisade (2.30 m)	20
Obedience	Heel on Leash	4	Heel on Leash	4	Heel on Leash	4	Heel on Leash	4
	Food refusal	10	Food refusal	10	Food refusal	10	Food refusal	20
	Heel off leash w/muzzle	8	Heel off leash w/muzzle	8	Heel off leash w/muzzle	8	Heel off leash w/muzzle	8
	Long Stay (down)	10	Long Stay (sit or down)	10	Long Stay (sit or down)	10	Long Stay (sit or down)	10
			Positions (start sit or down)	20	Positions (start sit, down or stand)	20	Positions (start sit, down or stand)	20
			Thrown Retrieve	4	Thrown Retrieve	4	Thrown Retrieve	4
					Seen Retrieve	8	Seen Retrieve	8
							Unseen Retrieve	8
							Send Away	12
Combativeness / Bitework	Defense of Handler	30	Defense of Handler	30	Defense of Handler	30	Defense of Handler	30
	Face Attack	30	Face Attack	30	Face Attack	30	Face Attack	30
			Guard of Decoy	30	Guard of Decoy	30	Guard of Decoy	30
			Fleeing Attack	30	Fleeing Attack	30	Fleeing Attack	30
					Search	40	Search	40
							Stopped Attack	20
							Guard of Object	30
	General Outlook	8	General Outlook	12	General Outlook	28	General Outlook	46
	TOTAL	**100**	**TOTAL**	**200**	**TOTAL**	**300**	**TOTAL**	**400**

A dog must defend its handler if he is attacked.

to move about the field, the dog must walk at the handler's feet.

Bitework: The dog develops its fighting abilities and is always under its handler's control. The most spectacular exercise is one in which the dog must stop without touching the attacker and heel upon its handler's command.

Obtaining Ranks

The dog must obtain 75 points (out of 100) to receive the title of Brevet for Dogs of Defense, have demonstrated no fear of shots fired and have obtained at least 22 points out of 50 in the two biting exercises. There is no particular title for Ring I, II, and III levels.

A PROGRESSION IN THE COMPETITIONS

As for any athletic discipline, there is a progression in the tests. The dog may not directly access certain ranks. It must follow a working route.

– Entry to the Brevet for Dogs of Defense:

Any pure breed dog belonging to the breeds authorized to compete that is at least 10 months old may present in the Brevet. It must have a working folder.

– Entry to Ring I:

Any dog holding a Brevet for Dogs of Defense or a Brevet de Campagne may present in Ring I.

– Entry to Ring II:

The dog must have twice obtained at least 160 points out of 200 in Ring I, from two different judges.

– Entry to Ring III:

The dog must have twice obtained at least 240 points out of 300 in Ring III, from two different judges.

Note:
As long as a dog has not twice received 300 points out of 400 in Ring II, it may compete in Ring II.

– Entry to French Ring Championship:

Three Ring III competitions called selection competitions are organized. The 24 best dogs at the national level will present at the French Championship.

Competitions in the Country

A completely French concept, competitions in the country appear to be the practical application of Ring competitions. They consist of a series of training tests in which the dog expresses its natural abilities in the fields of hurdles, obedience, fighting, and tracking. Just like the ring, competitions in the country pinpoint fundamental qualities of athleticism, dynamism, degree of obedience, stability of character, and courage in herding and guarding breeds. These tests are recognized as a way of bettering the canine species. To this end, the results appear on pedigrees and serve to inform breeders as to how to improve the species.

Organization of the Competition

Competitions in the country take place on free terrain in the form of a circuit where the animal is confronted with a variety of work situations in which it must show courage or initiative.

The locations most frequently used are castle grounds. Nevertheless it would be interesting to orient the work toward industrial areas or abandoned towns. The situational difficulties that the dog must resolve in urban areas would better correspond to the way in which dogs are used in administrations.

The free tracking tests and bloodhound tests are performed in nearby agricultural areas.

The Breeds Involved

A complete list of the breeds that are authorized for competition is attached.

The Different Exercises

Exercises in competitions in the country are divided into 3 categories:
Jumps. The dog must clear 5 types of obstacles (climbing a natural wall, high jumps - hurdles, trellis, netting - and long jump over a river). The size of the obstacles varies depending on the level reached by the dog.
Obedience brings together exercises in which the dog must listen to its handler. Moreover, during changes in exercise that require moving about the field, the dog must walk at the handler's feet. Unlike in the ring, the dog must be able to move about on any support (part of the exercises takes place in the water) and may be distracted during its exercise either as scheduled by the judges or not (one might remember the finale at the

List of breeds authorized to compete in Ring tests

Group 1

German Shepherd
Kelpie
Beauceron Shepherd
Belgian Shepherds
Brie Shepherd
Picard Shepherd
Pyrenees Shepherd
Scottish Collie
Bearded Collie
Border Collie
Dutch Shepherd
Australian Bouvier
Bouvier des Ardennes
Bouvier des Flandres

Group 2

Doberman
Hovawart
Tibetan Bulldog
Sharpei
Rottweiler
Boxer
Standard Schnauzer
Giant Schnauzer

Group 3

Airedale Terrier
American Staffordshire
 Terrier
English Bull Terrier
Staffordshire Bull
 Terrier
Black Russian Terrier

Competition in the Country in 1998: a dog was distracted during part of its time by a model airplane flying above its head).

Biting. The dog develops its fighting abilities, always under its handler's control. The exercises are performed at different distances and the dog must be tormented by different elements: an attacker in a costume, sound elements (alarm clock, trumpet, etc.)

Reaching Levels

To obtain the title of "Brevet de campagne" (certificate of competition in the country), the dog must obtain 112.5 points (out of 150), not be afraid of shots, and have bitten in a frontal attack during at least 10 seconds. There is no special title for levels of 350 points or 500 points.

PROGRESSION IN THE COMPETITION

As in any other athletic discipline, there is a progression to the tests. The dog cannot directly reach certain levels. It must follow a specific working route.

– Accessing the Certificate:
Any breed of dog that is authorized to participate may present the Brevet de Campagne. It must have a working file.

– Accessing the 350 points:
The dog must have a Brevet Campagne or Brevet Ring (ring certificate). It may also participate if it holds the titles Ring I, RCI I and II (note: if the dog obtains 280 points, it can access RCI III) or Schutzhund I and II.

– Accessing the 500 points/Selective:
The dog may participate in the 500 point tests if it holds a:
– Ring II having already twice obtained 240 points
– Ring III, RCI III or Schutzhund III
– 350 point level, having already obtained at least 280 points (80%) in the two tests, with two different judges.

Comments:
– Ring II dogs (with the above criteria), Ring III and RCI III dogs may participate in either of the two types of competition (350 points and selective).

– Competitors that receive 2 excellents (more than 350 points) in the Selective competitions may not participate in the "350 point competition in the country."

- Accessing the Championnat de France de Campagne (French Championship Competition in the Country):

The number of dogs in the Championnat de France is fixed at 12. They are selected based on the results they obtain during competitions considered as selection competitions for the Championnat de France.

List of exercises by level of Country competition (according to S. Migliano).

Exercise	Brevet		350 points		500 points/Selective	
Jumps	Hurdle (1 m)	10	Hurdle (1.1-1.2 m)	20	Hurdle (1.1-1.2 m)	20
			Wall (1.7-2 m)	20	Wall (1.7-2 m)	20
			Trellis (1 m)	10	Trellis (1 m)	10
			Netting (1 m)	10	Netting (1 m)	10
					River (3-4 m)	20
Obedience	Heel on Leash	4	Heel on Leash	4	Heel on Leash	4
			Heel off Leash	8	Heel off Leash	8
	Heel off Leash	8				
	Long Stay	10	Long Stay 2'	10	Long Stay 2' (Sit or Down)	10
	Food refusal (thrown)	10	Food refusal	10	Food refusal	10
	Retrieve in water	10	Seen Retrieve in water	8	Seen Retrieve in water	8
			Unseen Retrieve r in water	10	Unseen Retrieve in water	10
			Positions	18	Positions	18
					Send away in water	12
Combativeness/Bitework	Defense of Handler	30	Defense of Handler	30	Defense of Handler (with muzzle)	15
	Launched attack	30	Face or fleeing launched attack	30	Defense of Handler against Decoy	30
			Guard of Decoy	40	Attack at 80 m	30
			Search	40	Attack at 30 m	30
					Guard of Decoy	10
					Search	40
					False attack 80 m	20
					False attack 30 m	20
					Guard of Object	30
Tracking	300 m Tracking on-leash Retrieve of Object	30	On-Leash Tracking (10m leash)	40	400 m Tracking: Retrieve of Object, off leash	40
					400 m Tracking: Search for tracklayer, on-leash	40
	General Outlook	**8**	**General Outlook**	**12**	**General Outlook**	**25**
	TOTAL	**150**	**TOTAL**	**350**	**TOTAL**	**500**

Schutzhund competitions and RCI

Schutzhund competitions were created especially for the German Shepherd as an evaluation of the Working dog's behavior. They are now open to all breeds of Working dogs. RCI (International Competition Regulations) derive from this selection program. They were quickly adopted by many countries.

These two sports are very similar in their rules, developing the dog's natural abilities such as smelling and tracking, combativeness in bitework and obedience and sociability in obedience exercises. In all of the exercises, the dog must show enthusiasm and any indication of fear or submission is strongly penalized.

Organizing the Trials

The trials are divided into three categories that are separated from each other in time and space:
– tracking is done on a track where no other dogs are present and is laid out by a person that the dog does not know
– obedience and bitework exercises take place in the same field, but separately

The tracks must offer the same level of difficulty for all of the dogs of a given level. The field for the obedience and bitework exercises is enclosed and is often a club field.

THE BREEDS INVOLVED:

All working breeds that are recognized by the FCI are authorized to compete.
A complete list of the breeds may be found opposite.

THE DIFFERENT EXERCISES:

Schutzhund and ICR exercises are divided into three categories:
– Tracking: The dog must demonstrate perfect following of the track. It must track with a deep nose, not raise its head, track calmly, not leave the trail for more than 20 cm (8 inches) and not back-track.
– Obedience: All of the exercises take place in the same order. They mix pure obedience with jumping obstacles. Dynamic execution and perfect attentiveness to the handler are highly regarded.
– Biting: The dog must only bite the protective sleeve worn by the helper. The exercises take place in the same order. The dog must show a lot of initiative because all of the biting holds are executed without commands.

List of breeds authorized to compete in RCI tests.

Group 1
German Shepherd
Kelpie
Belgian Shepherds
Beauceron Shepherd
Brie Shepherd
Picard Shepherd
Pyrenees Shepherd
Scottish Collie
Bearded Collie
Border Collie
Dutch Shepherd
Australian Bouvier
Bouvier des Ardennes
Bouvier des Flandres

Group 2
Doberman
Giant Schnauzer
Standard Schnauzer
Boxer
Argentine Bulldog
Rottweiler
Sharpei
Tibetan Bulldog
Hovawart

Group 3
Airedale Terrier
Black Russian Terrier
American Staffordshire
  Terrier
English Bull Terrier
Staffordshire Bull
  Terrier

Only sociable dogs are able to interact with strangers.

The chart below lists the different exercises by category and by level for RCI trials. The exercises are not listed in their exact order, but do give a general idea of the progression.

Obtaining Qualifications

There is a progression in the trials :

– Entry to the ICR and the Schutzhund I:

The dog must be at least 18 months old and have already passed a temperament test with the judge.

Retrieving articles and jumping obstacles are joined together

– Entry to the ICR and Schutzhund II:

The dog must be at least 19 months old and have obtained at least 70 points out of 100 in tracking and obedience and 80 points out of 100 in bitework, and in the case of the ICR, at least 70 points out of 100 in the three disciplines.

It may also compete if it holds a Brevet de Campagne.

The dog must not touch the sleeve upon discovery

– Entry to the ICR and Schutzhund III:

The dog must be at least 20 months old and have obtained at least 70 points out of 100 in tracking and obedience and 80 points out of 100 in bitework in the Schutzhund, and in the ICR at least 70 points out of 100 in the three disciplines.

It may also compete if it has reached the rank of 350 points in Country trials.

The World Championship of the WUSV (Welt-Union der Vereine für deutsche Schäferhunde in German, or the World Union of German Shepherd Clubs) is the best known competition in the world for the Schutzhund. It is reserved for German Shepherds, which is the original breed for the competition. The WUSV brings together about 60 countries and organizes its show the first weekend of October each year.

It also determines the number of dogs from each country that are admitted to competition.

List of exercises by level of RCI competition

Exercise	RCI I		RCI II		RCI III	
Jumps	Hurdle Jump (1 m) and Retrieving a personal object	15	Hurdle jump (1 m) and Retrieving an Object (650 g)	15	Hurdle jump (1 m) and Retrieving an Object (650 g)	15
			Palisade Jump and Retrieving a personal object (1.60 m)	15	Palisade Jump and Retrieving a personal object (1.80 m)	15
Obedience	Heel on Leash	15	Heel on Leash	10		
	Heel off Leash	20	Heel off Leash	15	Heel off Leash	15
	Walking Sit	10	Walking Sit	5	Walking Sit	5
	Walking Down with Recall	10	Walking Down with Recall	10	Walking Down with Recall	10
	Retrieving an Object	10	Retrieving an Object (1 kg)	10	Retrieving an Object (2 kg)	10
	Send away with Down	10	Send away with Down	10	Send away with Down	10
	Down under Distraction	10	Down under Distraction	10	Down under Distraction	10
					Walking Stand-Stay	5
					Running Stand-Stay with Recall	10
Combativity/biting	Search	5	Search (6 hiding spots)	5	Search (6 hiding spots)	5
	Hold	5	Hold	5	Hold	5
	Bark	5	Bark	5	Bark	5
	Defense of Handler	35	Defense of Handler	35	Defense of Handler and Courage Test	45
	Courage Test	50	Test of courage	20	Escape of Attacker	10
			Escape of Attacker	10	Attacking the dog	25
			Attacking the dog	40		
			Escort	5	Escort	5
Tracking	Following of the Track	80	Following of the Track	80	Following of the Track	80
	Number of turns	2	Number of turns	2	Number of turns	4
	Retrieving 2 objects	20	Retrieving 2 objects	20	Retrieving 3 objects	20
	TOTAL	**300**	**TOTAL**	**300**	**TOTAL**	**300**

MONDIO-RING TRIALS

The Mondio-Ring was created by delegations from several American and European countries to become the relay for the existing national programs.
Its goal is to provide entertainment for the spectators, to be a game that becomes progressively more difficult for the participants and a competitive sport for trainers and their dogs. Finally, Mondio-Ring trials are designed to accentuate a dog's abilities, the quality of its training, its handler's expertise, and its genetic make-up.

Organizing the Trials

The trials are open to all level participants who wish to participate. To do so, the societies that organize a race alert the international organization.

The field is always in enclosed and must be less than 5,000 m² (1 1/4 acres).

THE BREEDS INVOLVED

All breeds are allowed, providing that the dog has a pedigree from a canine society that is recognized by the FCI.

THE DIFFERENT EXERCISES

The program is made up of three types of trials that must take place in the following order:

– Obedience: This is a group of exercises in which the dog must be completely attentive to its handler and respond to certain commands.

– Jumping: The dog must jump 3 types of obstacles (high jumps, climbing a palisade and long jump). The size of the obstacles varies depending on the dog's level.

– Bitework: The dog develops its combativeness, always under the control of its handler. The most spectacular exercise consists of stopped attacks in which the dog must not touch the attacker and must heel at its handler's command.

The order of the exercises is determined by a random drawing at the beginning of each competition. General outlook is not counted separately as in Ring Competitions, but rather is an integral part of how the exercise is graded, up to 10% of the total points being awarded in this exercise.

The table below shows the different exercises by category and by levelfor Mondio-Ring Competitions.

Obtaining Qualifications

As for any athletic discipline, there is a progression in the trials. A dog may not directly access certain levels. It must follow a working route.

– Entry to Mondio-Ring I:

Any pure breed dog belonging to the breeds authorized to compete that holds a Brevet de Ring or Brevet de Campagne may present in Level I of the Mondio-Ring. It must have a working folder.

– Entry to Mondio-Ring II:

The dog must have twice obtained at least 160 points out of 200 in Mondio-Ring I, from two different judges.

– Entry to Mondio-Ring III:

The dog must have twice obtained at least 240 points out of 300 in Mondio-Ring II, from two different judges.

– Entry to Mondio-Ring Finals:

Every year, a final competition of the best dogs takes place the 2nd weekend of October. The number of participants per country is defined by the final competition organizers.

The traditional accessories for attacking and retrieving can vary greatly

List of exercises by level of Mondio-Ring competition.

Exercise	Mondio-Ring I		Mondio-Ring II		Mondio-Ring III	
Obedience	Heel off Leash	6	Heel off Leash	6	Heel off Leash	6
	Long Down	10	Long Down	10	Long Stay (Sit or Down)	10
	Send away (20 m)	12	Send away (30 m)	12	Send away (40 m)	12
	Positions (5 m)	10	Positions (10 m)	12	Positions (15 m)	20
	Food Refusal (thrown)	5	Food Refusal (thrown and on ground)	10	Food Refusal (thrown and on ground))	10
	Retrieving a thrown object	12	Retrieving a thrown object	12	Retrieving a thrown object	12
	Searching for an object	15	Searching for an object	15		
Jumps	Palisade (1.80 m)	15	Palisade (2.10 m)	15	Palisade (2.30 m)	15
	Long jump (3 m)	15	Hurdle (1.20 m)	20	Long jump (4 m)	20
	Hurdle (1 m)	15			Hurdle (1.20 m)	20
Combativeness/bitework	**Face Attack with baton (30 m, no obstacles)**		**Face Attack with baton (40 m, no obstacles)**		**Face Attack with baton (50 m, no obstacles)**	
	Start	10	Start	10	Start	10
	Attack	30	Attack	20	Attack	30
	Out/Recall	10	Out/Recall	10	Out/Recall	10
	Fleeing Attack with Biting		**Fleeing Attack with Biting**		**Fleeing Attack with Biting**	
	Start	10	Start	10	Start	10
	Attack	30	Attack	10	Attack	10
	Out/Recall	10	Out/Recall	10	Out/Recall	10
	Defense of Handler	30	Defense of Handler	30	Defense of Handler	30
			Face Attack with accessories (30 m)		**Face Attack with accessories (30 m)**	
			Start	10	Start	10
			Attack	20	Attack	30
			Out/Recall	10	Out/Recall	10
			Search and Escort		**Search and Escort**	
			Find	10	Find	10
			Escort	30	Escort	30
					Stopped fleeing attack	
					Start	10
					Attack	20
					Guard of Object	30
	TOTAL	**200**	**TOTAL**	**300**	**TOTAL**	**400**

TRUFFLE HUNTING

Because of the geographic distribution of truffles, dog truffle competitions only currently take place in France. In other countries, the rarity of truffles causes a certain reticence in truffle hunters to perform this type of competition, preferring to search for truffles for fun rather than professional competition.

The first dog truffle competition took place in Dordogne in 1970. Truffle lovers, truffle growers and dog handlers gathered for the occasion. Neighboring regions followed suit some years later and created regulations. However, it was only on September 29, 1982 that the Société Centrale Canine (Central Canine Society) would standardize its first official rule.

In the beginning, dogs participating in these competitions were mostly (99%) non registered dogs. This tendency has clearly been reversed, since we now count only 30% of the dogs as non registered dogs. The competitions are open to dogs of all breeds, but only dogs that are registered and have a working folder will see their results standardized.

Two categories of competition were established:

Beginner Competition (Class A): this competition does not grant the CACT (Certificat d'Aptitude au Championnat de Travail-Working Champion Skills Certificate). It is reserved for young dogs (10 months) that have not yet acquired sufficient experience. A dog with two "excellent" scores may no longer compete in this category.

Open Competition (Class B): This is open to all dogs, providing they have already competed in Class A and that they at least one grade of "excellent."

Qualifying Grades are given based on the following point scale:
" Excellent "– for dogs obtaining at least 70% of the points
" Very Good "– for dogs obtaining at least 60% of the points
" Good " – for dogs obtaining at least 50% of the points
Less than 50% of the points, the grade of "insufficient" will be recorded in their working folder.

The CACT is awarded in Competition B to the dog with a grade of "excellent" and more than 80% of the points. One CACT is awarded per competition. In the event that two dogs have the same number of points, the CACT will be awarded to the dog who found the most truffles in the least amount of time. The CACT reserve may be also be awarded to the second-place dog. The title of working champion shall be awarded to a dog with 3 CACTs received from at least two different judges.

Truffières are organized as follows

Each truffière should hold 6 truffles arranged in no particular order. They must always be at least 30 cm (12 inches) apart and shall be buried at a depth of 3 to 10 cm (1 _ to 4 inches) no more than 36 hours beforehand. The truffles must be at least 2 cm (3/4 inch) and no more than 4 cm (1 _ inches) in diameter. The ground covering must not be such that the handler would suspect the location of the truffles. A precise plan for placing the truffles will be drawn up with a number for each truffle and will be provided to the jury. The organizers shall carefully plan the event so that the dogs can do their work without being disturbed by the spectators or by other dogs. The sides of the truffière are approximately 25 m (82 feet) long. An enclosure or a separation is highly recommended, but it must be placed 5 meters (16 feet) outside of the boundaries of the truffière to prevent the spectators from standing on the truffles to be found. The truffières must be separated by at least 5 meters (16 feet). Except for the handler, no one is admitting into the working area. Dogs that are obviously suffering from contagious diseases and mean dogs shall be excluded from the competition by the organizers. The necessary terms and conditions to this effect, as well as the organizing company's release from liability in the event of an accident caused by an animal will be specified on agreement forms signed by the competitors. Each truffière will have a number and passing over each of them shall be done after a random drawing among the competitors, all gathered at the start of the competition in the presence of the jury. The organizers will take all the necessary steps so that the drawing only takes place among the competitors and that they cannot later go and spot their truffière. Male dogs and female dogs shall be judged by group. The number of competitors for a given jury on a given day is limited to 15.

The handler and dog team may then appear before the jury to compete. The competition shall be judged based on a total of 200 points, broken down as follows:

Length of work: 72 points
Truffles found: 123 points
General outlook: 5 points

When his number is called, the competitor must present himself before the jury with his dog without going to the truffière in order to avoid any early indication of its location. Upon the signal from the judge, the handler takes his dog and once he arrives in the working zone, commands the animal. The clock starts as soon as the animal has two feet on the truffière and is only stopped once the dog has found the sixth truffle or after 12 minutes, whichever comes first.

Truffle hunting may only be done on leash in beginner competitions in Class A. It is preferable that the dog works alone on the truffière to avoid piling up the dirt, witch is technically advised against. The wearing of a muzzle is prohibited during the test.

The dog should tap with his paw to indicate the exact location of a truffle. The handler will go and retrieve the truffle without digging a surface of more than 20 cm_ (3 square inches). Any truffles found that are not immediately turned in to the jury for verification shall lead to elimination of the competitor. Identifying a spot without a truffle calls for a 10-point penalty. Identifying a spot from which a truffle has already been taken calls for a 5-point penalty. After a dog has identified a spot without a truffle designated on the map, the jury does not inform the competitor, who is free to decide to continue his search or not.

In the event that a dog identifies a location not indicated on the map and a truffle is in fact there, the points will be marked as if the truffle had been placed there by the organizers. Each location where a truffle has been found and retrieved shall be covered over again and smoothed off by the handler or he risks forfeiting the points awarded for the truffle found. The maximum working time is set at 12 minutes. Any stopping before 12 minutes is the equivalent of forfeit and the dog is not classed. For each truffle found, the jury will announce the time and chronological number of the truffle to the competitor, unless the competitor has previously requested that they not do so. All commands, signals, gestures, or pulling on the leash by the leader that could prevent the dog from identifying a location shall be penalized as though the animal marked a spot without a truffle.

The grade for general outlook must take into account obedience, eagerness to work, good behavior, as well as wandering outside of the truffière during the trial.

The record for such a competition in France is currently 52 seconds.

OBEDIENCE TRIALS

Obedience trials have long existed on an international level, especially in Nordic countries. They are often organized in a different manner, even if there is only one class in the International program. Comment: The French program is described below:

Organizing the Trials

Any enclosed field may be used for an obedience trial. Club fields are generally used.

BREEDS INVOLVED:

All breeds of dogs are authorized to compete. Trials are also open to non registered dogs, which will be classified separately.

DIFFERENT EXERCISES:

Regulations have been in effect since January 1, 1998. The exercises progress in 3 classes, providing entry to the French Championship and to the International class.

A chart shows the different exercises for classes 1, 2, and 3.

Each exercise is graded out of 10 and has a coefficient.

All breeds are admitted for competition

Class 1	Coef.	Class 2	Coef.	Class 3	Coef.
Sociability	1	Sociability	1	Heel off Leash	3
Heel on Leash	1	Heel off Leash	2	Stand/Sit/Down in Motion	3
Heel off Leash	2	Stand/Sit in Motion	3	Recall with Stand and Down on the way back	4
Stand in Motion	2	Recall with Down on the way back	3	Send away with Stand and Down in a square	4
Recall	2	Send away with Stand and Down in a square	3	Retrieving 2 Objects on Flat Ground	3
Send away with Down in a square	2	Retrieving an Object (dumbbell)	2	Hurdle Jump and Retrieving wooden or metal Object	3
Retrieving a personal Object	2	Hurdle Jump In and Out with Standing	2	Retrieving 4 scent articles	3
Hurdle Jump In and Out without Standing	2	Retrieving 3 scent articles	2	Positions from a Distance: Sit/Down/Stand twice	4
Retrieving 2 scent articles	1	Positions from a Distance: Sit/Down/Stand once	2	2 min. Long Sit in a group	3
Positions from a Distance: Sit/Down once	2	1 min. Long Sit in a group, Handler in sight	2	3 min. Long Down in a group under Distraction	2
1 min. Long Down, Handler out of sight	2	2 min. Long Down, Handler out of sight	2		
General Outlook	1	General Outlook	1		
TOTAL	**200**	**TOTAL**	**250**	**TOTAL**	**320**

Obtaining Qualifications

Ranking progresses as follows:

Entry to Class 1:

All dogs authorized to compete and at least 12 months of age may present in Class 1.

Entry to Class 2:

A dog with the grade of Excellent in Class 1 may present in Class 2.

Entry to Class 3:

A dog that has twice obtained the grade of Excellent in Class 2 under two different judges may present in Class 3.

Entry to the French Championship or the International Class:

A dog that has twice obtained the grade of Excellent in Class 3 under two different judges can enter the French Championship or the International Class.

Entry to the European Championship or the World Championship:

Given the results of the French Championship or in the International Class, the working group chooses the dogs that will participate in the European Championship and in the World Championship. Among other things, they must receive one or two grades of Excellent in these competitions.

Search and Rescue Team Competitions

For purposes that are not strictly athletic, but rather to compare and acquire preparatory methods for work, an international organization was created in 1994, under the initiative of German-speaking countries: the IRO (Internationale Rettungshunde-Organisation—International Rescue Dog Organization). This organization helped to establish Annual World Championships in the Czech Republic in 1995, in Austria in 1996, in Germany in 1997, in Finland in 1998, and in Slovenia in 1999.

Also organizing an annual international congress and training sessions, the IRO facilitates the exchange of information on teaching and training methods among dog team handlers all over the world.

LJUBLJANA, SLOVENIJA
JULY 1 - 4, 1999

Internationale
Rettungshunde-
Organisation

They can compare their practical experiences, learn more about each other, list the available resources and sometimes use complementary teams based in different countries.

The competition itself takes place over several days and involves three types of victim search by the teams:
– tracking (searching for a lost person with a reference scent articlel and a known point of departure)
– quest (searching for a lost person in a defined area without a reference scent article)
– disaster search (search for victims buried in rubble)

For each specialization, two other trials are added to the group and each graded on a scale of 50 points:
– An obedience trial including heeling on-leash and off-leash, behavior in a crowd of with sudden loud noises, recall and obedience from a distance exercises, retrieving on flat and over high jump, etc;
– An agility trial, including crossing unstable surfaces, dog walk, ladder, dangerous areas, and also jumping and crawling exercises.
The specific discipline is graded on a scale of 200 points and follows very precise grading conditions and regulations.

Currently, German, Austrian, and Czech teams dominate this type of competition, though in 1998 a French dog from the Brigade de Sapeurs Pompiers de Paris (Firemen's Brigade of Paris) was awarded the title of best disaster dog.

1999 World
Championship
in Slovenia.

THE SPORT OF AGILITY

Agility was invented in 1977. The basic idea came from John Varley, a member of the Cruft Dog Show who was looking for an original event to add some spice to the down time in the show. He contacted Peter Meanwelle for help in setting up the project. The two developed the first demonstration of agility in the world, which took place in 1978 during the Cruft Dog Show in London.

The demonstration was extremely well received and from 1979 on agility has been officially recognized by the Kennel Club. From that point on, and thanks to Peter Lewis in particular, agility demonstrations have developed very quickly.

In 1989, the FCI also recognized the sport of agility. This worldwide organization created a specific commission to establish uniform regulations by which the trials would be judged and which would determine the characteristics of the obstacles used. It was used on an international level for the first time in 1991.

In 1993, the MINI category of agility trials appeared. These were the first official competitions adapted for small dogs (standing less than 40 cm/15 3/4 inches at the withers).

Agility is an educational and athletic discipline, which is related to equestrian jumping competitions. It is open to all dogs and consists of having the animal run off-leash through a series of different obstacles within a given amount of time. It is not only a race against the clock, but also a test of precision movements. The difficulty of the sport is that the animal must be both fast and accurate in its performance.

It is therefore necessary for the dog to have a foundation of training and obedience. Once he has mastered these, you can start with the obstacles. This training is not aimed at the handler gaining control over the dog, but rather reinforcing their relationship and developing trust. The dog must be balanced, sociable, and completely alert to his partner.

A Sport for All Dogs

This sport has the advantage of being open to all dogs, whether or not they are registered, pure breeds or mixed breeds. The canine species comes in very many forms. Many different breeds participate in the trials. All body types lend themselves to this discipline: from the little Pyrenees to the Rottweiler. Nevertheless, the breeds that are best suited are medium-sized breeds such as the Spaniel and large breeds such as the Belgian Shepherd. The canine species is also characterized by a wide range of sizes. This has led the professionals to create different categories. A dog that measures 40 cm (15 inches) at the withers can hardly jump an hurdle that is 60 cm (24 inches) high as easily or safely as a dog that measures 60 cm (24 inches) at the withers.

There are therefore 4 separate categories based on the size of the dog. In each category, the size of the obstacles has been adapted to the dog's body.
Category A: Adapted for dogs measuring 35 cm (13 3/4 inches) at the withers. The specific dimensions of the obstacles are:
  – height of single hurdle: 30-35 cm (11 3/4 to 13 3/4 inches)
  – long jump: 60 to 75 cm (23 1/2 to 29 1/2 inches)
  – river hurdle: 20 cm (7 3/4 inches)
  – the height of the axis of the tire jump is 55 cm (21 1/2 inches)
Category B: adapted for dogs measuring 35 to 50 cm (13 1/2 to 19 1/2 inches) at the withers
Category C: adapted for dogs measuring more than 50 cm (19 1/2 inches) at the withers
  For these two intermediate categories, the specific dimensions of the obstacles are:
  – height of hurdle: 40-50 cm (15 3/4 to 19 1/2 inches)
  – height of axis of the tire jump: 65 cm (25 1/2 inches)
Category D: adapted for very large, heavy or slow breeds. The specific dimensions of the obstacles are:
  – height of single hurdles: 60 to 75 cm (23 1/2 to 29 1/2 inches)
  – height of axis of the tire jump: 90 cm (35 1/2 inches).

The creation of categories allows us to avoid many accidents. Animals that are too excited or too motivated don't hesitate in front of obstacles that are too big, but rather expend all their energy into overcoming the obstacle, which can cause trauma to joints, muscles, and tendons.

There are certain predominant breeds among all of those in competitions. They are the:
  – Border Collie, a herding dog, which represents 80% of the participants in Great Britain.
  – Belgian Shepherd or Tervuren that can be seen in agility competitions.
  – Shetland, the most common breed in MINI agility competitions.

Terrain and Course of the Agility Trials

An agility course cannot be placed on just any kind of terrain. It must measure 20 x 40 meters (65 1/2 x 130 eet).

The floor must be soft, flat, not too slippery, and not too hard. This helps to avoid injuries to the pads, sprains, and luxations.

The course is made up of 12 to 20 obstacles chosen from those that have been standardized by the ICF. There are various types of obstacles:

Descending A-Frame

– **Contact zone obstacles: the contact zone** is a mandatory passage for the dog, on which it must place at least one foot to avoid penalization.

• Dog walk – A-Frame - Seesaw

– **Jumps:**

– Height jump: These have similar dimensions, but differ in form. The height of the obstacle varies depending on the category of dog.

– Long jump: this is a river and strict long jump.

– **Tire jump:** the axis of the tire through which the dog jumps is adapted to its category.

– **Spread** (obstacle made up of multiple jumps) 30 cm high (12 inches).

– **Tunnels:** open and closed.

– **Other types of obstacles:**

– Table and pause box: for these two obstacles, the principle is the same: The dog must hold a position previously chosen by the judge for 5 seconds (sit, down, stand).

– Weave poles: the dog must slalom between poles always starting on the right side of the obstacle. This is an impressive element that deals with the dog's skills in obedience.

All of these obstacles have precise dimensions and some vary depending on the category of dogs. They must also be completely safe and therefore have safety mechanisms such as:

– cleats in the contact zones

– sand paint on the pause table.

Running through the weave poles

During trial, regardless of level, the course must always include at least 7 jumps and 2 changes in direction. It must cover 200 to 300 meters (330 to 650 feet).

The obstacles must be spaced 5 to 7 meters (16 to 23 feet) apart unless they are part of a combination, in which case they must be 3.5 meters (11 1/2 feet) apart.

The difficulty of the course is related to the obstacles chosen and to their arrangement on the field. For each level, the regulations call for specific obstacles to be used.

Name	Obstacle	Dimensions Length	Width	Height
		CONTACT OBSTACLES		
A-Frame		Inner angle 90°	Minimum 90 cm	Highest point: Min. 1.7 m Max. 1.9 m
Seesaw		3.65 m minimum 4.25 m maximum	30-40 cm	70 cm (1/6 of the length of the plank)
Dog Walk		Minimum 1.20 m Maximum 1.35 m	Minimum 30 cm Maximum 40 cm	Minimum 3.60 m Maximum 4.20 m
		JUMPS		
Hurdle			Minimum 1.20 m	Min. 30-35 cm Standard 40-50 cm Max. 60-75 cm
Hurdle with brush			Same	Same
Viaduct			Same	Same
Wall			Same	Same
Tire			Diameter: 38-60 cm	Axis of tire: Min. 50 cm Standard 65 cm Max. 90 cm
Long Jump		120-150 cm	120 cm	Wooden: 15-28 cm Poles: 120 cm
		TUNNELS		
Open Tunnel		360 cm	Diameter: 60 cm	
Closed Tunnel		90 cm	60-65 cm	60 cm
		MISCELLANEOUS		
Table		90-120 cm	90-120 cm	50 cm
Weave Poles		50-65 cm between the 8, 10, or 12 poles		100 cm

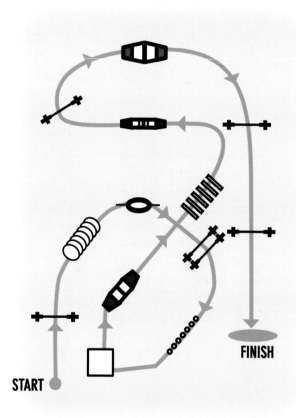

START

FINISH

Example of Agility Course

– **First level trials**: The dog clears max. 3 contact zone obstacles, the position held on the platform or the stop zone is always "lying down."

– **Second level trials**: The dog may encounter 4 contact zone obstacles; the position to be held on the table or in the pause box twill be indicated by the judge before the start of the competition and will be the same for all competitors.

The arrangement of the obstacles follows certain rules:

– the wave poles can only be done once per course

– the contact zone obstacles as well as the table and pause box cannot be placed at the start or finish

– the tire jump and long jump cannot be at an angle

The judge determines the course. He designs it such that the dog can proceed easily and smoothly. The goal is to find a happy medium between controlling the dog to avoid faults and reaching optimum speed of performance.

During relay competitions, there are two identical courses arranged side by side on the field. They must be separated by barriers and located 10 meters (33 feet) apart.

Program of the Trials

Before the start, the judge who designed the course checks that:
– the obstacles are in all in accordance with the regulations
– they are properly installed in the course
– the length of the course is exactly as it should be.

He then gathers the competitors to explain the details of the trial to them as follows:
– the standard race time: To establish the time, we use the speed in meters per second chosen for the evolution of the standard course as reference criteria.

– Standard race time = length of the course/speed of evolution

The speed of evolution, and therefore the standard race time, depends on the level of the trial:

1.8 m/s (6 ft/s) < speed of evolution < 3.5 m/s (11 1/2 ft).

– maximum course time: In general this is equal to twice the standard race time, but it may never be less than 1.5 times the standard race time.

The judge reminds the competitors of the regulations for the competition and the criteria for grading the results. The dogs cannot be previously trained on the course. Only their handlers are allowed to walk through the course, without the dog.

When a competitor enters the course, he must:

– place the dog in a held position (sit, down, stand) behind the starting line.

– Remove the dog's leash and collar (it is against regulations to wear a collar during competition for safety reasons).

– Take his position on the course wherever he would like.

– After receiving the order from the judge, give his dog the order to start. As soon as the dog crosses the starting line, the clock starts.

– Guide his dog through all of the obstacles in the correct order, but without touching the obstacles or the dog and without overcoming any of the obstacles himself.

When the dog has finished the course and crossed the finish line, the clock is stopped. The handler replaces the dog's leash and leaves the field.

Agility Trials

Competitions are organized around the same design in most of the member countries of the FCI. In each of these countries, this federation oversees all tests of agility through the national canine organization.

As has been mentioned earlier, all dogs (registered or not, mixed or pure breeds) may compete in agility trials. But they do not all have access to the same trials (registered or non registered dogs).

STANDARDIZED TESTS

Only dogs registered in a stud book recognized by the FCI can participate in these competitions. Among other things, they must:

– be at least 15 months old
– be vaccinated and tattooed
– belong to a club from a national canine organization of the FCI

They then have a working file in which the results of all trial will be recorded.

These trials lead to the acquisition of a certificate of agility and to national trials and the European Championship of the FCI. They are made up of three classes:
- first level class
- second level class
- third level class

A dog that arrives at a competition for the first time will first participate in first level trials to get a certificate of agility. To do so, it must obtain two excellent grades or two very good grades in official first level tests. This will allow it to enter the second level trials.

If the dog obtains three excellent grades or three very good grades in the official second level trials, it will then be allowed in the third level trials and then the regional championships. If it makes it and obtains an excellent or a very good grade in the competition it can participate in the national championship.

Since 1997 there has been a world championship for agility, which has a standard agility test and a jumping test.

NON-STANDARDIZED TRIALS

All dogs are allowed to participate. They do not need to be registered in a stud book recognized by the ICF or be pure breeds. Entry regulations are similar to those already mentioned.

These trials are quite varied because they depend on the initiative in each country. Certain ones are very well know because they are sponsored by big names in dog food (master Royal Canin, Slalom d'or, etc.)

Free tests are sometimes organized in canine clubs and can be interesting:

- jumping: we also see jumping in standardized competitions. As its name implies, it is almost completely made up of jumps.

- Competition by elimination: Two dogs run identical courses that are set up side by side. The one who wins qualifies for the next round.

- Speculators' trial: Obstacles are arranged but in no specific order. They are arranged by type and each one is given a value. The dogs have 60 seconds to do as many obstacles as possible.

- Team trial: here there are groups of four dogs that compete in a course for jumping or a second level course. The winning team is the one with the best cumulative score for the points earned by each dog.

- Relay: teams of two or more dogs run an agility or jumping course one after the other

The discipline of canine sports is booming and trials are the perfect answer for handlers who want to provide a foundation of obedience and sociability necessary for the dog's harmonious integration into everyday life. Each year, this sport reaches an ever-more remarkable level of performance.

Catching the ball

FLYBALL

Flyball was invented at the end of the 1970s. As legend would have it, Herbert Wagner held the first demonstration on the Tonight Show with Johnny Carson, filmed in California and aired to an audience of millions of Americans. From the beginning of the 1980s, the sport has been very popular and official competitions have been organized throughout North America. In 1984 canine sport professionals founded an organization called the North American Flyball Association (NAFA). It still represents the authority and world reference for Flyball. In Great Britain, the sport has taken longer to develop. The first competition only took place in 1991 and in 1993 the British Flyball Association was founded, based on the model of the NAFA. Its goal, like that of NAFA, is to establish regulations and oversee all official competitions.

Flyball has therefore rapidly developed over the last twenty years in English-speaking countries (United States, Canada, England, Australia). In France, however, the activity is not yet recognized and is generally considered more of a game suggested by canine clubs for dog owners.

The principle of Flyball is simple. It is a relay race in which two teams, each made of up of four or more dogs, compete in identical courses that are placed side by side. To complete the relay, each dog must bring a ball to the handler.

The Course

There are three important elements on the field:
– a line that serves as the starting line and the finish line

– four identical hurdles, the height of which must be between 10 and 18 inches (depending on the height at the withers for the smallest dog in the group). These hurdles are each placed 10 feet apart. The first hurdle is placed 6 feet from the starting line and the last is 10-15 feet from the box.

– A Flyball box: this contains a device on a spring that allows the dog to release a tennis ball using a pedal

In countries where Flyball is popular (United States, Canada, England, Australia, Belgium), many professionals have invented different types of boxes especially adapted for Flyball. The most commonly used boxes in these countries are characterized by a concave front that allows the dog to turn much faster while catching the ball, like swimmers.

Program of the Trials

During official competitions, the first dogs are positioned on the starting line. Upon the judges signal, the two dogs start. They jump the four hurdles. Once they arrive at the box, they press the pedal to make a ball come out, catch it mid-air to lose as little time as possible. Then they return to their respective masters by jumping the same four hurdles on their way back, bringing the ball. Once the last hurdle has been jumped, the next dog on their team starts.

The clock stops when the last competitor on a team completes the course.

Flyball is truly a test of speed. The best dogs take less than 20 seconds to complete the course. The current world record is 16.7 seconds.

Advantages of Flyball

This sport has numerous advantages, which have surely contributed to its success in English-speaking countries.

First of all, Flyball is open to all dogs, regardless of their origin, breed, or size. And, unlike in agility competitions, the master does not need to run alongside the dog, which makes the sport accessible to older and handicapped owners.

It is a very simple, non-technical game that requires practically no training. The dog mainly becomes conditioned to the sport. The hardest thing to teach the dog is to press the pedal to make the ball come out!

Flyball therefore allows the master to improve the relationship he has with his dog, and also allows his companion to perform a minimum of physical exercise. This is a game—a fun activity that can easily be enjoyed in urban areas.

FIELD TRIALS

History

Field trials are geared toward comparing the skills of hunting dogs. The first field trial took place in 1865 in Coutil (Bedfordshire). This type of trial then appeared in Germany in 1876, in Holland in 1878, in Belgium in 1882, and in France in 1888.

The first competition in England was only for Setters and Pointers.

These trials rapidly gained success and from 1867 on, landowners offered their property for the organization of new competitions. The dogs ran in pairs (braces) and the loser was eliminated from the competition.

But their success was only temporary and the number of competitions dropped. Only those organized by the National Kennel Club remain. This sport has continued to develop in other countries where pointers are popular.

In 1889 in Boran, two types of trials were specified: long quest trials (200 meters [650 feet]for dogs from any country) and limited quest trials (40 meters [130 feet], with mandatory retrieving exercises). The following year the mid-length quest was added (100 [330 feet] meters, reserved exclusively for dogs trained in France). With the competition's being divided into several trials, the rules became more and more country-specific.

In 1897, for the first time, dogs were allowed to run solo and judges took the dog's skills and training into account in the ranking.

Over the next several years, the regulations became more refined and the trials grew in number. Dogs ran in braces or solo, in spring or in summer, and were arranged by age, the youngest dogs competing first.

In 1963 the following trials were defined: a long quest for English dogs without shooting of the game, French field trials for English and continental pointers without shooting of the game, and finally a practical hunting trial for all pointers, with shooting of the game.

In 1979 there were five disciplines:
– long quest (in braces, with partridges)
– French trials without shooting of the game (English solo, English brace, Continental solo)
– Amateur practice trials.

Continental pointer breeds are primarily Braques, Spaniels, and Griffons. Among the English pointers used are the Pointer, the English Setter, the Irish Setter, and the Gordon Setter. In competitions, the most commonly represented breeds are the English Setter, the Pointer, the German Braque, and the French Spaniel.

Procedures

The trials often take place on several different sites. The dogs are divided into groups of twelve for shot game, fifteen for spring trials, with a distribution that is proportionate to their participation in the competition. Each group forms a separate competition. If a given participant has several dogs, the rules state that he must divide his dogs among no more than two trials.

Anyone may participate in an open trial: professional trainers, amateur trainers and hunters. Amateur trials are reserved for the last two categories.

The normal work time for a dog is fifteen minutes. This may be extended if the dog is excellent and has not encountered anything. A judge may also call a dog back after all of the competitors have performed, in order to sharpen his judgment.

At the beginning of the trial, the dog must be placed with its nose to the wind. To determine this in low winds, some people use the smoke of a cigarette or toss a handful of grass in the air. During the first minute, called the "warming up minute",the points count, but not the errors. The end of this minute is announced with a trumpet call. Each dog or brace of dogs then has 14 minutes in which to find the birds, slither and point them out, flush them, without chasing them in flight and upon the gun shot.

The end of the course will be announced with a trumpet call and the competitor shall then call his dog, leash it and leave the course.

Hunting with two dogs

Types of Trials

There are three types of trials:
– Spring competitions, which take place in a field, with a pair of wild partridges
– Summer competitions
– Fall competitions or trials with shot game, during open season, with the death of the game

SPRING TRIALS

Depending on the extent of the quest, we distinguish between the long quest and the French quest.

The Long Quest:

This is a large-scale competition involving only English dogs. Their speed and resistance are put to a very difficult trial. This quest is actually a race with loops as far across as 500 meters (1/3 mile). These dogs are generally endowed with exceptional olfactory abilities, which sometimes allows them to locate a pair of birds at a hundred meters (about 300 feet).

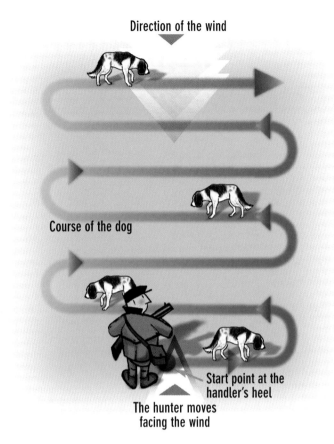

Direction of the wind

Course of the dog

Start point at the
handler's heel

The hunter moves
facing the wind

Progression
of the Dog
in a Field Trial

A lead dog is mandatory in this trial, which is run with partridges and in braces. When one of the competitors points, the other must also point out the partridge. The pair of dogs is chosen randomly and led by their respective handlers.

This type of trials involves primarily professional trainers or seasoned amateurs. French quest trials draw a greater number of participants.

French Quests

These trials take place in the Spring in fields of unripe grains. Points only count for marking birds. The judges do not award points for pointing out hares. Nevertheless, even if the hare does not count in the awarding of prizes, it is a factor in the ranking because a dog that chases a hare will be eliminated.

There are four categories in the French quest: the English solo, the Continental solo, the English brace, and the Continental brace. The solo trials are reserved for dogs that do not hold the title of "Solo Working Champion." Once a dog has obtained this title, it may no longer work alone.

During a brace trial, the lead dog, though not mandatory, will be highly regarded and taken into account in the ranking.

In English trials, the quest is generally more spread out than for Continental dogs. The dog must explore as much of the field as possible in the fifteen minutes of the trial. To do so, the exploration must be done in regular loops with the same distance on either side of the handler (80 to 100 meters) (260 to 320 feet). The handler must slowly walk straight ahead, as in hunting. Often the partridges are alerted by the noise and run away on foot to the sides. This way, the dog is more likely to find them at the end of a loop. If there is a difference in the vegetation on a side (the field has been worked), the dog must explore the border where partridges often seek shelter. Dogs that search in a disorderly fashion pass the game and lead the judges into it. They are eliminated.

In a trial the dog must never double back (at the end of a loop, it should not go backwards, but rather take the turn with its nose to the wind). Neither should it go too close to the handler or behind him. In these two cases, the dog wastes time exploring ground that has already been covered.

Finally, the dog must demonstrate decisiveness. It must go directly into the wind once it has recognized partridges, otherwise it will not be able to block them. After a hesitant and indecisive dog has made several passes, the partridges walking about will ultimately fly away by themselves, in which case the dog will be eliminated.

In these trials, if a dog flushes out game without knowing it was there, the dog is eliminated. It is not always the dog's fault. He may simply be unlucky or the handler may have made an error.

Pointing must be firm and held. Any dog that flushes its game on its own will be eliminated. Once it has blocked game, it must remain still until its handler has arrived. Once the handler is present, the dog flushes the game out and remains still.

Upon flight of the game, the handler shoots a warning pistol to simulate a shot taken at the game. The dog must remain immobile and will then be leashed on the spot.

In Spring trials, the game is often on foot and only flies afterward, once the dog is not longer still or far away. The first example means elimination; in the second case, the point is denied.

Spring trials are generally very difficult because there are a lot of external contributing factors.

Dog slithering towards the game.

SUMMER TRIALS

These are held in July and August. The rules are practically the same, except for the fact that points on pheasants and quail, or other feathered game, may rank the dog in prizes. However, partridges must be pointed out at least once.

TRIALS ON SHOT GAME

These are divided into two categories: breeding birds (partridges, pheasants, and quail) and natural birds (partridges, woodcocks, and snipe). They may take place solo or in pairs. Trials with pheasants are held in beet fields or in the woods and are the most common. In all cases, the game shot must be retrieved.

In these trials, in addition to the judges and the handler, there is an official marksman, because the handlers are is not allowed to shoot.

A quest of approximately forty meters in front of the handler is the most appreciated, even if it is a bit disorganized.

The dog must also remain perfectly still upon flight of the game and during the shot. This is hard for impatient dogs because they are being asked to retrieve the game right after the shot. While retrieving the game, the dog must not drop it or chew it. It must sit and deliver the game upon the handler's command.

Judging

The composition of the juries varies from one trial to another:
– long quest: three judges, two of which have qualified in the long quest
   – pair trials: two judges who have qualified
   – solo trials: two judges, one of which has qualified

A dog is judged on its speed, training, sense of smell, passion for the hunt, extent of its quest, the way in which it carries its head and its style.

To be ranked, a dog must complete the course in 15 minutes, receive the grade of "Very Good," and have pointed (pointing followed by flushing upon command, remained still as the game takes flight and during the shot, and be put back on a leash by the handler).

ERRORS

Five errors are grounds for elimination:
– overall lack of qualities
– out of hand (the dog gets too far away from the handler, does not obey his command, and abandons the quest)
   – chasing game after having failed to point or not (this is grounds for elimination with feathered game)
   – marked fear of the shot
   – discovering game by accident

CANINE CROSS COUNTRY AND SLED RACES

Sled, ATV and Cross Country races are very popular in the world of canine sports. Participants have one or more dogs pull elements in fields free of snow.
Sled competitions are often organized when there is no snow, allowing mushers to continue training their dogs.
All of these sports are also under the authority of Sport Sledding Federations in most countries.

Describing Sporting Practices

Cani-Cross

This is a race in the country pairing master and dog. Each participant moves on foot for a clearly defined distance on a specific trail. He is accompanied by a single dog that he holds on a leash. For greater ease, the use of a harness, long elastic leash and large belt is recommended.

All-Terrain Bike Cross

All-terrain bikes are needed to practice this sport because the trails are always over rough ground. A single dog is attached to the front of the bike. It is recommended that participants use a harness and a long elastic leash or specific devices equipped with shock absorbers. Due to the risks of frequent falls, it is highly recommended that the master wear protective leg and arm gear, as well as a helmet.

Harness Tests

These require the use of a manually-powered two- or three-wheeled vehicle with a brake system. The light cart has three wheels and is most often used, even though it is entirely possible to use a bike with blocked pedals or without a chain. There must be at least three dogs in the harnessed team.

Harness tests are the most like dogsleds since the dogs are always pulling, unlike the Cani-cross or Bike Cross in which the master can pass his dog, though he cannot pull it.

Organizing the Competitions

Conditions for Participation

The tests are open to all dogs and all masters, often ranked in three categories: children, adults, and veterans.

Regulations

Based on the tests in question, departures are done in groups or spaced out in time. Everyone uses the same trail.

The actual regulations are quite similar to those in dog sledding and have a "test" portion (planned, number of dogs admitted to compete, etc.) and a "conduct to follow" portion of the course (rules for passing, leaving the trail, etc.).

Distances

The distances covered are based on the sporting categories (Cani-cross, Bike Cross or Harness) the age of the participants (children, adult, or veteran), and the number of dogs.

The shortest course is the Cani-Cross Children's event and the longest is the multiple dog harness test.

These distance may be modified based on the atmospheric conditions (the warmer it is, the shorter the distance). The courses may also be cancelled if the weather is too hot (competitions should be cancelled if temperatures exceed 16 to 18o C).

UTILITY SEARCH TRIALS

In utility search and rescue trials, the tracklayer is playing the role of a lost person. This discipline may also be used as a starting point for real interventions in searches for missing people, since, given the case, the certificate offers the possibility of participating in searches for missing people with public authorities (but not in searches for criminals on the run).

Organizing the Trials

Utility Search trials are organized in a variety of areas and fields. Only the tracking dog is allowed on the track, with the exception of spectators' dogs or dogs of local inhabitants.

The track's route must be previously drawn on a map that is provided to the judges and the tracker.

THE BREEDS INVOLVED:

These tests are open to all breeds of Working dogs with working folders.

THE DIFFERENT EXERCISES

The goal of Utility Search Trials is to find personal objects along the track and also the tracklayer at the end of the course. The trials become more and more difficult as level increases.

The track is designed by experienced tracklayers who know the region perfectly.

The handler is free to lead or help his dog at any point in the tracking. He may remove the dog's leash if necessary (to clear obstacles), put him back on the trail, or order him to search to pick the trail up again. The handler may also pick up objects, question people along the trail, or let his dog rest

Class 1 Tracking Trial

Age of the track: Two hours
Length of the track: Approximately two kilometers (1 1/4 miles)
Time allowed to find the tracklayer: Approximately one hour
Attitude of tracklayer while laying the track: Walking
Objects along the track: First personal object dropped ten paces from the start of the track. Five objects dropped along the track at intervals of 500 paces.

Difficulties encountered: Dirt path and grass. Electric fence for cows. Barbed wire. Walking alongside then crossing a road with limited traffic. Ditches to cross.

Position of the tracklayer when found: Lying down or hidden in a ditch, under a shelter, or behind a hedge or section of a wall.

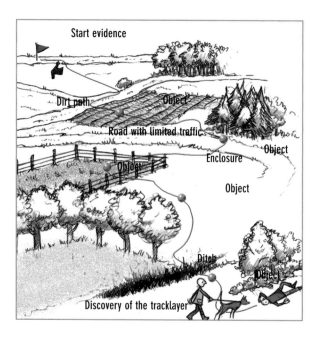

Class 2 Tracking Trial

Age of the track: Three hours
Length of the track: Approximately two kilometers (1 1/4 miles)
Time allowed to find the tracklayer: Approximately one and one half hours
Attitude of tracklayer while laying the track: Walking
Objects along the track: First object dropped 150 paces from the start of the track. A reference object, enclosed in a plastic bag, is given to the handler before the start. Five objects dropped along the track at intervals of 500 paces.

Difficulties encountered: A stranger will introduce his scent at the starting line half an hour before the tracker is brought to the line. Dirt path and grass. Electric fences for cows. Barbed wire. Walking along-side, then crossing a road with little traffic (distance of 50 steps). Ditches, thick hedges, forest with thick undergrowth. 1.5 meter (5 feet) obstacle to go around. Pass by an isolated house.

Position of the tracklayer when found: Lying down or hidden in a ditch, under a shelter, or behind a hedge or section of a wall, in a parked vehicle or a vehicle stopped alongside a road.

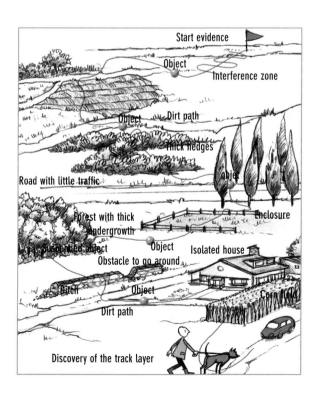

Handler/Dog Utility Tracking Certificate

Age of the track: Six hours
Length of the track: Approximately three kilometers (1 7/8 mile)
Time allowed to find the tracklayer: Approximately two hours
Attitude of tracklayer while laying the track: Walking, with some areas crossed at a run and one or two three minute stops.

Objects along the track: First personal object dropped 150 paces from the start of the track. Five objects dropped along the track at intervals of 625 paces, of which one may be attached 1.5 meters (5 feet) above the ground.

Difficulties encountered: A stranger will introduce his scent at the starting line fifteen minutes before the tracker is brought to the line. Dirt path and grass. Electric fences for cows. Barbed wire. One or more roads to walk alongside and cross. Ditches, thick hedges, forest with thick undergrowth. 1.5 meter (5 feet)obstacle to go around. Pass by an isolated house. Walk on a road for approximately 100 steps. Go through ruins and a farmyard. Pass by a small group of three or four isolated country houses.

Position of the tracklayer when found: Lying down or hidden in a ditch, under a shelter, in a parked vehicle or a vehicle stopped along-side a road, in a room, in a tree, in a farmyard, with a group of people, or behind a hedge or section of a wall.

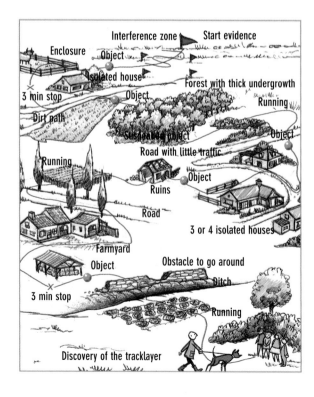

Obtaining Qualifications

The handler-dog team will qualify as follows:

Qualification for Class 1 and 2:

The handler-dog team must obtain three grades, with at least 1 Excellent, 1 Very Good, and 1 Good from two different judges.

Qualifiers for classes 1 and 2:

Excellent: The dog found at least 2 articles and the missing person
Very Good: The dog found 1 article and the missing person
Good: The dog found the missing person

Qualification for the Certificate:

The handler-dog team must obtain a grade with the qualifier of Excellent, Very Good, or Good.

Qualifiers for the Certificate:

Excellent: The dog found at least 3 articles and the missing person
Very Good: The dog found 2 articles and the missing person
Good: The dog found 1 article and the missing person

PROGRESSION IN THE TRIALS:

As for all athletic disciplines, there is a progression in the trials. The dog may not directly access certain levels. It must follow a working route.

Entry to Practical Utility Search Class 1:

Any dog belonging to the breeds authorized to compete that has a working folder may present at this level. It must pass the shot test. Two shots are fired at about 15 meters from the dog and the animal must not show any signs of fear.

Entry to Practical Utility Search Class 2:

Any handler-dog team with a qualification in Class 1 may present in Class 2. The dog must pass the shot test.

Entry to the:= Handler and Dog Utility Search Certificate:

The Certificate trial is open to all handler-dog teams with a qualification in Class 2. The dog must pass the shot test.

The primary characteristic of Utility Search trials lies in the fact that they are based on the principle of a handler-dog team. If the dog is presented by another person, this new team must make its way through all of the qualifications again, regardless of its level.

TRACKING TRIALS AND COMPETITIONS

Commonly called French tracking, these trials and competitions center around the dog's olfactory qualities and concentration.

Organizing the Competitions

Tracking competitions are organized in large open fields in which the surface allows for different tracks to be established. Each dog works on a fresh track from the other dogs. It is therefore necessary that all of the fields allow the same level of difficulty for each competitor.

THE BREEDS INVOLVED:

All working breeds are allowed to participate in tracking trials.
A complete list of breeds authorized to compete may be found in the appendix.

THE DIFFERENT EXERCISES:

Tracking is divided into two categories:

List of breeds authorized to compete in Tracking trials.

Group 1
German Shepherd
Kelpie
Belgian Shepherds
Schipperke
Beauceron Shepherd
Picard Shepherd
Pyrenees Shepherd
Scottish Collie
Bearded Collie
Border Collie
Shetland Shepherd
Komondor
Kuvasz
Mudi
Puli
Pumi
Bergame Shepherd
Maremma Sheepdog
Dutch Shepherd
Schapendoes
Podhale
Nizziny
Cuvac
Russian Meridional Shepherd
Sarplaninac
Australian Bouvier
Bouvier des Ardennes
Bouvier des Flandres

Group 2
Doberman
Giant Schnauzer
Standard Schnauzer
Boxer
Bull Mastiff
Bordeaux Bulldog
Mastiff
Rottweiler
Tibetan Bulldog
Hovawart
Caucasian Shepherd
Landseer
Leonberg
Newfoundland
Saint Bernard
Central Asian Shepherd
Bernese Bouvier

Group 3
Airedale Terrier
Fox Terrier
Black Russian Terrier
American Staffordshire Terrier
English Bull Terrier

Group 5
Siberian Husky

Group 7
Korthals

Group 8
Chesapeake Bay Retriever
Curly-Coated Retriever
Flat-Coated Retriever
Labrador
Golden Retriever
Barbet
Wetterhoun
Spanish Water Dog
Portuguese Water Dog

Group 9
Giant Poodle
Standard Poodle
Tibetan Terrier
King Charles Spaniel
King Charles Cavalier

- free tracking, for classes A, B, and C
- blood hound tracking, for the ranks of Legal Police, Cold Track, and Identification

A chart listing the different exercises by category and by rank for tracking competitions may be found in the appendix.

List of exercises in free tracking.

Track A		Track B		Track C	
Warm track length (in m)	400	Warm track length (in m)	600	Warm track length (in m)	600
Number of 90° turns	2	Number of 90° turns	2	Number of 90° turns or wide turns	3
Number of objects at the end of the track	1	Number of sharp turns	2	Number of sharp turns	2
		Number of objects at the end of the track	1	Number of objects at the end of the track	1
				False track	1

Track A Grading		Track B Grading		Track C Grading	
Retrieving the object	40	Retrieving the object	40	Retrieving the object	40
Following of the track	45	Following of the track	45	Following of the track	45
Temperament/speed	5	Temperament/speed	5	Temperament/speed	5
Obedience/presentation	10	Obedience/presentation	10	Obedience/presentation	10
TOTAL	**100**	**TOTAL**	**100**	**TOTAL**	**100**

List of exercises for 10 m LeashTracking

10 m LeashTracking		Cold Track		Selective 10 m LeashTracking	
Type of track	W	Type of track	1 h	Type of track	W
Length of track (in m)	800	Length of track (in m)	800	Length of track (in m)	800
Number of 90° or wide turns	3-4	Number of 90° or wide turns	3	Number of 90° or wide turns	3
Number of sharp turns	3	Number of sharp turns	1	Number of sharp turns	2-4
False track	1	Number of objects on the course	3	False track	1
Number of objects on the course	2			Number of objects on the course	3
Discovering the tracklayer	1			Discovering the tracklayer	1

10 m LeashTracking Grading		Cold Track Grading		Selective 10 m LeashTracking Grading	
Following of the track	30	Following of the track	55	Following of the track	30
Temperament, speed	5	Temperament, speed	5	Temperament, speed	5
Presentation, obedience	10	Presentation, obedience	10	Presentation, obedience	10
Uncovering objects (2x15)	30	Uncovering objects (2x15)	30	Uncovering objects (2x15)	30
Discovering the tracer	10			Identification	25
Manifestation	15				
TOTAL	**100**	**TOTAL**	**100**	**TOTAL**	**100**

Note: W indicates warm track.

Obtaining Qualifications

Dogs that obtain at least 75 points (out of 100) are awarded the grade of "Excellent." Those that obtain at least 60 points receive the grade of "Very Good" and those with less than 50 points receive the grade of "Good."

PROGRESSING IN THE COMPETITIONS

As with all athletic disciplines, there is a progression in the trials. Dogs cannot directly enter certain ranks. They must follow a working route.

Entry to the Class A Trial:

Any pure breed dog belonging to the breeds authorized to compete may participate in the Class A tracking trial. It must have a working folder.

Entry to the Class B Trial:

Any dog with a grade of "Excellent" or "Very Good" in Class A may present in Class B.

Entry to Class C Trial:

Dogs must have received 2 grades of "Excellent" from two different judges in Class B or 1 grade of "Excellent" in RCI II in tracking alone (90 points).

Discovering the tracklayer is a key moment in tracking.

Entry to the Legal Police Competition:

The dog must have obtained 2 grades of "Excellent" from two different judges in Class B or 1 grade of "Excellent" in RCI II in tracking alone (90 points).

Entry to the Cold Track Competition:

The dog must have obtained 2 grades of "Excellent" from two different judges in Class B or 1 grade of "Excellent" in RCI II in tracking alone (90 points).

Entry to the Identification Competition:

The dog must have obtained:
– 4 grades of "Excellent" from 2 different judges in Legal Police competitions, one of which must be from outside of the region
– 2 grades of "Excellent" from 2 different judges in Cold Track
– 2 grades of "Excellent" from 2 different judges in Class C, one of which is from outside of the region

PREPARING SPORTING AND UTILITY DOGS

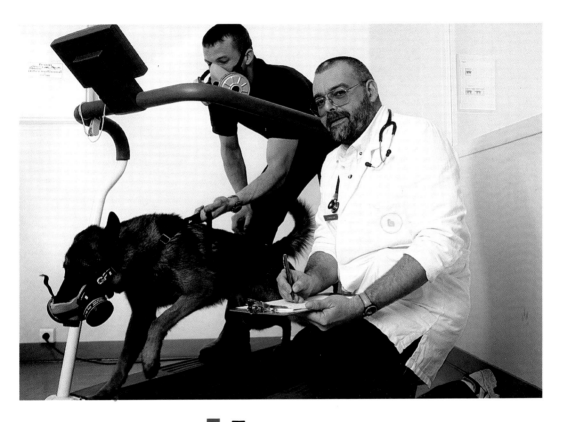

*L*ike any athlete, sporting and utility dogs need physical, nutritional, and behavioral preparation not only to improve their performance, but also to help prevent the onset of specific diseases.

PHYSIOLOGICAL CONSEQUENCES OF PHYSICAL EFFORT

Intense work and competition can cause psychological and physical stress for dogs as well as for humans. Dog owners can therefore benefit from a basic knowledge of the physiological changes caused by physical effort by better understanding how to prepare their dogs for competitions and preventing as many potential pathological problems as possible.

Metabolic Bases

Muscular work very directly affects the type and amount of energy required and also greatly affects the animal's overall balance through the physiological stress it causes. It is not our intention to readdress the many theoretical elements covered in so many other works, but rather to simply limit ourselves to those aspects that are new or truly essential in understanding the physiological bases of effort in dogs.

THE ENERGY OF EFFORT

The chemical energy involved in muscular contractions comes solely from "phosphate" links that are rich in adenosine triphosphate energy (ATP). Intracellular ATP is, or tends to be, lowered during effort. It is then instantaneously rebuilt on site in four processes: the transfer from phosphocreatine (PCr), the destruction of glycogen, the oxidation of glucose, and the oxidation of fatty acids. It is the relative contribution of each of these processes to the rebuilding of the ATP supply that determines the specific metabolic aspects of each type of effort.

PHOSPHAGENS

Phosphocreatine allows ATP to be rebuilt so quickly within the muscle cell that ATP and phosphocreatine make up an integrated system

Control of oxygen consumption in dogs during exertion

ATP production by unit of substrata consumed according to the metabolic diagram in question

Reaction			ATP/mol	Resp. Quot.
		Substrata	O_2	
Glycogen	→ Lactate	3	-	-
Glucose	→ Lactate	2	-	-
Lactate	→ $CO_2 2H_2O$	17	5.7	1.00
Glycogen	→ $CO_2 + H_2O$	37	6.2	1.00
Glucose	→ $CO_2 + H_2O$	36	6.0	1.00
AGLP	→ $CO_2 + H_2O$	138	5.6	0.71
Acetoacetate	→ $CO_2 + H_2O$	23	5.7	0.73
ß hydroxybutyrate	→ $CO_2 + H_2O$	26	5.8	0.80

called the phosphagen system. This energy system is preponderant during supra-maximal effort lasting only a few seconds (jumping, starting races, etc.). The bio-availability of muscular phosphagens is not at all influenced by training or diet.

GLYCOGENOLYSIS

ATP can also be generated through anaerobic glycogenolysis, which frees up lactic acid. The rate of renewal for ATP through anaerobic glycogenolysis only represents one-third to one half of that generated by the phosphagen system. As a result, the lactic anaerobic system can only develop half of the maximum power (work/time) generated by the alactic anaerobic system (phosphagens). The power from lactic anaerobiosis is probably at its maximum after three to ten seconds and remains predominant for a maximum of about thirty seconds.

OXIDATION OF THE GLUCOSE

Glucose is transported in the blood, then enters the muscle cell to be oxidized there in the mitochondria. Its degree of oxidation largely depends on the ability to enter the muscle cell, in relation to the glycemia and its regulating hormones of insulin, glucagon, the growth hormone, and cortisol. The rate of renewal for the ATP from the oxidation of the glucose is about 50% of that obtained from anaerobic glycolysis, with an equivalent ratio of power.

The anaerobic metabolism of glucose, like that of glycogen, generates lactic acid, the two having a major point in common: the conversion of pyruvate to lactate or acetyl-CoA. This conversion is triggered by the dehydrogenated pyruvate complex, an enzyme that is dependent on the cofactors derived from thiamine, lipoic acid, pantothenic acid, pyridoxin, and niacin. It is also influenced by dichloracetic acid (a molecule that is presumed toxic) and without a doubt by dimethylglycin N.N. (DMG).

The oxidation of the glucose is probably the primary source of muscular energy during effort lasting from 60 seconds to a few minutes. It is encouraged by the ingestion of slow carbohydrates and can be reduced by meals that are too rich in fats or by fasting.

OXIDATION OF LIPIDS

The oxidative metabolisms of glucose and fatty acids are integral to the functioning of the muscle cell, but are nonetheless two metabolic paths differentiated from energy production. The oxidized fatty acids in the

Percentage of muscle fibers with high ATPase mysosin activity (fast-twitch fibers) in different muscle groups in the Greyhound, cross-breeds, and the Foxhound

	Greyhounds	Cross-breeds	Foxhounds
Deltoid	99.8 ± 0.3	74.4 ± 3.0	56.6 ± 6.8
Triceps brachii caput longum	94.2 ± 5.4	77.2 ± 2.7	64.9 ± 4.4
Vastus lateri	96.6 ± 1.7	61.4 ± 10.2	80.7 ± 8.2
Gluteus medius	97.4 ± 0.7	68.6 ± 5.6	65.3 ± 4.9
Biceps femoris	88.6 ± 2.2	67.2 ± 1.3	63.1 ± 1.5
Semi-tendinous muscle	98.9 ± 0.8	85.2 ± 2.6	69.6 ± 6.8

muscle cell are from those with long chains freely circulating in the plasma (plasmatic free fatty acids or AGPL).

Several stages along the way to oxidation make up potential limiting factors for their oxidation. The AGLP enter the cell by diffusion, which results in an increased entrance when their plasmatic concentration is increased.

Once in the muscle cell, carnitine plays a very important role in their transport, linked to acetyl-CoA, through the mitochondrial membrane, which is the final step before the beta-oxidation of the fatty acids.

At the same time, some ACLP can be taken from their path and transformed into ketone bodies released into the blood, aceto-acetate and beta-hydroxybutyrate then being oxidized in the muscle cell and particularly by the myocardium, for which they are a preferred energy substratum.

The oxidation of the AGLP is the primary source of energy for the muscle during long periods of medium- to low-intensity effort, approximately semi-maximal. It is increased, as are the ketone bodies, by fasting, under-nutrition, and training, particularly when training is accompanied with too small a diet that is high in fat (adaptive phenomenon).

PROTEIN CATABOLISM

Ramified amino acids (leucine, isoleucine, and valine) can make up five to 10 percent of the muscular oxidative energy supply. The amino groups are transferred to pyruvate to form alanine and to glutamic acid to provide glutamin. Alanine and glutamin are released into the blood, then taken by the liver where they are used in glucose synthesis. The glucose is then released into the blood, where it becomes available for intramuscular oxidation.

At the same time, alanin-amino-transferasis activities, from aminotransferasis aspartate and glutamate-dihydro-amino-transferasis are increased by 80%. The urinary excretion of urea increases and the nitrogen level drops. After effort, methylhistidine is increased in the blood and reduced in the muscle, which translates to a restriction of the synthesis of actine and myosin during muscular work. Such phenomena can be qualified by determining the amino-acidemia, ammoniemia, and uremia, or even by urea and urinary proteins dosage.

ROLES OF THE LACTIC ANAEROBIC ENERGY SYSTEM

Lactates in supra-maximal effort

During intense muscular exercise reaching a power greater than that allowed by the oxidative systems (aerobiosis), supra-maximal effort is reached (like for racing Greyhounds). In this case, the anaerobic hypercatabolism of the muscular glycogen leads to a massive and sudden release of lactic acid that accumulates in the muscle before returning to the blood. In Greyhounds, for example, the result is hyper-lactacidemia, which can reach or exceed 14 or even 22 mmol/l. Under such conditions, the lactic anaerobiosis is, clearly, quite preponderant in covering the muscular energy requirement.

According to an evaluation of the lactic acid produced and the oxygen saved by anaerobic glycolysis, an equivalent energy of lactates formed in vivo was determined to be approximately 220 calories per gram of lactates formed, in humans.

The only data of this type that we have for dogs concerns gastronemia, isolated and perfused using the "stop-flow" technique. In such a case, the formation of 1 gram of lactates corresponds to the release of 248 calories, figures which are very similar to those in humans.

This approach could prove useful in the fundamentals of better determining the quantitative energy requirements for dogs such as racing Greyhounds. It does, however, have certain limitations:

- The blood lactates general reach their peak a few minutes after the effort, then fall again exponentially with a half-life of fifteen minutes.

- In this type of effort, there is a gradient of concentration of blood lac-tates during exercise in the muscle, blood, and urine, and the increase of lactatemia cannot be considered as entirely representative of the lactates generated by the system.

Regardless, the accumulation of lactic acid has several adverse affects, including:

– inhibiting glycogenolysis and glycosis
– inhibiting lipolysis
– causing osmotic muscular swelling
– reducing the lactic acid flow to the muscle cell

The Notion of Oxygen Debt

During brief and intense effort, the muscle uses more energy than the aerobic system can provide. It therefore develops an energy debt during this period referred to as an "oxygen debt." During the recuperation peri-od, the amount of oxygen provided beyond the maintenance need repre-sents the payment of this oxygen debt. This allows the re-synthesis of glycogen from the lactates, including the energy lost during the process, with the yield being lower than one.

Nevertheless, we must not forget that a large part of the lactates is oxi-dized for energy purposes during recuperation and as a result is not taken into account in the evaluation of this oxygen debt, which means the debt is underestimated. Overall, the two processes compensate for each other, which means that the reimbursed debt most often appears identical to the debt contracted.

More recently, the evaluation of the oxygen lactic debt was made based on the lactates accumulated in the blood and the oxidative energy that was saved as a result. This analysis shows that, without considering the hypothesis regarding the multi-sector distribution of blood lactactes, 1 mmol of cumulate lactates correspond to saving 3.3 ml of oxygen per kilo-gram of body weight.

Based on the maximal lactacidemia observed in Greyhounds (15 to 20 mmol/l), we can estimate the oxygen lactic debt to be between 1.7 and 2.2 liters of oxygen in a Greyhound weighing 30 kilograms. If we accept an average thermal coefficient of 5 kcal per liter of oxygen and a muscu-lar energy yield of 22 percent, we can estimate the lactic anaerobic ener-gy (LAE) expended by a Greyhound (weighing 30 kilograms) during as race as follows:

$$LAE = \frac{2(1\ Ox) \times 5\ kcal \times 100}{22} \approx 46\ kcal$$

This corresponds to approximately 2.7 percent of the maintenance energy requirement of such a dog.

What happens to lactic acid after effort:

After effort, as we have seen, the energy used in oxidizing the lactates can be valued by the body by deducting it from the use of other energy molecules (glucose, lipids, etc.). The energy needed for the re-synthesis of glycogen from lactates represents an added metabolic charge. From the data, it appears that lactic acid is oxidized after effort when the amount accumulated is low and when the metabolic level during the recuperation period is higher than for maintenance.

In such a case, the body has no oxygen debt to reimburse. This is the case with combined aero-anaerobic efforts such as those in ring and agility tests. On the other hand, when a large amount of lactic acid has been accumulated (like for the racing Greyhound), and the recuperation is passive, a very large part of the lactates is taken for glycogen re-synthesis, with a relatively large oxygen debt.

Estimate of the respective contributions of the three energy systems during a competitive Greyhound race

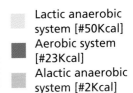

Lactic anaerobic system [#50Kcal]
Aerobic system [#23Kcal]
Alactic anaerobic system [#2Kcal]

RACING GREYHOUNDS: RESPECTIVE PARTS OF THE DIFFERENT METABOLISMS

We have seen that during all effort, three distinct metabolic networks are closely linked and one of them becomes preponderant depending on the type of effort involved. As the archetypal sprinter, the case of the racing Greyhound is useful to consider because it demonstrates the differences in levels that exist between these three networks.

In racing Greyhounds, the phosphagen system (alactic anaerobiosis) is used at 50 percent of its total capacity, providing approximately 2 kcal, whereas as we have seen the lactic anaerobic path provides nearly 50 kcal. Recent studies have shown that even during very brief 30-second periods of effort, 28-30 percent of the energy comes from the aerobic path.

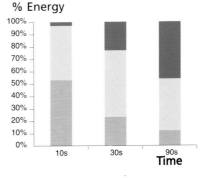

By integrating this information to the case in question, aerobiosis would then contribute 23 kcal to an overall energy expenditure for the race close to 75 kcal, or 4.5 percent of the maintenance energy requirement for a Greyhound.

Estimate of the respective contributions of the three metabolic energy paths during three short-term exertion tests (expressed in percentage of total work provided).

ROLES OF THE AEROBIC ENERGY SYSTEM

When effort is over a long period (more than a few minutes) and of average intensity (50-70 percent of the maximal oxygen consumption, which is still poorly quantified in dogs), aerobiosis becomes the system for covering the muscular energy need. It is not useful to repeat information that has already been published concerning aerobic metabolism here. We shall simply note that during an endurance test, the fatty acids, in considerable part derived from the tissue lipolysis, make up the primary energy source for the muscle cell in that:

– the basic training of the animal is appropriately managed,
– the diet is rich in fats,
– the level of plasmatic free fatty acids is high,

Prolonged muscle work would then be responsible for a clear increase in ACLP that is earlier and more effective in cold times. In fact, it is the adipic tissue that provides the dog with the majority of its energy when it is cold. At low temperatures, the level of AGLP in the blood may be multiplied by 1.88. The renewal of these acids and their speed of oxidation are increased by 4.5 and 8.3 respectively, whereas at the same time, the relative participation of the AGLP in the formation of carbonic gas increases 36 to 64 percent. This observation is compared to that of sled dogs, in which we observe an increase of nearly 50 percent for lipids circulating in winter.

Other than supplying energy to the muscle cell, the aerobic system therefore allows the body to fully take advantage of the pre-existing metabolic adaptation, and especially to conserve the animal's supply of glycogen, the exhausting of which is a great limiting factor for prolonging effort.

Different sources of energy for muscular exertion

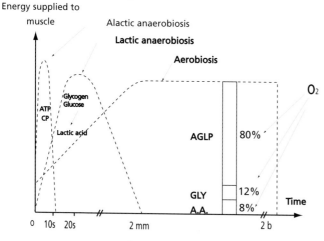

The Notion of Metabolic Fatigue

Among the determining factors for fatigue are:

– substances for which the concentration is reduced during effort (ATP, glycogen, etc.)
– substances that accumulate during exercise (lactates, hydrogen ions, etc.)

The passage of lactic acid from the muscle to the blood is encouraged by an increased blood flow and by the presence of bicarbonates in the blood. This accumulation of lactates in the blood (hyperlactatemia) is traditionally associated with anaerobic metabolism and the oxygen debt. This debt is not limited to dogs practicing brief and intense effort.

In fact, in sled dogs, we can find cases of hyperlactatemia associated with hyperglycemia, which reflect the animal's excitation and the fatigue it causes by encouraging anaerobic metabolism of the glucose. In light of such observations, it is recommended for sled dogs (and also in all dogs that participate in relatively long periods of effort: ring, tracking, field, hunting) that the dogs be kept calm prior to the competition, which is actually contrary to certain traditional methods.

Muscular glycogen is another major determinant of fatigue. Its level can be considerably increased prior to competition by a dietary carbohydrate supply, even by using dissociated type diets that are of no use to the dogs in which they increase the risk for muscular problems.

At the same time, we know that muscular glycogen is saved through the oxidation of fatty acids, and in particular after a long metabolic adaptation to them. Then the other dietary strategies such as carbohydrate supplies and adaptation to fats must be adapted, in their respective intended supplies, to the different levels of intensity and to the duration of the effort in question.

Power vs. Speed

In Sporting dogs, as in humans and horses, a balance will be established between power and speed during effort, and have an affect on the nutritional options. The relationship between power and speed will vary based on a certain number of external factors linked to the type of ground surface, the related effort of traction, the speed, and the wind resistance.

For dogs that exceed 50 km/h, the variation of speed is correlated to the square root of the power, which corresponds to the metabolic aspects developed earlier. Therefore, if the developed power doubles, the speed is multiplied by 1.4 (approximately the square root of 2). For power that is tripled, the speed increases by a factor of 1.7. Studying the racing animal's speed then allows us, conversely, to appreciate the power developed and therefore the metabolism in question.

With the current different types of competition (speed, medium distance, long distance) for this discipline taken into consideration, dog sledding is a very representative illustration of these theoretical notions.

Sled dogs that have been trained in endurance can maintain an "Iditarod" type trot (about 16 km/h) for ten to fourteen

Relative intensities of the different metabolic energy paths used during exertion in dogs

Type of Sport	Alactic Anaerobiosis	Anaerobiosis	Aerobiosis
Jumping	+++	+	#0
Short Attack	++	++	+
Greyhound Race	+	+++++	++
Agility	#0	++++	++
Ring Competition	#0	+++	+++
Field Trial	#0	++	+++
Newfoundland	#0	+	++++
Tracking/Country	#0	#0	++++
Herding	#0	#0	+++
Hunt	#0	#0	++++
Sled Racing	#0	#0*	+++++

*except speed races: + to ++

hours per day, for several days in a row, and they can only do it with a diet that is predominantly lipids. It is therefore reasonable to assume that in these dogs, the preferred energy source is through the oxidation of fatty acids, and to assign it a 1 as the degree of power (equivalent of approximately 0.25 mmol/kg/second in human muscles, for comparison).

Glucose can be oxidized, which (given the previous information) generates a power developed two times greater (degree of power: 2), and as a result increases the speed by a factor of 1.4 or approximately 23 km/h. This speed corresponds to a moderate gallop or a fast trot that good dogs can maintain for several hours per day for several days (medium-distance "Alpirod" type races).

The use of glycogen ensures a yield of developed power that is two times greater than that of glucose oxidation. Sled dogs use this in speed races to run at speeds greater than 30 km/h (32 to 34 km/h for the best teams), a rhythm maintained by good teams during speed tests taking place in two or three legs of 25 to 35 kilometers.

Finally, phosphagens can intervene by generating a power that is two to three times greater than anaerobic glycolysis, allowing the sled dog to reach maximal speeds near 45 km/h for periods of thirty seconds and even speeds of 50 to 55 km/h for a few seconds.

The theoretical diagram of three clearly separate metabolic energy paths leads to the superposition of these metabolisms in practice that have to be taken into account in training and rationing. From a strictly aerobic metabolism in pure endurance, we can go to an aero-anaerobic metabolism when the test is shortened (but the aero-anaerobic transition zone corresponding to the emergence of the anaerobic threshold is still poorly defined in dogs), or even to the valuation of lactic anaerobic catabolisms (glycogen) or alactic anaerobic catabolisms (phosphagens) during the speed peaks considered to be sprints.

This being the case, it is possible to feed and train the canine athlete in order to encourage oxidative yields and the necessary balance between the use of fatty acids or glucose as energy fuel. We can also increase the supply of muscular glycogen and anaerobic glycolysis with different methods that are from the same field. But we do not currently know of any way to influence the metabolic behavior and supply of phosphagens.

Cardiovascular and Respiratory Adaptation

Cardiovascular and respiratory adaptations during effort are intended to ensure the oxygen supply and nutrients needed for muscular activity and to allow for the elimination of wastes, particularly carbonic gas and heat, produced by muscular metabolism. These adaptations are indispensable not only for the completion of the sporting test in good conditions, but also to continue effort beyond the first instants. Two types of responses of the organism can be distinguished:

– an immediate response adapted to the instantaneous needs of the organism, therefore concomitant with the effort
– a more long term response that anticipates the organism's needs and corresponds to the adaptations caused by the organism

DURING PHYSICAL EXERCISE

Changes in the circulatory function during work are primarily to increase the blood flow and thereby supply oxygen to the tissues that are experiencing increased metabolism, particularly the muscles. The organism reaches this state by increasing the heart rate and redistributing the blood mass to the zones of activity to the detriment of the zones that are at rest. These changes are accompanied by an increased capacity of the blood to carry oxygen due to a contraction of the spleen that allows a large number of red blood cells to be sent into the blood, thereby increasing the hematocrit and amount of hemoglobin.

The heart flow can increase considerably and reach ten times its level at rest. The frequency of heart beats increases very noticeably in relation to the intensity of the effort, it can reach 300 beats per minute in racing Greyhounds, and 200 in sled dogs. The working muscles are at the center of intense vasodilatation; dilating the blood vessels allows muscles to increase their internal blood flow. The breath rate evolves in several phases during effort:

– during the first three to four seconds, the breath rate increases dramatically
– a plateau is then reached that will be maintained until the end of the effort
– during the recuperation period, a low decrease in respiratory frequency will occur, going from more than 200 movements per minute to approximately 30.

THE EFFECTS OF TRAINING

After daily training for 4 to 5 weeks, the dog's body will present significant modifications in its cardiovascular and respiratory systems. Cardiac

THE SYSTEM OF GASEOUS EXCHANGE.

CO_2 | C_2

Ambient air

Respiratory System

Alveolo-capillary wall

Circulatory System

Capillary walls

Interstitial Fluids

CO_2 O_2 Cellular membranes

Cells

The consumption of oxygen may be calculated using Fick's equation:
$VO2 = Q (CaO2 - CvO2)$

Q = Cardiac output, determined by:
- heart rate
- volume of systolic ejection

$CaO2$ = O2 content of arterial blood, determined by:
- ventilation
- hemoglobinemia
- degree of saturation of hemoglobin

$CvO2$ = O2 content of combined venous blood (right heart cavities), determined by:
- consumption of oxygen by the tissues

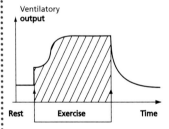

Ventilatory output

Rest   Exercise   Time

Ventilatory changes during exercise.

From the beginning of exertion, ventilation increases rapidly, then a second phase of slower increase appears and exists until ventilation is stabilized at a plateau. Once work has stopped, ventilation suddenly decreases, then more slowly decreases to return to its normal rate at rest.

and hemodynamic modifications due to repeated physical exercise tend to minimize the energy needed for cardiac work, as well as to develop the capacity for the heart to pump. In trained dogs, the heart rate at rest is lower than that for sedentary dogs and arrhythmia is more marked. Their plasmatic volume is increased and the return of venous blood is improved, which results in an overall increase in heart flow.

Intensive training sometimes leads to hypertrophy of the heart. In Greyhounds, for example, six months of intense training causes an increase of 50 percent of the thickness of the heart wall and an increase of 30 percent of the volume of the left ventricular cavity. Training will also cause an increase in the number and density of capillary blood vessels in muscle. Finally, contrary to popular belief, in dogs with good health, regular physical exercise brings no or little modification to the respiratory system. It is the body's overall capacity to consume oxygen that is considerably increased through endurance training (we speak of "VO2Max," the maximum consumption of oxygen). These changes can only take place optimally in dogs with good overall health. Any change or insufficiency of these functions will limit the possibilities for adapting to the conditions of effort and, as a result, also limit performance in sports or work.

Average amounts of VO_2 max known in dogs

Amount of VO_2 max observed	Breed	Author
90	Common	Certelli, 1964
125	Common	Bailie, 1961
160	Common	Wagner, 1977
135	Beagle	Young, 1959
112	Foxhound	Ordway, 1984
143	Foxhound	Hsia, 1992
100	Common	Certelli, 1963
125	Malinois	Thiebault, 1998

DOGS AND THE FIVE SENSES

Dogs are in constant contact with the matter that makes up the Earth. The way they perceive this matter is depends entirely on their five senses: taste, smell, hearing, touch, and sight. All the senses are essential to dogs who work, whether for amusement (canine sports) or utility. Thanks to these sensory tools, dogs can adapt quickly to any change in the environment.

Taste

The sense of taste is associated with the taste buds in the mucosa of the tongue, palate, and pharynx. Nerves carry sensory input from the taste buds to the brain. This input is produced when the chemical substances in food dissolved in saliva interact with the taste buds.

DOGS HAVE A UNIQUE SENSE OF TASTE:

–They have a clear preference for sweet flavors. This preference is even stronger in bitches.

– The way sour flavors are perceived depends on molecular size: The larger the acid molecule, the more sour the sensation it produces.

– Dogs perceive salty flavors only after a certain concentration of salt in the food has been reached. Levels below this concentration are perceived as sweet.

– Bitter flavors are perceived even in very weak concentrations. This prevents dogs from ingesting poisons like strychnine, a particularly bitter substance.

A dog's sense of taste and his dietary preferences are strongly influenced by experience. Young dogs fed a single type of food become adapted specifically to this food. In addition, since taste sensations fade very little in dogs, they can eat the same food every day if they find it palatable. For this reason, it is acceptable to accustom a dog to receiving the same balanced food every day.

Smell

The anatomy of a dog's nose promotes a high level of olfactory sensitivity:

– The size and placement of the nostrils give dogs a greater olfactory range than humans.

– The turbinate bones separate the air into two currents:

– Most of the air passes through the nasal cavities to the larynx and then the trachea and bronchial tubes; and

– A smaller amount of air is forced upward to the olfactory epithelium, covered by a mucous membrane lined with olfactory cells.

Olfactory area of the dog

1. Frontal sinus
2. Lamina of the ethmoid bone
3. Ethmoidal nerve
4. Olfactory nerves
5. Nasal part of the laryngeal cavity
6. Caudal nasal nerve
7. Vomero-nasal nerve
8 and 9. Nasal branches of the ethmoidal nerve

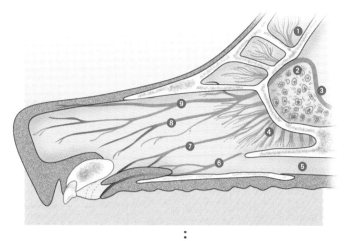

The shape of a dog's muzzle influences his sense of smell. Mesocephalic dogs therefore have a more developed sense of smell than other types of dogs. The shortness and shape of the skull in brachycephalic dogs inhibit air circulation, and the long nosebridge in dolichocephalic dogs limits the flow of odors to the olfactory epithelium.

ODOR DISPERSION

All living organisms produce molecules that have odorous, gustative, or color properties. Odor molecules are volatile and have a molecular weight below 300 d.

The dispersion of odors in the environment depends on various mechanisms:

– Odors are produced by particles emitted by humans and animals. These particles are very small (14 mm, with an average weight of 70 ng) and are produced abundantly every day.

– Air currents flow over the surface of the body. In humans, these currents have been found to originate at the feet and travel up the body to a height of 40 cm above the head. They carry odor particles which are then dispersed in the ambient air. The lightest particles are dispersed most in the environment and are the most sensitive to climatic changes.

– An organism's odor profile assumes various forms, depending on body movement:

– An immobile body in a calm environment becomes enveloped in an odorous hemisphere, of which it is the center;

– In the presence of wind, the odor of an immobile body takes the form of a cone, with the body at the summit; and

– A body in motion deposits odorous particles over a certain width in space, creating a trail. This trail is known as the "scent" of quarry in hunting.

Climatic variations modify a body's odor profile:

Wind displaces particles in the atmosphere. A trail created in a cross wind may therefore be displaced laterally by several dozen centimeters.

In addition, wind strength affects the shape of the odorous cone surrounding an immobile body: A weak wind increases the diffusion of odor molecules, while a strong wind limits the remanence of an odor by dispersing its molecules.

– Air temperature and hygrometry modify air density and therefore affect atmospheric movement. These factors may also dry the mucous membrane of the nose and sinus, limiting olfactory sensitivity.

Weather factors have a greater influence on atmospheric odors (lightweight particles) than on trail odors (heavy particles).

Odor diffusion in snow

The difference between the temperature of a body buried in snow and the surface temperature produces ascending air currents which carry odor

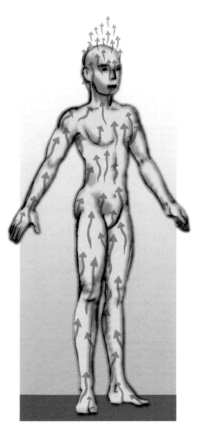

Body air currents
(according to Syrotuck)

molecules. The type of snow affects how easily odors travel: Powdery snow contains a large amount of air, which increases the flow of warm air currents. In more compact snow or in snow containing patches of ice, odors may travel through the snow and emerge several meters away from the buried body.

OLFACTORY PHYSIOLOGY IN DOGS

In order for a dog to recognize an odor, molecules must become attached to the receptors of the mucous membrane of the nose and sinus. The location of these receptors (more or less specific to an odor) is precise and well-defined, such that their activation or inhibition produces a "nasal image" specific to an odor. This image is analyzed by the brain, which then recognizes the odor inhaled by the dog.

Dissemination of fragrant particles on a track as a function of wind

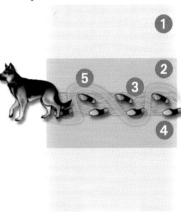

In order to increase the volume of air reaching the mucous membrane of the nose and sinus, dogs develop a sniffing behavior that produces a greater air current, greater air speed, and increased air flow to the roof of the nasal fossae.

A dog's olfactory sensitivity is linked to various factors:

– The surface area of the mucous membrane of the nose and sinus is greater in dogs than in humans: 200 cm^2 in the German Shepherd (or 200 million olfactory cells) versus 10 cm^2 in humans (or 10 million cells). The number of olfactory cells depends on breed:

– German Shepherd: 200 million cells
– Fox Terrier: 147 million cells
– Dachshund: 125 million cells
– Labrador Retriever: 220 million cells
– Cocker Spaniel: 67 million cells

– Olfactory sensitivity depends on the size of the olfactory area in the brain compared to total brain size. In humans this area is 0.29%, while in dogs it is 10.1%.

– The pigmentation of the mucous membrane of the nose and sinus has a direct influence on sense of smell. In fact, albinos have an imperfect sense of smell known as "partial anosmia." Dark-coated dogs therefore have greater olfactory sensitivity.

– The sensitivity threshold (or minimum perceivable concentration) is lower in dogs than in humans and depends on the odorous substance and the dog's training.

– Dogs have a molecular sense of smell, that is, each molecule corresponds to one odor. Dogs therefore have a qualificative power of discrimination: They can differentiate the 250,000 combinations of different

1 - Band of very light fragrant particles
2 -Band of light fragrant particles
3 -Band of heavy fragrant particles
4 -Footprints
5 -Path followed by the dog
6 -Direction of wind

odors created from the seven primary odors (camphorlike, musky, floral, peppermintlike, ethereal, pungent, and putrid).

– Bitches are generally more sensitive to odors than males, but this sensitivity varies depending on sexual cycle. Experiments have shown that the sense of smell is partially linked to sexual hormones: Injecting testosterone in a male increases olfactory sensitivity, while castration greatly decreases it. Similarly, injecting estrogen in a bitch increases olfactory sensitivity.

– The olfactory acuity of the same dog may vary with biological changes: A generally weakened state (weight loss, illness, etc.) speeds the onset of olfactory fatigue; hunger increases an animal's basic acuity, while satiation decreases it; and digestion causes a decrease in olfactory sensitivity in the hour following a meal.

RESEARCH ON CANINE OLFACTION:

The practical applications of canine olfaction vary widely:

– Odors left by animals or humans on a trail are easily detected by hounds or tracking dogs (canine sporting events or utility tracking); and
– Detecting the source of an odor from a distance is the purpose of pointers and dogs who search for wreckage and avalanche victims and detect various substances, including explosives, drugs, and truffles.

Olfactory sensation is slow in its manifestation: Reaction time is estimated at 0.5 to several seconds in humans ("latency of appearance"). Yet the perception persists for some time after the odorous source is removed ("olfactory persistence"). These two notions are illustrated by a tracking dog who follows a trail even after the olfactory stimulus as such (an unknown human odor) is below the dog's olfactory threshold: The addition of various stimuli makes it possible to surpass the olfactory threshold. Perceived intensity can therefore be linked to the number of inhalations. During tracking in which the target scent is not presented at the beginning, the trail must be a minimum of 600 to 1,000 meters long for a dog to be able to detect an individual odor. A dog will then be able to distinguish, for example, the person who created the trail from other people or follow the same animal even after it reaches others.

The discrimination between dromic direction (the direction of a tracked animal's flight) and antidromic direction seems to be linked to a dog's ability to detect differences in time and stimulation intensity between the two nostrils (as in humans, but to a higher degree). The dog then sets out in the direction where the odor seems strongest.

English Setter puppy pointing game

When a dog's olfactory apparatus is stimulated constantly or by many odors in rapid succession, the odorous sensation decreases, then disappears—this phenomenon is known as adaptation. Maximum sensation occurs in two to four minutes. The time required to recover normal sensitivity ranges from three to four minutes to an hour. Adaptation is specific to an odor. The olfactory apparatus may thus become adapted to one odor but remain sensitive to others.

After one to two hours of intense work involving the sense of smell, a phenomenon known as olfactory fatigue occurs in dogs and is accompanied by general fatigue. For this reason, periods of work should be alternated with periods of rest for the dog if the search is long.

A dog's auditory "radar"

A dog's erect pinna

TRAINING THE SENSE OF SMELL:

Regardless of a dog's highly developed sense of smell, training makes it possible to:

– decrease the threshold of perception. This is done by having a dog work repeatedly on the same odor. In this manner, similar to a person who works with perfumes, the dog will become more sensitive to a specific odor that he is exposed to regularly; and

– increase the dog's power of discrimination. An experienced dog can thus differentiate the various odorous components on a trail.

It is important to remember that not long ago, dogs relied on their sense of smell to find food, a primary motivation. For this reason, it is necessary to motivate a dog by rewarding him when he discovers an odor. This encourages the dog to indicate the odor's presence.

Turn toward the source of the sound...

Hearing

Like the sense of smell, hearing is highly developed in dogs.

Very wide frequency range:

Dogs can perceive frequencies from 15 to 40,000 Hz and even 80,000 Hz. In comparison, humans can perceive sounds only in the 20 to 20,000 Hz range. Ultrasound whistles can therefore be used without disturbing people nearby.

The human voice, which falls between 128 and 3,072 Hz, and the movements of an object or animal, which fall between 2,000 and 3,000 Hz, are therefore easily perceptible by dogs. In addition, dogs can detect differences of 1/9 tone and therefore clearly distinguish vocal timber and intonation. For this reason, they can differentiate two different words in a group of several hundred.

and the dog turns its head toward the noise to hear it better with both ears

Low *audibility threshold*

Dogs can hear sounds that humans cannot. A dog can hear from a distance of 25 meters a sound that a human cannot hear further than 4 meters away. On average, dogs can hear humans up to 350 meters away.

Ability *to locate the source of sound*

A dog's ear acts like a radar to detect sound and locate its source. This ability is greatest in sheepdog breeds with large, erect, mobile pinnae. After a dog perceives a difference in time or sound intensity between the two ears, he cocks his head toward the source of the sound to maximize perception with both ears. Dogs are thus able to hear sounds up to 100 meters away at an angle of 0° to 90° relative to the skull axis.

These auditory abilities are a major asset to the tracking dog: In the field he can hear and locate noises and calls; he can also distinguish one sound from another and react based on his auditory memory.

Touch

There are many tactile corpuscles in a dog's skin, especially on his paw pads (for exploring the ground). They are also found on the upper lip and the nose, combined with hairs and vibrissae.

Together with their sense of touch, dogs rely on kinesthesia to perceive joint movement, using receptors in the muscles, bones, and joints. Walking is therefore semi-automatic in dogs—they can move over any type of terrain without watching where they place their feet.

Sight

A dog's eyesight is less important than his sense of smell:

– Dogs are good at perceiving motion at a distance but not stationary objects at the same distance. Still, they perceive shapes accurately.

– Dogs have more highly developed vision at night and in partial darkness than humans. Their retinal cells have more rods than cones:
– Rods are stimulated by luminosity (the more rods in the retina, the better the vision in weak light).

– Cones ensure clear vision and color vision (the more cones in the retina, the clearer the vision and the better the perception of colors). In

Difficult progression for dog and handler

fact, dogs see only violet to green (wavelengths ranging from 390 to 540 nm). Dogs therefore have similar vision to colorblind humans, though not as clear.

– With good binocular vision, dogs can perceive depth and perspective.

There are differences between breeds in terms of the angle of vision:

– Herding dogs have the widest field of vision, for optimal herd surveillance. Their eyes are set wide apart on the sides of the head in order to cover this wide field.

– Hunting dogs have the best binocular vision. Their eyes are located on the front of the head, for seeing prey clearly.

– In dogs, six muscles enable the eyes to move laterally, vertically, and in all intermediate directions. For this reason, even with his head motionless, a dog can scan a larger field of vision in a shorter period of time.

A ranking of the senses in dogs

If one were to rank a dog's senses by relative importance to canine work, the order would be as follows:

1. Smell. Dogs are extremely sensitive to odors, especially those they know, both in closed and open environments.

2. Hearing. Dogs have more effective hearing than humans.

3. Touch. Moving semi-automatically, dogs can focus fully on the work at hand.

4. Sight. In their work, dogs makes excellent use of their daytime vision. They can also locate moving objects at night.

5. Taste. All dogs must automatically reject poisonous substances to prevent any contact with them. For this reason, taste is never used by dogs during their work.

The five senses do not work separately from one another. They work together and are a magnificent tool for both dog and owner.

The German Shepherd: a Herding dog with very wide monocular vision

The Brittany Spaniel: a Hunting dog with highly developed binocular vision

THE BASICS OF CANINE NUTRITION

All living organisms must eat. Dogs rely on their owner to provide a perfectly balanced diet every day. Some fifty nutrients are now considered essential for dogs, and the quality of a particular dog food is based on how well it solves and adapts the highly complex "puzzle" of canine nutrition.

Proteins (meat, fish, eggs), fiber (green vegetables), fats (plant and animal), minerals, and vitamins must be included in the ideal diet, and the amount of these various elements must reflect:
– The dog's size (obviously, a 2-kilogram (4 1/2 pound) Chihuahua will not have the same diet as an 80-kilogram (175 pound) Saint Bernard!);
– The dog's physiological condition (dietary requirements are affected by growth, gestation, nursing, athletic activity, and old age); and
– The dog's health (in many cases, nutrition has become an important tool in the medical treatment of disease).

Owners of canine athletes or utility dogs already know the importance of nutrition. For this reason, the present section will cover only the basic elements, in order to give all readers a good understanding of all the elements necessary to create the best possible nutritional balance.

50 essential nutrients with an important role

Just like humans, dogs are creatures whose survival depends on the hundreds of millions of cells that make up their body and work like tiny fires to provide energy. These "fires" are essential to life. They require a constant supply of fuel—food—and combustive—oxygen, to produce heat and energy. The body thus maintains a constant temperature and can build and strengthen itself, and thereby survive, without ever ceasing to renew itself.

To feed a dog well, an owner must have a good understanding of the role of nutrition, defined as "all exchanges between an organism and its

Nutrients and their sources

Nutrients	Food Sources
Protein	Meat (raw or slightly cooked), cooked fish, cooked eggs, milk (if the dog reacts well to it), cheese Avoid: scraps with too many tendons, raw eggs, raw fish
Starch	Well–cooked grains (rice, pasta, corn, wheat). Avoid: potatoes, bread, raw grains
Bulk	Green vegetables (green beans, carrots, cooked greens, bran—very small amounts) Avoid: cabbage, onions, turnips
Fats	Animal fats (suet, lard/poultry), vegetable oils (soy, corn, borage) Avoid: rancid or cooked fats
Vitamins and Minerals	Ground bone, calcium carbonate, mineral supplements, yeast (vitamins), dairy products (calcium) Avoid: Any excess of supplements

environment that allow the organism to assimilate foreign substances and produce the energy it needs to survive."

The role of nutrients

A nutrient is a simple element that must be included in a dog's diet in an amount that will help maintain the dog's health. Every day, dogs require each of the fifty essential nutrients because each has an important role, and their body cannot synthesize them.

WATER: THE MOST IMPORTANT OF ALL

It may seem unnecessary to list water as a nutrient, but it is important to remember that while an organism can go weeks without eating, it cannot survive more than three days without drinking. A dog's body is two-thirds water, and all its tissues are bathed in water. Muscles, for example, are 80% water by weight.

While dogs can lose all their body fat and half their protein and still survive, a loss of only 10% of the water in their body leads to death. With its many significant functions, water is the most important nutrient for dogs and all other living organisms. Dogs on a maintenance diet require approximately 60 ml of water per day for each kilogram of body weight (and sometimes quite a bit more, in cases such as strenuous exercise, gestation, and lactation).

PROTEIN: THE BODY'S BUILDING BLOCKS

Protein does have nutritional value, but it serves mostly as a building block for bones, muscles, nervous structures, etc.—in short, everything a dog needs to survive. A protein is a molecule consisting of amino acids, a sort of train made of cars (nonessential amino acids) and locomotives (essential amino acids). There are differences in the nutritional value, especially during digestion, of "good" proteins (red or white meat, fish, eggs, etc.) and "bad" proteins (tendons, connective tissue), which are indigestible and will be passed in the stools. A protein that is well-digested (and thus absorbed in the form of amino acids) will not necessarily be well-used (metabolized) by the organism. It may lack certain essential amino acids without which the dog's body cannot synthesize its own proteins. It is therefore useful to speak of the "biological value" of proteins and to compare essential amino acids to pieces of, red, white, and blue cloth: With enough of each color, American flags can be made, but if one color is lacking, this will not be possible. Similarly, when one essential amino acid is missing, protein synthesis ceases, and the remaining amino acids are wasted. [

It is important to remember that a food high in protein is not necessarily high in quality. Instead, the type of protein used in a particular food must be considered.

Finally, insufficient calories in the diet can cause an organism to "burn" its proteins instead of saving them as building blocks. The balance of calories and protein in a food is thus also essential.

FATS: NOT JUST A SOURCE OF CALORIES

The main role of fats is to provide energy in the form of calories.

Dogs digest fats very well, much better than humans, and greatly enjoy the flavor (this can lead to overeating if a strict portion size is not adhered to). But the palatability of fats should never undermine the nutritional balance of a dog food. This explains why approximately 50% of the dogs in the United States are overweight, compared to only 25 to 30% of the dogs in Europe.

Chemically speaking, dietary fats consist of fatty esters and esters of glycerol that form a chain of a certain length and degree of saturation. A food's caloric content is based more or less on the amount of fat it contains. Carbohydrate-protein substitution is, in fact, nearly isocaloric in dogs, while any extra fat represents an additional 50 calories per kilogram. An increase in caloric density and fat content makes food more palatable to dogs. Because this can lead to overeating, it is necessary to exercise great vigilance over portion size.

While dogs can easily handle high levels of fat in their diet, fatty foods should be reserved for active dogs and dogs with high caloric requirements, such as lactating bitches. Depending on their origin, fats consist of various fatty acids and therefore have different nutritional values. Fatty acids play a dual role:

• primarily non-specific, in that they simply provide calories. All fatty acids contribute calories, but the so-called saturated fats in tallow (from ruminants) and lard (from pigs) do not play only this role; and

• specific, in that fatty acids play a structural role as a component of all cellular membranes, as well as a functional role as precursors of cellular and hormonal transmitters.

This dual role is played by so-called "essential" fatty acids—essential, because a dog's body cannot synthesize them and must obtain them from the diet. There are two families of essential fatty acids (also called polyunsaturated essential fatty acids), that are important to know despite their strange names:

• the "omega-6" series, more naturally found in vegetable rather than animal oils, except poultry. A deficiency in this type of fatty acid leads to skin dryness, desquamation, alopecia (hair loss), and a dull coat. This is one of the main nutrients for a beautiful coat.

• the "omega-3" series, found mainly in fish oils, play an important role in preserving cell membranes and in the functioning of the nervous and immune systems. These fatty acids now are also used for their anti-inflammatory qualities (in treating many cases of skin irritation) and their "oxygenating" properties (they improve oxygen flow in the cells and increase the deformability of red blood cells, interesting properties for sporting dogs and older dogs).

Whatever the type, all fats are particularly fragile raw materials that deteriorate rapidly. Rancidity leads primarily to the decreased palatability of food and especially to physiological ailments in dogs: digestive intolerance, pancreatic disorders, liver damage, etc. In commercial dog food, antioxidants are added to prevent dietary fat from becoming rancid. In the case of homemade dog food, it is best not to give a dog cooked fats.

CARBOHYDRATES

Carbohydrates are nutrients consisting almost exclusively of plant matter; food ingredients of animal origin contain virtually no carbohydrates. The building blocks of carbohydrates are simple sugars, the most common of which is glucose, the primary component of starch and cellulose. Other carbohydrates, such as pectins and gums, are more complex molecules consisting of uronic acid produced by the oxidation of simple sugars. Some carbohydrates (starches and sugars) can be digested and assimilated by a dog's body. Indigestible carbohydrates (fiber and cellulose) serve as bulk to stimulate and regulate intestinal flow. Like all other animals, dogs have a metabolic need for glucose, which is a primary source of energy for certain organs, including the brain, and is also an essential building block in many organic molecules. Nevertheless, dogs and a few other animal species, have one basic difference: Their body can maintain its glycemia (the level of glucose in the blood) without any carbohydrates in the diet. Dogs and a few other animal species use certain amino acids found in proteins to synthesize glucose. For this reason, dogs are not at risk of glucose deficiency.

Digestible carbohydrates

Among the digestible carbohydrates, lactose is fairly important for puppies. Canine mother's milk contains half the lactose of cow's milk. While puppies can use lactose, their ability to digest it is limited, and any excess leads to digestive problems. Replacement mother's milk for dogs therefore must not contain too much lactose. Adult dogs are even more lactose intolerant. In fact, milk consumption can lead to diarrhea in adults.

Starch

Starch is a ramified complex of glucose polymers encased like a capsule called a "grain" (of starch). The shape of a particular starch depends on its botanical origin. A dog's body uses amylases, enzymes from the pancreas, to digest starch. Digestibility is greatly improved by cooking, which gelatinizes starch. Found in grains (wheat, corn, rice, etc.) and potatoes, starches provide the body with a quick source of energy, provided they are well-cooked. The rice used in homemade dog food should be "sticky" to ensure digestibility and prevent diarrhea. Two cooking methods are used for commercial dry dog foods: extrusion (kibble) and flaking (so-called "dinners"). These methods ensure that starch is cooked perfectly and therefore highly digestible.

Dietary fiber

Although dietary fiber cannot be assimilated by a dog's body, it is considered a necessary part of the canine diet. Dietary fiber consists of all carbohydrates that are not digested upon exiting the small intestine: cellulose, hemicellulose, lignin, pectic matter, etc. Some indigestible proteins, including keratin found in feathers, may also be included.

Fiber regulates the activity of the digestive tract, slowing it down or speeding it up when necessary. Since intestinal action in dogs is dependent of stress and activity level, the amount of dietary fiber in dog food must be adapted quantitatively. Fiber also serves as a substrate for the fermentation of intestinal flora and helps maintain the balance of this material in the large intestine. For this reason, any abrupt change in the source of dietary fiber can cause a temporary imbalance, with uncontrolled fermentation, flatulence, and diarrhea.

Although fiber is necessary for healthy digestion, it does have some drawbacks:

– Fiber decreases the digestibility of food (this is true especially of wheat bran); and

– In combination with complex substances known as phytates, fiber can decrease the availability of certain minerals during digestion.

Still, fiber can be used to decrease the digestibility of food for less active dogs or to lower the calorie content of food for overweight dogs. In these cases, the goal is to reduce the assimilation of food and obtain a degree of dilution that will not excessively limit bolus volume. Certain types of fiber can maximize these properties while limiting the drawbacks. Because of the decreased digestibility of high-fiber dog foods, it is necessary to raise the nutrient content of these foods.

MINERALS: MANY FUNCTIONS

Minerals account for a very small proportion of a dog's weight, but each plays an essential role. For this reason, the mineral content in a dog's diet should be monitored very carefully. In addition, all minerals can interfere with each other in digestion or metabolism. Therefore, it is necessary not only to ensure that each is present in the proper amount, but also to avoid any imbalance, which can harm the organism as much as a simple deficiency.

In the field of nutrition, minerals are divided into two groups:

– macronutrients, for which the dietary requirement is expressed in grams for a standard-sized dog, including calcium, phosphorus, magnesium, sodium, potassium, and chloride; and

– trace minerals, for which the dietary requirement is expressed in milligrams per day (or less), including iron, copper, manganese, zinc, iodine, selenium, fluorine, cobalt, molybdenum, etc.

Quantitatively speaking, calcium and phosphorus are the most important mineral elements: They are the building blocks of the skeleton and also have other important metabolic functions: For example, phosphorus is involved in energy transfer inside the cell. The skeleton is a substantial buffer reserve of phosphorus on which an organism can draw in the case of a deficiency. This explains the occurrence of bone disease when phosphorus and calcium levels in the diet are unbalanced. Magnesium is also involved in bone metabolism, but more importantly, it is found together with potassium in the intracellular fluid essential to many chemical reactions.

Generally speaking, trace minerals are necessary not only in the production of red blood cells, but also in oxygen transport, skin pigmentation and preservation, the functioning of enzymatic systems, the synthesis of

Minerals: Roles and Sources

Minerals	Roles in the organism	Sources
Calcium (Ca)	Foundation of the skeleton, transmission of nervous impulse phosphate	Bone powder, calcium carbonate, calcium
Phosphorus (P)	Foundation of the skeleton, foundation of the cell membranes, energy metabolism	Bone powder, phosphates
Sodium (Na) Potassium (K)	Cell balance, regulation of hydric balance, energy metabolism	Kitchen salt, potassium salts
Magnesium (Mg)	Foundation of the skeleton, nervous system, energy metabolism	Bone powder, magnesia, magnesium salts
Iron (Fe)	Foundation of red blood cells, cellular respiration, enzymes	Meat, iron salts
Copper (Cu)	Formation of hemoglobin, formation of bone, cellular oxidation	Bone powder, copper salts, meat
Cobalt (Co)	Formation of hemoglobin, multiplication of erythrocytes	Bone powder, yeasts
Manganese (Min.)	Enzymatic activation, formation of cartilage	Manganese salts
Iodine (I)	Synthesis of thyroid hormones	Sea salts, fish
Zinc (Zn)	Enzymatic systeMS, skin integrity, reproduction	Zinc salts

thyroid hormones, etc. Each trace mineral fulfills one or more roles in a number of bodily functions.

VITAMINS: NEITHER TOO MANY NOR TOO FEW

Everyone has heard of vitamins, nutrients essential for life that include a wide variety of substances. When even a single vitamin is completely or partially lacking in the diet, an organism exhibits clinical symptoms of deficiency that can eventually lead to severe illness. As a group, vitamins have two distinguishing features:

– A dog's daily requirement for each vitamin is expressed in milligrams or even micrograms; and

Vitamins: Roles and Sources

Minerals	Roles in the organism	Sources
Vitamin A (retinol)	Vision, growth Resistance to disease	Fish liver oil, liver, eggs
Vitamin D (calciferol)	Metabolic balance Phosphocalcic, Improved absorption of calcium	Sun (UV) Fish liver oil, Eggs
Vitamin E (tocopherol)	Antioxidant Prevention of muscular pathology (exertion)	Milk, cereal grains, eggs
Vitamin K	Production of elements in coagulation	Fish, liver, grains
Vitamin B1 (thiamine)	Energy metabolism (carbohydrates) Good nerve function	Grains, bran, yeast
Vitamin B2 (riboflavin)	Metabolism of amino acids and fats	Grains, milk, yeast
Vitamin B6 (pyridoxine)	Metabolism of proteins, fats, carbohydrates, and iron	Grains, milk, fish, yeast
Vitamin PP	Integrity of tissues (skin)	Grains, yeast, fish, eggs
Folic acid	Metabolism of proteins, synthesis of hemoglobin	Yeast, liver
Vitamin B12 (cyanocobalamine) Panthotenic acid	Metabolism of proteins, synthesis of hemoglobin Integrity of tissues (skin)	Iron, fish, dairy products Liver, fish, dairy products, rice
Vitamin H (biotine)	Integrity of the skin, metabolism of carbohydrates, lipids, and proteins	Yeast, natural ingredients
Vitamin B14 (choline)	Metabolism of fats, liver protection	Natural ingredients

– Vitamins are organic substances, unlike trace minerals such as iron, iodine, and zinc, which are just as essential.

Vitamins are found in food and are either liposoluble (soluble in fats) or hydrosoluble (soluble in water).

Dogs require thirteen different vitamins. Each plays a specific role or roles, from ensuring good vision, proper growth, and the efficient use of fats, to preserving the skin and maintaining the blood vessels and nervous tissue.

It is important to note that excessive amounts of certain vitamins (particularly vitamins A and D) in the diet can be very dangerous. While these vitamins are necessary and useful in certain amounts, they are harmful and even toxic in others. However, some vitamins, including vitamin E, are well-tolerated even in large amounts. In fact, large amounts of vitamin E have a curative and preventative effect on cell membranes. So far, no signs of hypervitaminosis from this vitamin have been reported in dogs. Amounts of vitamin E above the physiological requirement may therefore increase the quality of a specific food.

Finally, owners should remember that brewers' yeast is a rich natural source of B vitamins, which can be a great aid to improving the appearance of the coat.

Basic nutrional requirements: the maintenance diet

The so-called "maintenance diet" is designed for young adult dogs (under 6-7 years old) with no special physiological conditions (that is, not in a reproductive or athletic period) or illnesses (in perfect health). The nutritional requirements of this "model" dog are used as a basis for determining the adjustments necessary for dogs who are active, pregnant, elderly, or chronically ill.

Dogs rarely have no level of physical activity. For this reason, a proper maintenance diet serves not only to simply maintain a dog but to preserve an optimal state of health by preventing any tendency toward becoming overweight, a frequent problem in dogs.

A good "maintenance" food has two main characteristics:

– It maintains the animal's healthy weight because it is highly digestible without providing too much fat; and
– It promotes healthy skin and a beautiful coat because it is sufficiently enriched with essential fatty acids, essential amino acids, and B vitamins.
The food must be fortified to reflect the following nutritional balance, optimal for a medium-sized adult dog:

– 25% protein;
– 12% fat;
– 5 to 7% dietary fiber;
– 1.1% calcium; and
– 0.8 to 0.9% phosphorus.

In addition, once a dog reaches adulthood, he requires a certain number of calories to maintain his weight. However, the greater the increase in weight (relative to size), the lower the caloric requirement per kilogram of body weight. In fact, the basic caloric requirement is 132 calories of metabolizable energy per kilogram of body weight raised by a factor of 0.75.

Consequently, a small breed needs a diet with a higher concentration of calories, and therefore fat, than a medium-sized breed. And this increase in caloric concentration must be accompanied by an increase in the concentrations of protein, minerals, and vitamins in the diet. For large breeds, an increase in caloric density makes it possible to decrease portion size and thus minimize the risk of poor digestion.

Examples of variations of energy requirements in dogs (in multiples of the Maintenance Energy Requirement)

Maintenance	1
Work, 1 hour	1.1
Greyhound training	1.2
End of growth	1.25
Work, 1 day	1.4
Maintenance at 0° C	1.5
Growth period	1.6
End of gestation	1.4
Beginning of growth period	2
Puppy, non-weaned	2.5
Lactation	2-4
Sled dog	2-4
Animal in hospital cage	0.8-0.9

Seasonal modifications to Maintenance Energy Requirements in dogs living outside

Increase (%) of calories ingested	Continental	Climate Oceanic	Mediterranean
January	100	60	30
February	100	60	30
March	70	30	15
April	40	15	10
May	10	5	0
October	10	5	0
November	40	15	10
December	70	30	15

Dietary balance and portion size are the two key concerns in feeding a dog properly. The attached tables provide the reader with all the necessary numerical data. The suggested quantities shown are for information only, given that outside temperature, the nervous disposition of the breed, and daily environment can modify amounts. The same is true of commercial dog food, for which it is necessary to follow the manufacturer's recommendations.

Diet must be adapted to a dog's size and age

Of all the animal species, the dog exhibits the greatest range in weight. From the Chihuahua, weighing under 1 kg (2 pounds), to the Saint Bernard, weighing over 80 kg (175 pounds), the ratio is one to eighty, while it is never greater than two or three in cats or humans. It goes without saying that this wide range is accompanied by significant anatomical and physiological variations between breeds, and these variations lead to specific nutritional requirements and therefore a specific diet.

**Energy
requirements
per kg and per day**

Kcal/kg/day

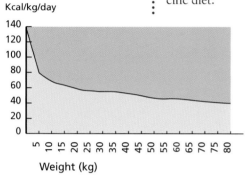

Weight (kg)

Many factors related to a dog's size must be considered in determining his diet: growth period and extent, tooth size, caloric requirements, relative weight of the digestive tract, and average life expectancy. To best meet a dog's requirements and ensure that he remains in good health, adjustments must be made to his diet at each stage of his life.

To understand the key points of a dog's diet that must be customized, owners must simply keep in mind the following factors:

SPECIFIC NUTRITIONAL REQUIREMENTS FOR PUPPIES, BASED ON SIZE

Differences between breeds are visible as early as birth. For example, a Poodle bitch delivers puppies weighing 150 to 200 g (5 to 7 oz.) each, while Newfoundland puppies weigh 600 to 700 g (21 to 25 oz.) at birth. Even though an adult dog of a large breed weighs twenty-five times more than a dog of a small breed, the ratio of birth weight to adult weight ranges only from one to six. Growth period therefore differs depending on breed. The extent and duration of growth are proportional to a dog's final weight.

**Relationship
between birth
weight and adult
weight**

Half adult weight is attained around three months by a puppy of a small breed and not until five or six months by a puppy of a large breed.

Poodles reach adult weight around eight months, when they have attained a weight twenty times their birth weight. Newfoundlands grow until they are eighteen to twenty-four months old, when they have attained a weight approximately one hundred times their birth weight.

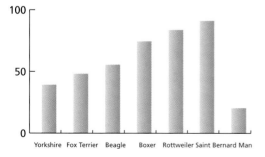

Yorkshire Fox Terrier Beagle   Boxer   Rottweiler Saint Bernard Man

Regardless of breed, puppies require many more calories and much more protein, minerals, and vitamins than adult dogs. Puppy foods thus have certain features in common: high caloric density, a high concentration of all essential nutrients, and a maximum amount of starch. Still, breed size makes some adaptations necessary.

Fundamental differences between small dogs and large dogs:

Differences	Mini (Chihuahua)	Variation Factor	Max (St. Bernard)
Duration of Growth	8 months	3 times longer	24 months
Amplitude of Growth	Weight at birth x 20	5 times greater	Weight at birth x 100
Size of Teeth	Length of a canine tooth: 4-5 mm	3 times longer	Length of a canine tooth: 15-16 mm
Energy Needs	1,32 kcal/kg of body weight	3 times greater per kg	45 kcal/kg of body weight
Relative weight of the digestive tract	7% of body weight	More than 2 times greater	2.8% of body weight
Average Life Expectancy	> 12 years	Almost 2 times greater	7 years

All of these particularities must be taken into consideration in diet. To respond best to the dog's needs and to help maintain the animal's good health, adjustments will be necessary at each stage of life.

– At three months old, a terrier puppy weighs 2-3 kg (4 1/2 to 6 1/2 lb.), while a puppy of a large breed weighs 18-20 kg (39 to 44 lb.). Obviously, their jaws are not the same size! Medium-sized kibble would be difficult for the terrier puppy to handle but would be wasteful for the large breed puppy. It is therefore a good idea to offer appropriate sizes of kibble to small, medium, and large breed puppies.

– Large breed puppies are particularly susceptible to growth problems, including defects in stance and limb position, bone deformation, and joint lesions. These problems are often caused by a diet too high in calories that leads to very rapid weight gain. By limiting the caloric density in the diet of large breed puppies and providing appropriate portions, growth can be better controlled and the risks therefore minimized.

– Large breed puppies require more calcium than small breed puppies. Yet a 20-kg (44 lb.)

Coefficient multiplier of birth weight at one year

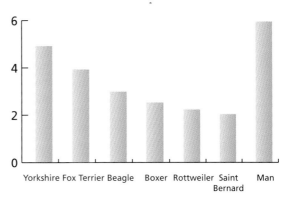

lpuppy eats only 1.5 times more than a 10-kg (22 lb.) puppy of the same age. If both dogs are given the same food, the 20-kg (44 lb.) puppy may suffer a calcium deficiency. For this reason, the calcium concentration should be increased in foods designed for large breed puppies.

– The length of time dogs should be fed puppy food varies, depending on breed: eight to ten months for small breeds, ten to fourteen months for medium-sized breeds, and fourteen to twenty-four months for large breeds.

SPECIFIC NUTRITIONAL REQUIREMENTS FOR ADULT DOGS, BASED ON SIZE

Once a dog reaches adulthood, he requires a certain number of calories to maintain his weight. The more his weight increases, the fewer calories per kilogram of body weight he requires. Consequently, a small breed needs a food with a higher caloric—and therefore fat—concentration than a medium-sized breed. An increase in caloric concentration must, in turn, be accompanied by an increase in the concentration of protein, minerals, and vitamins.

Additional fat increases a product's palatability. Indeed, palatability is a key feature for small breeds, who are often difficult because their owners give in easily to their whims. Small breeds will more readily eat small kibble.

For large-sized breeds, an increase in caloric density makes it possible to slightly decrease portion size and thereby minimize the risk of poor digestion. Smaller portions also help prevent gastric dilatation and torsion, a frequent problem in large breeds. The presentation of the food is also important: large kibble which is not too dense may help to slightly slow a dog's eating.

SPECIFIC NUTRITIONAL REQUIREMENTS FOR MATURE DOGS, BASED ON SIZE

In dogs, as in all other animal species, the aging process begins particularly early. For this reason, certain dietary measures aimed at slowing or reducing the negative effects of aging should be taken as soon as a dog reaches adulthood. The first signs of aging are invisible: the gradual deterioration of some cells, particularly in the kidneys. Contrary to popular belief, limiting protein in the diet will not prevent the kidneys from losing their filtering capacity. However, it is now recognized that reducing the level of phosphorus in the diet can have a positive effect.

Relative weight of the digestive tract in relation to body weight in adult dogs

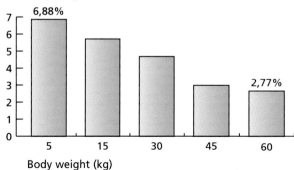

Relative weight of digestive tract/body weight (%)

Body weight (kg)

The mechanisms of aging are linked to the oxidation of the fatty acids in cell membranes. Enriching the diet with vitamins E and C can help the body protect itself from the molecules that cause this oxidation.

As a dog ages, his muscle mass tends to decrease, while his fat reserves increase. His physical activity decreases, as does his resistance to infection, and his coat becomes duller. All these problems are due in part to the body's less efficient use of nutrients. To combat this, it is therefore necessary to provide all the necessary elements—amino acids, fatty acids, trace minerals, vitamins—in a more easily assimilated form. Changes in portion size, together with a marked decrease in phosphorus and an increase in vitamins E and C, should be made at different times, depending on breed: around six years old for large breeds, seven years old for medium-sized breeds, and eight years old for small breeds.

The guidelines for caloric density for mature dogs match those for adult dogs: an increase in calories for small breeds because of their increased requirements and an increase also for large breeds in order to compensate for their limited digestive capacity.

As a dog ages, he becomes more susceptible to oral and dental problems. To ensure that older dogs continue eating normally, they should be given food that is easier to handle, thanks to a kibble size proportional to the size of the dog.

**Energy Recommendations for Elderly Dogs
(kcal of metabolizable energy per day)**

Weight (kg)	Very Calm Dog	"Normal" Dog	Nervous Dog
2	140	165	190
4	240	280	320
6	325	380	430
8	400	470	530
10	475	555	630
12	545	640	725
14	610	720	810
16	675	790	900
18	740	870	980
20	800	940	1060
22	860	1005	1140
24	920	1080	1220
26	980	1140	1290
28	1030	1200	1360
30	1080	1270	1440
32	1140	1330	1510
34	1190	1390	1580
36	1240	1450	1650
38	1290	1515	1720
40	1350	1575	1785
50	1590	1860	2110

Most of the dog food on the market is designed for any and all dogs, regardless of size. Even the most complete product lines are based only on the different stages of a dog's life. Yet genetic selection by humans has produced breeds that vary greatly in morphology and life style. In order to respect these differences, it is necessary to provide owners with products truly adapted to their dogs. A diet that fulfills a dog's requirements as precisely as possible, combined with regular exercise and periodic veterinary examinations, can help improve a dog's well-being and extend his life expectancy.

The digestibility of food

The digestibility of food, characterized by what we call its Digestive Value Coefficient, is a concrete piece of information that reflects the way in which the food is used by the dog's digestive tract. While digestibility is considered a fundamental criterion of the nutritional quality of food, by nutritional veterinarians and owners alike, the practical approach they each use is different.

For the nutritionist, the digestibility of food corresponds to the relationship between what the animal retains (digests) of the food and that which it had consumed.

For the owner, the digestibility of food is appreciated by the quantity, frequency, and quality of his dog's feces (excrement).

Two parameters determine the overall aspect of a dog's feces, reflections of the animal's nutrition and health:

– the digestibility of the dry matter in the food (called DM)

$$CUD.DM = \frac{DM \text{ ingested} - DM \text{ excreted}}{DM \text{ ingested}}$$

Therefore, for a dog that consumes 100 grams of dry matter (the part of the food remaining when the water is removed) and emits 20 grams of dry matter in its excrement, the digestibility of the food is 80%. If this dog retained 85 grams of the food instead of 80, the digestibility would be improved by 5 points, which would represent a decrease in dry matter excreted in the feces by 5/20 or 25%! We note that a slight improvement in the digestibility of a food (5%) can mean a significant drop in the daily amount of excrement (25%), which explains the research efforts made by good manufacturers in this area.

The moistness of feces is also important, since feces contain 65-75% water. A drop in their water content will therefore significantly reduce their volume and improve their consistency.

This being the case, several parameters can change the value of the digestibility of food, starting with the dog itself: Compared to a Beagle, for example, a Fox Terrier digests the same food better, with a spread of digestibility of about 5 points. The quantity of food consumed can also significantly affect this parameter: An increase of the amount consumed by the dog in a single meal means poorer digestibility, which often leads to a suggestion of smaller, more frequent meals throughout the day for dogs with sensitive digestive tracts or those with increased nutritional needs (sports, nursing, etc.).

Digestibility is an important concept for healthy dogs and greatly determines the difference between good and bad food.

Dry food with flakes used to make a soup

Dry food for small-breed dogs (less than 10 kg).(22 lb.) Top to bottom for adult dogs, mature dogs, and puppies.

Dry food for medium-sized breeds (10-25 kg).(22 to 55 lb.) Top to bottom for adult dogs, mature dogs, and puppies.

Dry food for large-breed dogs (>26 kg).(> 55 lb.) Top to bottom for adult dogs, mature dogs, and puppies.

Dry food for a giant dog (over 45 kg) (over 100 lb). Top to botom: For an adult dog, for a mature dog and puppy.

THE NUTRITIONAL SPECIFICS OF PHYSICAL EFFORT

As in humans and horses, intense work and competition cause a specific energy expenditure in dogs, as well as physiological and psychological stress. But in dogs, unlike in the other species, the aspects of size and build come into play. These aspects give rise to nutritional specifics that must be considered in a dog's diet.

Nutritional adaptation is therefore necessary and must take into consideration quantitative and qualitative energy needs associated with muscular work, and also modifications in nutritional requirements based on a dog's build and stress level. Generally speaking, food formulated for sporting or working dogs should:

- provide an optimal quality of energy in adequate amounts;
- minimize the volume and weight of the intestinal bolus as much as possible (highly digestible and highly concentrated foods);
- help keep the animal properly hydrated;
- take into account the dog's body shape;
- possibly have a buffer effect on the metabolic acidification that can be caused by work;
- help maximize results of other ergogenic activities (training, etc.);
- fill physiological voids created by stress;
- be a true preventive factor for effort-related gastrointestinal problems.

It should also respect the animal's particular body type through a scientifically-based "mini," "medium," or "maxi" approach.

Quantitative changes in energy requirements

The daily energy requirements of a working dog are certainly higher than those for the maintenance diet of the same dog, but many variables are involved in determining the exact difference, which can sometimes be difficult to predict. Every trainer should aim primarily at maintaining the dog's proper weight by weighing the dog each week and adapting the amount of food administered accordingly.

A certain amount of data has helped define this approach for the very different cases of the racing Greyhound and the sled dog.

For Greyhounds, the strict energy requirement generated by a single race of under 30 seconds can be estimated by calculating the oxygen debt incurred, giving a result of approximately 75 kcal.

Another simulation borrowed from humans shows that for a given effort, the energy expenditure linked to movement is independent of speed for non-aerodynamic forces and dependent on speed squared for air resistance. This includes the energy required for initial acceleration, in which the dog's body moves from an initial speed of zero to racing speed. A Greyhound participating in a 480-meter race ($\approx 1/3$ mile) at a speed of 17 meters (56 feet) per second expends approximately 70 kcal of energy in this example, which is quite close to our calculation and represents about 4% of the maintenance energy requirement.

Modification of hematocrit in relation to the quantity of proteins in the ration: case of the Husky in long distance race

Still, other factors that will affect the animal's energy requirements must be added to this theoretical approach:

– The number of races per day: If one race represents 4 to 5% of the maintenance energy requirement (approximately 1,800 kcal for a dog weighing 30 kg, based on 132 kcal ME/ kgO.75), two or even three races per day (as is the case for UICL races), combined with being placed in the starting box, will clearly increase the animal's energy requirements;

– Climatic conditions: A drop in the ambient temperature from 15° C to 8° C (27 to 14°F) causes a 25% increase in the metabolizable energy requirement for dogs. In warm climates, glycogen reserves appear to be more rapidly depleted in the body during work, given the considerable energy required for thermoregulation.

Thus, for a given dog and a given amount of effort (a racing Greyhound), the energy requirement will be in the range of 150 to 190 kcal per kilogram of metabolic weight (weightO.75).

Variations in energy requirements with ambient temperature.
Case of a dog working for one hour.

Average Temperature (oC)	Energy Requirements (kcal ME/kg 0.75)
-20	270
-15	255
-10	240
-5	225
0	210
5	195
10	180
15	165
20	150
25	165
30	195
35	210
40	225
45	240
50	255

Sled dogs have very different energy requirements than other sporting dogs. First, their maintenance level requirement is lower at equal weights, particularly for the Siberian Husky (10 to 110 kcal of metabolizable energy per kg O.75). The reasons for this are a higher metabolic energy efficiency, reduced thermoregulation expenditures because of the thermal insulation of the animal's coat, and the breed's body temperature, which is slightly lower than the norm.

Particularly detailed scientific research has been conducted on these dogs, given their irrefutable value as an example of extreme endurance effort. Double-marked water (with deuterium and tritium) has been used to determine the exact daily energy requirements of sled dogs in various racing conditions. In an "Iditarod"-type race day (approximately 200 km [125 miles] covered at a temperature of −35° C[-63°F]), this figure exceeds 11,000 kcal (approximately ten times the dog's maintenance requirement!). In a training or racing situation, the requirement depends on the type of effort, the length of effort, and the ambient temperature, as summarized in the attached table.

Evolution of the energy requirements in practicing sled dogs. Case of a dog weighing 20 kg

Period	Energy Requirements
Maintenance	1000-1200
Training (5 to 8 km/day)	1300-1400
Training (10 to 20 km/day)	1700-1800
Training (30 km/day)	2000-2400
Speed race	1400-1800
Long distance race	2500-3000
Iditarod	7000-8000

For other dogs, generally speaking, one hour of work leads to an increase of about 10% in the base energy requirement. This may mean increasing the energy ingested by 40 or 50% for a "day" of work or sport.

In fact, the vast majority of canine sports fall somewhere between the two extremes of racing Greyhounds and sled dogs. Agility, for example, is closer to the brief effort exerted by Greyhounds: 30 to 60 seconds of racing and obstacles over a distance of 100 to 200 meters (328 to 656 feet), repeated five or six times in one day. Ring events are also a series of brief exercises, but with a steadier rhythm over a longer period of time. With these other dogs, variations in ambient temperature seem to have a greater impact on the energy requirement than for sled dogs, whose "thermal neutrality zone" appears to be broader.

The notion of "energy quality"

The quality of energy administered to the dog during effort is extremely important and leads us to define the criteria for optimal energy for sporting and working dogs. In addition to the type of nutrients used, two qualitative aspects must be considered:

1. The energy must be quickly and easily available where it is needed (muscle cells);
2. The energy compounds must be balanced such that combustion occurs at a maximum efficiency, produces a minimum of waste, and does not carry the risk of metabolic blockage.

ENERGY AVAILABILITY

To reach the site where it will be used, energy must first be digested and then metabolized. To fully understand the recommendations mentioned, it is important to examine briefly how the families of energy-providing nutrients behave with regard to the changes in digestive motility and the physiological adaptations found in sporting dogs. These families include fats (9 kcal ME/g), nitrogen-free extract (4 kcal ME/g), and proteins (4 kg ME/g), with values given for dry, "premium" quality, highly digestible food.

When considering food energy, it seems necessary to take into account that effort accelerates digestive transit.

First, the time of gastric transit must be optimized. If it is too short, it can cause diarrhea due to the poor pre-digestion of proteins and exacerbated by stress; if it is too long, it can induce gastric stasis leading to vomiting and especially stomach torsion. In the absence of a true scientific study of the problem, experience shows that at this level, the physical presentation of the food is to blame, as the best results in sporting dogs have been obtained using dry, extruded food that is slightly rehydrated a half hour before mealtime. Trainers should look for kibble that "holds together" after rehydration, that retains its initial shape without becoming soupy.

The digestibility of food sources must also be considered. Indeed, when transit is accelerated, digestive enzymes have less time to do their work.

In terms of starches (the bulk of nitrogen-free extract), digestion often peaks because of the sometimes mediocre activity of amylase in dogs, particularly working breeds like the German Shepherd and Nordic dogs. In the intestine, the speed with which amylase attacks starch depends primarily on the botanical origin of the starch. The physico-chemical treatment of food can destroy certain links, thereby increasing the surface area exposed to amylase attack. In this way (in the case of boiled starch), amylase digestion can be made up to one hundred times more efficient. Dextrinization is a dry, thermal treatment that reduces amyloses and amylopectins into short-chain molecules called dextrins. However, this term is not completely accurate for the starches used in food for domestic carnivores (this food is boiled or extruded), since the treatment of this food does not alter its physical structure. For sporting dogs, highly digestible starch sources must be used. In fact, compared to fats, which have a caloric value almost two and one half times greater, starches significantly

Nutritional recommendations for Sporting Dogs

Type of Exertion	Maintenance	Brief Effort	Intermediate Effort	Long Endurance Effort
Energy (kcal ME/kg 0.75)	132	150-190	200-400	400-800
Proteins (g/1000 kcal ME)	50-60	70-80	80-90	80-90
Proteins (%ME)	20-25	30	35	35-40
Proteins (%100DM)	24-27	30-35	35-40	35-40
Fats (%DM)	5-10	20-25	20-30	30-40
FA n-6 (%DM)	1	2	3	3
FA n-3 (%DM)	0.2	0,4	0.6	0,6
Short FA (%DM)	-	2.5-5	5-7	8-10
Fiber (%DM)	2-5	3	2.5	2
Calcium (%DM)	0,9-1,1	1-1.1	1,1-1,2	1.2-2.0
Phosphorus (%DM)	0,7-0,9	1.0-1.2	1,0-1,3	1,0-1.5
Potassium (%DM)	0,2	0,4-0,8	0.4-0.8	0,4-0,8
NaCl (mg/kg)	240	240	240	240
Magnesium (%DM)	0.04	0,10	0,15	0,15

increase the ration volume for animals requiring high levels of energy for sporting activity.

But any increase–however slight–in the volume ingested reduces digestibility and causes wetter feces that can lead to softening. In addition, carbohydrate digestion can modify the absorption of other compounds in the ration, such as proteins, some electrolytes, and water. Poorly digested starches reduce the prececal and complete digestibility of proteins in dogs; at the same time, a significant decrease in sodium and potassium absorption is observed. A final, very negative aspect for sporting dogs is that water turnover in the intestine is also modified by the ingestion of poorly digested carbohydrates.

Dogs can digest large quantities of protein, especially animal proteins (actually, plant proteins are no problem, except for the associated carbohydrates and some exceptions related to antitrypsic factors). While relatively rare in dogs in general, digestive problems related to protein intake are more of an issue in sporting dogs. Thus, the consumption of protides that are resistant to pancreatic proteases but are biodegradable (scleroprotein in feathers, collagen in tendons and horns, undercooked eggs, etc.) can lead to intestinal dysmicrobisms that compromise the overall digestibility of the ration, thereby increasing fecal volume and contributing significantly to the occurrence of diarrhea.

Finally, fats must be mentioned, as they are the best source of energy for sporting dogs. Fats have the advantages of being highly palatable, highly digestible, and very well tolerated by dogs (provided that organoleptic quality is optimal). Let us note that, in terms of quality, two categories of fatty acids have digestive virtues for sporting dogs:

– short- or medium-chain fatty acids (coconut, copra, and palm kernel oils, etc.), which are easy to digest because they are digested passively, without the involvement of bile salts;

– omega-3 essential fatty acids (basically purified fish oils) which help preserve the intestinal mucosa, thanks to their local anti-inflammatory virtues. Indeed, when the bolus is too large or too high in fiber in sporting dogs, the intestinal mucosa may undergo traumatic micro-erosion.

To make energy readily available and easy for the body to use during effort, it therefore seems essential to seek highly digestible foods and low alimentary and fecal obstruction, while also considering the information discussed above. Food can be evaluated easily by comparing fecal volume to ingested volume, with the optimum for sporting dogs being 45 to 50 grams of feces for 100 grams of ingested dry matter. While difficult to obtain with homemade rations, this goal is still too rarely achieved using commercial foods.

In the context of making energy available to muscle cells, we must consider the hormonal control of energy metabolism during physical exercise. Indeed, hormonal factors play a key role in the mobilization and use of various energy substrates.

Generally speaking, these factors act either as receptors at the membrane level, by stimulating the production of a second hormonal messenger, or by crossing the membrane and binding with a cytosolic receptor. The first process modifies the activity of certain enzymatic and other reactions and is short in term, while the second increases the amount of enzymatic material and has more long-term effects.

All hormonal messages are prompted during physical exercise, with the degree of variation depending on two factors: intensity and length. From this we note that during effort, the drop in insulinemia and the rise in glucagon and catecholamines are factors that can boost the production and use of carbohydrate reserves, while the mobilization of fat reserves depends only on the rise in plasmatic catecholamines and the drop in insulinemia.

While the mobilization of fat reserves in adipose tissue is controlled by a number of hormones, the use of free plasmatic fatty acids (FPFA) seems to be influenced by relationships between metabolites that are relatively independent from hormones. FPFAs penetrate the muscle cell by diffusion, and their cellular oxidation is controlled by enzymatic stages regulated by other metabolic channels, such as glycolysis.

In terms of metabolism, the concept of optimal energy must take into account this adaptive endocrine and enzymatic data. Thus, administering excessive non-membrane carbohydrates (starches and sugars) to sporting dogs can exacerbate an oversupply of glycogen which, during effort, promotes lactic anaerobiosis with excessive lactate production. Alternately, giving a dog simple sugars before training or competition can induce secondary hypoglycemia at the start of effort through a hyperinsulic reaction.

During extended effort, food energy should be supplied primarily by fats. But because of the hormonal and enzymatic adaptations produced, fats must be incorporated into the ration gradually, in increasing quantities. When this is done, while at the same time reducing the volume of the daily ration and limiting the impact of stress-induced diarrhea, the increase in fat can significantly improve athletic performance in dogs doing endurance work.

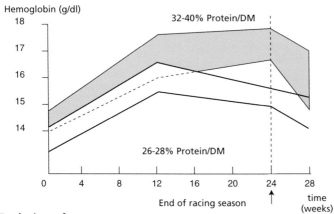

Evolution of hemoglobinemia as a function of the percentage of protein in the ration during racing season

THE CAUSES OF VARIATIONS IN ENERGY EFFICIENCY

The energy supplied to dogs must be adapted qualitatively to the physiological objective and the type of energy metabolism involved. This being the case, the accumulation of metabolizable wastes and certain risks of metabolic blockage can substantially reduce muscle energy efficiency.

Thus, the excessive accumulation of lactates in the blood can impede tissue lipolysis, thereby reducing the efficiency of aerobic metabolism, while the resulting release of protons causes a drop in intramuscular pH, impeding all energy reactions. The accumulation of extracellular potassium can further exacerbate these phenomena. Similarly, nitrogen hypercatabolism during effort can cause the excessive release of ammonia and increase muscle fatigue.

Finally, the sharp drop in glycemia or the lack of glucogenic amino acids (overall protein deficiency) can, during extreme endurance efforts, lead to real metabolic blockage through the accumulation of cetone bodies, although the risk remains slight in dogs, given their ability to use cetone bodies in energy production.

Adapting the qualitative supply of energy should therefore help offset these risks, especially since certain ergonenic nutrients help improve muscle energy efficiency (see specific chapter).

The nutritional impact of stress

While the notion of stress as defined by Selye is extensive, it is certainly true that sporting dogs, like all human athletes, undergo stress that is both physiological (training, competition, etc.) and psychological (transportation, psychological environment, spectators, temperature, noise, etc.). Like the strict energy expenditure incurred by effort, this modifies the animal's nutritional needs. Some contemporary authors would like to extend the concept of stress to include more than the body's central response. The central catecholamine response normally corresponds to various emotional upsets and can be lessened by reducing or eliminating the emotional component of any stressful situation. In fact, the relative importance of the central component of stress decreases as a situation recurs. In our case, we can understand this as one of the important consequences of well-administered training.

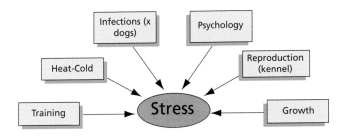

Sources of stress in Sporting Dogs

STRESS AND PROTEINS

The stress of effort modifies the regulation of cerebral serotonin (5-hydroxytryptamine or 5HT) synthesis and activity. This neurotransmitter is involved in the regulation of many physiological functions (ingestion, sleep, blood pressure, energy metabolism, etc.), and its precursor is tryptophan. Overall, the cerebral metabolism of serotonin is increased by effort, depending on the type of training. The primary nutritional consequence of the stress of effort in dogs is therefore an increased need for neutral amino acids and tryptophan, in other words, high-quality proteins that are rich in essential amino acids (high biological value). At the moment, it is impossible to quantify this phenomenon accurately.

Numerous studies on sled dogs have shown that stress causes sometimes severe anemic processes that can be prevented through a minimum supply of protein in the diet of at least 30 to 35% of the metabolizable energy of the ration, in the form of high-quality proteins.

In correlation with the concentration of energy in the ration, the protein content for sporting dogs must exceed 35% compared to dry matter.

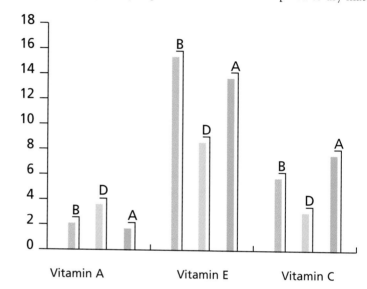

In dogs, stress means narrowing the protein requirement range, though this range is quite broad in a maintenance diet.

The stress of membrane oxidation and its consequences

THE STRESS OF CELLULAR OXIDATION

During cellular metabolism, the biochemical reactions involving oxygen constantly generate toxic compounds called free radicals. Thus, stable oxygen (O_2) can give rise to active compounds like singlet oxygen ($'O_2$), the superoxide free radical ($O_2°$), or much more reactive compounds like the hydroxyl radical ($OH°$). Research conducted in recent years has demonstrated clearly that these free radicals are involved in inflammatory mechanisms, particularly during effort. In terms of the stress induced by physical exercise, free radicals are now considered a basic cause of lesions affecting the entire cell, including proteins and nucleic acids, but especially membrane fatty acids.

These compounds can initiate self-boosting radicular reactions that, when they exceed the reactive capacity of the body's antioxidant systems, cause considerable molecular oxidation affecting unsaturated membrane fats in particular; it even seems that they can form through a simple mechanical influence involving articular or traumatic compression.

The peroxidation of polyunsaturated fatty acids in membrane phospholipids weakens their carbon chain, which eventually breaks. Membrane fluidity and resistance then decrease, leading to changes in cross-membrane exchange that compound the changes generated by the hypoxic altitude process in the case that interests us.

This breakdown generates end products that are then eliminated (dimalonic aldehyde in the urine and pentanes—primarily ethane—through respiration). The hydroperoxides that are formed are released into the cytoplasm, where they become available for forming new free radicals. In addition to modifying cell structure, these new free radicals denature certain proteins and lead to a decline in cytosolic enzyme activity. This process also contributes to the onset of muscle fatigue during effort.

What interests us is that the peroxidation of membrane fats decreases the fluidity or deformability of cells, which lose the ability to maintain their ionic gradients. It also causes general cell swelling and the onset of tissue inflammation.

THE EFFECTS OF PHYSICAL EXERCISE

Even moderate exercise generates free radicals in muscle which cause the peroxidation of polyunsaturated fatty acids in cell membranes. Although the details of the mechanism are not yet well known, the oxidative stress of effort seems to be better tolerated by trained subjects, provided that effort remains moderate.

This protective effect of training might involve a reduction of available iron. In fact, many recent studies have shown a correlation between the content of free iron and the biochemistry of free radicals in many pathological processes. Free iron can apparently diffuse under the stress of effort in the membranes, where it interacts with ascorbic acid and thiol groups to initiate lipoperoxidation. Finally, endurance training significantly increases (by 50 to 70%) the concentration of antioxidant enzymes (glutathione peroxidase and reductase, glucose 6 phosphate dehydrogenase, catalase) in cardiac and skeletal muscles.

While basic training seems to help fight these harmful phenomena, a certain number of nutritional adaptations can also prevent them, at least in part.

A NUTRITIONAL APPROACH TO THE PHENOMENA OF MEMBRANE PEROXIDATION

As we have clearly established, the effects of oxidative stress, or the appearance of reactive types of oxygen that destroy various cell compounds, appear during physical exercise.

This being the case, the organism has defense mechanisms against the production of free radicals and can either fight them off or repair the tissue damage they cause. This system of antioxidant defense consists of:

– enzymes, primarily superoxide dismutase, glutathione peroxidase, and catalase, as well as secondary enzymatic structures such as glutathione reductase, glucose-6-phosphate dehydrogenase, and glutathione S transferase;
– antioxidant nutrients that destroy the free radicals produced, the best known being vitamins E and C, beta carotene, and selenium;
– secondary antioxidants that act in vivo, such as urates, xanthine dehydrogenase, and ubiquinone or the famous polyphenols in Bordeaux wine, etc.

Vitamin E

Alpha-tocopherol (vitamin E) is, without a doubt, the most important destroyer of membrane and lipoproteinic free radicals. It inhibits lipoperoxidation by breaking the chains of peroxide radicals and capturing oxygen singlets. Many studies of vitamin E deficiency in animals have shown clearly that this vitamin significantly increases the cell's sensitivity to lipoperoxidation.

In addition, vitamin E deficiency significantly affects physical performance, particularly in terms of endurance, whether the animal is trained or not. Endurance training also causes a considerable drop in the level of vitamin E in the muscles.

Fewer studies have been conducted regarding the effects of vitamin E supplementation on the consequences of the oxidative stress of effort.

Together with Royal Canin's research center, the UMES has conducted a number of scientific field experiments (the "Dogs of Cimes – Licancabur " expedition and tests conducted in Alaska and Wyoming on the sled dog team of France's Jacques Philip) since 1996 in an effort to pinpoint the preventive virtues and effective dosage of E vitamins in food. These experiments show that 400 IU (mg) per kilogram of food consumed is usually optimal for sporting and working dogs. Only extreme conditions (long-distance sled races, work in altitude hypoxia, intense stress, etc.) may require doubling or even tripling these recommendations.

Vitamin C

Ascorbic acid is the most abundant hydrosoluble antioxidant and can destroy many free radicals, including peroxide radicals, thiols, hydroxyls, superoxides, and singlet oxygen. It is also directly involved in the regeneration of vitamin E in cells. However, in the presence of free transition metals (iron, copper), vitamin C acts as a prooxidant. This can occur under normal conditions when the ions are chelated, for example by ferritin or transferrin.

Although not a vitamin for dogs, which synthesize ascorbic acid, the usefulness of vitamin C supplementation in stressful situations is well established, as this vitamin significantly decreases ascorbemia. The optimum dosage for stress is 0.25 mg of ascorbic acid per kcal ME consumed.

Beta carotene

Beta carotene has antioxidant properties completely independent of its role as a precursor of vitamin A. This is actually its primary role in cats, a species unable to convert it to vitamin A. Beta carotene deactivates singlet oxygen and traps peroxide radicals. Its effectiveness as an antioxidant during ischemic processes has also been shown. Still, its precise active mechanisms remain relatively unknown, as does the optimal daily dosage.

Other antioxidant compounds

While the antioxidant enzymes alpha-tocopherol, ascorbic acid, and beta carotene are the body's most effective means of defense against the oxidative stress on cells, some small molecules—though most not directly linked to food—also have antioxidant properties (additionally, the UMES is currently working on a vectorized superoxide dismutase, or SOD, extracted from melons that seems effective at 10 to 20 mg/kg of body weight). Ubiquinols are the reduced forms of electron carriers in the respiratory chain. It has been shown that the presence of respiratory substrates helps fight the peroxidation of mitochondrial membranes by maintaining a high level of ubiquinone in a reduced form. Ubiquinols do not deactivate fat radicals directly, as alpha-tocopherol does, but they do help regenerate alpha-tocopherol in mitochondrial membranes in the same way as ascorbic acid.

Uric acid is hydrosoluble and has considerable antioxidant properties. It effectively traps many types of hydrosoluble radicals as it permanently deteriorates. It also significantly decreases the reactivity of free iron with active oxygen compounds through complexation. In addition, current research is aimed at developing medicated antioxidant molecules from alkylated derivatives of uric acid and 5-6-diamino-uracil.

Obviously, nutritional antioxidants are both a new and effective approach to fighting the effects of stress in dogs. It is interesting to note that they also have an important application in this species in terms of increasing life expectancy by fighting cell aging (geriatry) and diseases such as tumors, cataracts, and cardiovascular illnesses.

The hydroelectric consequences of dehydration

Dehydration is one of the main problems for sporting dogs, especially since it modifies the animal's ion and acid-base balances, thereby increasing the risk of rhabdomyolysis, collapse, and post-effort tetaniform syndrome.

In racing Greyhounds, recent work by Blythe has uncovered some interesting information. In American races, a dog with a variation in weight over 1 kg from the weight stated at the pre-race weigh-in may be eliminated from competition. After the initial weigh-in, qualified dogs are kept together in a kennel with nothing to drink until the race (in order to prevent the possibility of doping). This waiting period lasts from two to six hours. Dogs are weighed again twenty minutes before the race. When weight loss between the two weigh-ins exceeds 1.5 kg, the race veterinarian is called in to decide whether the animal can participate in competition. The loss of water through urine and saliva due to the stress of this waiting period leads to significant pre-effort dehydration. At this point, 5% of dogs exhibit dehydration greater than 2.4%, although their performance may not suffer.

From this the author concludes that, given the repeatability of these well-known dehydration factors, the clear correlation between the pre-race waiting period in the kennel and dehydration level, and the systematic waiting period of the same dogs, these dogs should be identified and allowed to participate in only the five first competitions of a single meet in order to reduce their waiting period in the kennel. This type of regulation, establishing that dogs cannot be given anything to drink while waiting to race, is now reaching European races, thereby highlighting the negative side of antidoping regulations that are so strict as to verge on stupidity. The objective of these regulations is, nevertheless, respect for the animal. The true impact of extracellular dehy-

Number of races

Male
Female

% of Ponderal Decrease

Distribution of the percentages of the ponderal decrease in competing Greyhounds, Study of 2552 races (Blythe)

dration is not yet clearly defined for brief and intense effort in dogs, but significant post-effort changes are still observed:

- an increase in natremia, correlated with hyperlacticemia;
- a drop in kaliemia and bicarbonates;
- a steady drop in magnesemia;
- return to normal after two hours of recovery.

The actual potassium requirement depends on two essential factors: the athlete's initial potassium level and the losses incurred through effort. Past studies have shown an increase in the concentration of potassium in the muscles of trained animals. In properly trained subjects, the potassium content of non-fatty body mass is much higher than in sedentary subjects. This being the case, short training programs lead to an increase in the total potassium level in the body, but this phenomenon seems linked to an increase in relative body mass. Subsequently, athletes in training need a diet high in potassium to fill an increased requirement related to the increase in muscle mass and the concentration of intramuscular potassium.

Whatever the case may be, hypokalemia can also result from digestive loss through stress-induced diarrhea, excessive sodium ingestion, or exercise in excessive heat. This can lead to an increase in muscular and cardiac sensitivity, the escape of intracellular enzymes, and even premature supraventricular contractions, all of which cause a marked decrease in performance.

Clearly, potassium supplementation is necessary for sporting dogs and should be part of a balanced diet.

Magnesium is a cation that activates some 300 enzymatic systems. In particular, it serves as an activator at the membrane level of Na-K-ATPase, which operates the sodium pump and allows potassium to enter the cell.

Trained animals have been shown to exhibit an increase in magnesium in the cells. Changes affecting magnesemia during physical activity depend essentially on the length of effort. Brief physical exercise (Greyhound race) leads to a significant increase in magnesemia (10 to 20%, probably related to the increase in hematocrit), while any sort of extended effort (hunting, sled racing), is accompanied by a drop in magnesemia of 2 to 5 mg/l. Magnesemia is physiologically important, especially because it affects free plasmatic magnesium, or approximately 65% of all circulating magnesium. Magnesium leaving the plasma is captured by the erythrocytes, muscle cells, and fat cells. Given that physiological reserves of labile magnesium do not exist, post-effort hypomagnesemia can sometimes lead to the clinical onset of possibly tetaniform muscle spasms in poorly trained animals that have undergone intense tissue lipolysis. Here again, an increase in magnesium in the diet is necessary for sporting dogs, especially since increasing fat in the ration affects the digestibility of this mineral.

Most cases of dehydration and electrolyte disturbance observed in sporting dogs are the result of insufficient drinking (during extended effort, a dog needs 2 or 3 times more water), stress, or changes in mineral metabolism.

Necessary mineral and vitamin adaptations

In terms of minerals, it seems necessary to take different approaches for brief and extended effort and to consider the size of the dog involved.

Thus, dietary calcium must be slightly increased for dogs exerting brief or medium effort, in order to prevent joint pain and the osteofibrotic processes frequent in sporting dogs. However, it is necessary to use caution in these cases, in order not to increase the risk of osteochondrosis.

In addition, high-fat diets administered to dogs exerting extended effort can stimulate the loss of calcium and magnesium through the feces (soap formation). It therefore seems necessary to establish a relationship between the ration's fat content and its calcium content.

In terms of magnesium, we have discussed the plasmatic changes during effort and determined that the magnesium content in the diet must be increased, particularly when the diet is high in fat. In sporting dogs, chronic magnesium deficiency appears as:

- decreased endurance and resistance;
- a decreased ability to adapt to heat and cold;
- a loss of motivation;
- changes in neuromuscular sensitivity;
- asthenia with cramps;
- ligament laxity.

Sodium chloride should be limited in the diet, since dogs perspire only minimally through the interdigital gaps. Excessive salt consumption, based on recommendations for humans or horses, soon leads to polyuropolydipsia. In a hot or very cold climate, this can cause extracellular dehydration and collapse. Diarrhea can also occur when electrolyte solutions formulated for horses are administered (this is common in the world of canine sports).

Without going into too much detail, all trace elements should be doubled in the sporting dog diet, as opposed to the maintenance diet, in order to create a safety zone, to account for the higher energy concentration of the food, and to offset the negative effects of calcium on digestibility. Particular attention should be given to the following trace elements:

Nutritional characteristics of special dry food for Sporting and Working Dogs

Size Parameter	Small	Medium	Large
In %/Food			
Protein	30	33	31
Fats	22	30	25
Bulk Fiber	2,5	2,5	2,5
Dietary Fiber	5,5	5,0	5,5
Calcium	1,3	1,4	1,3
Phosphorus	1,0	1,1	1,0
Sodium	0,35	0,35	0,35
Potassium	0,6	0,6	0,6
Magnesium	0,15	0,15	0,15
In mg/kg Food			
Iron	200	220	210
Zinc	210	210	210
Manganese	65	65	65
Copper	35	0,4	0,4
Selenium	0,4	0,4	0,4
Iodine	4,0	4,0	4,0
Vitamin A (IU)	15000	15000	15000
Vitamin D 3 (IU)	1200	1200	1200
Vitamin E	400	400	400
Vitamin C	300	300	300
Vitamin B1	12	12	12
Vitamin B2	5	5	5
Panthotenic Acid	40	40	40
Vitamin B6	6	6	6
Vitamin B12	0,3	0,3	0,3
Niacin	25	25	25
Biotin	0,8	0,8	0,8
Folic Acid	1,0	1,1	1,2
Choline	3000	3000	3000

– iron, which helps prevent anemia. Let us mention, however, that it is important to avoid any excess in iron for strictly digestive reasons, as iron salts frequently cause the hemorrhagic appearance of stress-induced diarrhea and rectal bleeding;

– copper, which can also help prevent certain anemias, improves the solidity of the bone matrix and of cartilage;

– zinc, which is involved in muscular contraction and is the active metal in the enzyme LDH and the plasmatic carrier protein of vitamin A;

– iodine, which activates thyroid functioning and can help prevent muscular dystrophy;

– selenium, which, together with vitamin E, preserves muscle cells.

Finally, with regard to vitamins, the distinction must still be made between long-term, biological preparations and a sort of "doping" often administered at race time. Let us first establish that if the first condition is fully met, a vitamin overdose in the days or hours preceding competition provides little or no benefit. Vitamins C, B, and E are the only vitamins with demonstrated virtues for sporting dogs.

We have now clearly established a certain amount of scientific data on the nutritional specifics of sporting dogs. This data may seem excessive to trainers but is one of the keys to success in competition and work, in a constantly developing sphere of activity.

PRACTICAL RATIONS

In practical terms, a Sporting or Working dog's ration must:

- be nutritionally balanced in the elements mentioned above
- be concentrated and highly digestible
- be appropriately adapted to and consumed by the dog
- take into account the dog's size (small, medium, large)

We can then consider foods for Sporting dogs as being a series of specific adaptations around the three following themes:

- meeting maintenance needs
- increasing the energy content and nutrients of the food while decreasing the amount of fecal matter
- enriching the food for effort and induced stress (providing empty carbohydrate calories and especially lipid calories)

When choosing a type of food or evaluating a food, you should first to consider its energy density insofar as the energy requirement is significantly influenced by the amount and intensity of the exercise involved, making the ration size a limiting factor. It is then clear that there is no place in this context for dry complete industrial foods (excluding table scraps and moist food) that could possibly include supplements adapted to the specific needs of each sport practiced. In the long term, the owner must not lose track of the fact that the nutrients, if they meet the energy requirement, are also the only way for the animal to ward off the effects of stress.

The Relationship between Training and Diet

An animal's diet should be carefully adapted to changes in training:

– rest period: high-quality maintenance food, adapted to the size of the dog
– training period: gradual progression to a working ration (transitions over a week for each modification) or increasing addition of a working dog's dietary supplement to the maintenance ration

– racing period: the added stress to the work may call for additional nutritional adaptations. Quantitatively, the ration is adapted to the change in the weight of the animal

– post-training period: gradual return to the maintenance diet

Of course, owners cannot expect any particular performance from a dog that is well-fed but poorly trained or well-trained but without a proper diet! Regardless of the canine sport in question, it isn't the egg yolks on Monday or the sardine on Thursday or the secret magic powder that will make the animal a winner, but rather a rational approach that respects a real dietary plan that is based on nutritional information and carefully thought out for the entire season.

Choosing the Foods

The quality of raw materials or complete foods used to meet nutritional needs is of the utmost importance for Sporting or Working dogs insofar as they must be extremely digestible, ensure optimal energy yield for the animal, and allow for optimal detoxification.

Protein Sources

All protein sources with a low availability of amino acids and a low biological value (balance of essential amino acids) should be avoided. The same is true for proteins that are not easily digested and that are rich in collagen (the total collagen/protein ratio should not exceed 20%). We recommend:

– (red and white) meat
– meat and fish powder with at least 55-60% protein in relation to the dry matter
– whole egg powder

De-lactosed caseine (which, in order to be perfectly balanced, requires the addition of about 2% of methionine)

Carbohydrate Sources

Foods or raw materials that are high in starch should be chosen for their quality and should undergo an optimal heat treatment in order not to cause intestinal problems. Quick sugars are prohibited. Fiber will be introduced in limited amounts (2-3% cellulose in the food), because it is too great in volume, decreases the overall digestibility of the ration, and causes water to be retained in the feces, which is harmful to the dog's hydration. Only certain "soluble" fiber is useful in the dog's digestive health.

Lipid Sources

These should be thought of in terms of the category of fatty acids that they transport and should be carefully monitored for non-oxidation and spoiling:

– lard, suet, poultry fat (long saturated fatty acids)

– coconut, coprah, and palm oils (short or medium fatty acids)

– sunflower, soy, and corn oil (essential fatty acids from the Omega 6 series)
– purified fish oils (essential fatty acids from the Omega 3 series)

Vitamin and Mineral Sources

Here again, we should look for mineral sources that can be perfectly assimilated, such as calcium phosphates and carbonates. Used systematically, yeasts are an excellent source of B complex vitamins. Liposoluble vitamins will be provided in commercial forms.

Complete Industrial Foods

For the many reasons cited above, it seems that only complete dry dog food should be used for Sporting dogs.

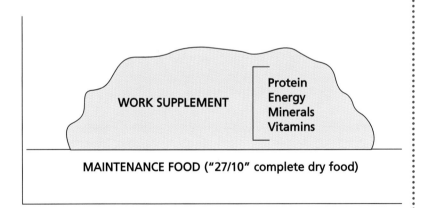

Rationing plan for Sporting Dogs – Solution #1

Maintenance Food

For some owners, the easiest approach is still increasing the daily ration based on the increase in the energy requirement, without changing the food. In this case, no specific dietary approach is used, and the result is a less-than-optimal performance for the animal.

The following more effective examples could be used:

1) The same maintenance food is used all year long. It is gradually supplemented during the training and competition periods. In this case, the best basis is provided by a 25/10 type food (25% protein, 10% fat for the unfinished product, which corresponds to about 27% protein and 11% fat in relation to the dry matter) that is highly digestible (with an optimum of 50 grams of fecal matter for every 100 grams of dry matter ingested). Based on current knowledge, we would recommend a food that is adapted to the animal's size and shape, and one that targets the first period of adult life (often called "Adult 1"). Use this food as a constant dietary base for the whole year, supplementing it during training and competition periods with lean meat or fish for brief periods of exertion and fats for longer periods of exertion. At the peak of training, we would then gradually reach a ration that is one fourth to one third dry food and three fourths to two thirds meat or fish. An adapted vitamin and mineral supplement would then be necessary.

2) The maintenance diet is only used during the rest period. It should meet the previously described qualitative conditions and will gradually be changed to a specific complete food once training becomes intense. Dietary transitions should be spread out over three to seven days.

Rationing plan for Sporting Dogs – Solution #2

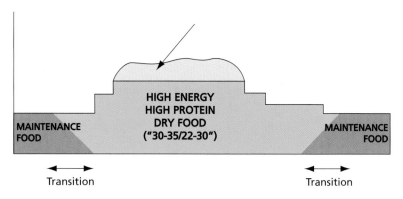

Specific Foods

Ideally we would recommend a 30-32/22-25 type food for short to medium periods of exertion and a 35/30 type food for long periods of exertion. Here again, the food needs to be highly digestible and ensure small intestinal and fecal amounts. Ration size should also be adapted to changes in the dog's weight. When taking into account the extreme aspects of some types of exertion, Greyhounds and sled dogs may be considered separately. For a sled dog, a 35/30 type food would be quite sufficient for most of the training period as well as for "small" categories of harness competition (3 to 6 dogs). Beyond that, specific supplements for protein, fats, vitamins, and minerals appear necessary and may used in either a homemade or industrial form. For long distances, the gradual

Composition of work supplement for Sporting Dogs during brief periods of exertion (ex: Greyhounds)

Semi-industrial Food

Meat powder (60% protein)	# 50-60%
Egg powder	# 15% F (anaerobic training)
Fats	# 10-20%
Yeast	# 5%
Calcium Carbonates	# 2%
Calcium Phosphate	# 1%
Minerals, trace elements, vitamins	qps
Energy:	3500 kcal/kg

Daily amount = $\dfrac{\text{Energy Requirement Linked to training} - 1700 \text{ (maintenance energy req.)}}{3500} = \text{kg}$

Example of daily ration for racing Greyhound weighing 30 kg

Lean meat	#750 g
Rice (before cooking)	#150 g
Bone meal	2 teaspoons
Corn oil	1 teaspoon
Liver	#30-60 g

Vitamin and trace element supplements

change to a type 36/36 complete semi-moist food seems to be an excellent solution, but poses a problem for industries in that this section of the market is still rather small and does not justify the necessary investments. Nevertheless, a rationing program that calls for gradually increasing the proportion of the specific supplement in the daily ration may still be implemented.

Practical Distribution Methods

In addition to respecting the dog's nutritional needs when choosing the proper food and respecting an adapted dietary program that changes over the course of the year, appropriately feeding a Sporting or Working dog also entails certain practical methods for distributing the meals. These methods help to:

– prevent problems such as stomach torsion, an obsessive fear for owners of certain large dogs

– minimize the incidence of stress-related diarrhea
– allow the body to find the energy it needs when it needs it

– maintain the body's level of extra-cellular hydration

Composition of special food for brief periods of exertion in large dogs

Special Complete Dry Food

Protein	31-33%
Fat	22-25%
Fiber	2%
NFE	38-40%
Calcium	1.1-1.2%
Phosphorus	# 1.0%

+ other minerals, trace elements, vitamins ÷ Specific recommendations

Special ration (1,200 g/day for a dog weighting 30 kg)

Red meat	# 60%	
Cereal flakes	# 30%	Protein: 33%
Soy oil	# 2%	Fat.: 14%
Coprah oil	# 2%	CFE: 45%
Fish oil	# 2%	Energy: 2250 kcal ME/kg
Specific CMV fish oil	# 4%	

Dogs should never be fed right before exertion. It is also best to break up the daily ration into as many meals as possible. A series of very small meals is greatly preferable to a single very large meal. To best prepare a dog for exertion, give the animal a quarter (for short periods of exertion) to a third (for long periods of exertion) of its daily ration approximately three hours beforehand so that its stomach will be empty when the period of exertion begins.

This "preparatory" meal should be extremely hydrated (with three to four times more water than food) so the dog will be able to compensate for the fluids used by the effort. With this system, owners should not have to worry about the affect of the peak of insulin caused by the meal. Thirty to forty minutes before the work, they dog may again be allowed to drink, but this time a more limited amount (200 ml for a dog weighing 20 kg (44 pounds), for example).

Practical rationing for Sled Dogs based on the distribution of complete dry food and adapted work supplement:

Proportion Dry Food*/ Supplement**	Kcal ME/kg (% DM)	Protein (% DM)	Fats%	Protein Calories***
80/20	# 4550	37	34	31.5
70/30	# 4650	38	36	31.6
60/40	# 4750	39	38	31.6
50/50	# 4850	40	40	31.7
40/60	# 5000	41	42	31.8

* "35/30" Type Complete Dry Food
** "45/45" Type Work Supplement
*** Essential Respect of Protein/Calorie Relationship

Approximately two hours after the exertion the dog will be given the rest of its daily ration, except for the case of sled dogs racing in legs or long distance, in which case the food may be distributed sooner to prevent stress-related diarrhea the next day. In contrast, the dog may be allowed to drink immediately following the exertion, by breaking up the amounts over the hour following exertion.

So, rules that are specific

to the practice of a real physical activity should be added to the classical rules governing balanced dietary rations. A dog's diet during competition or when faced with working activity is a fundamental part of preparing the animal and preventing problems. It should be specifically adapted, of the highest quality, and take precedence over the numerous "secret recipes" that serve no other purpose than to placate the owner's psyche.

ERGOGENIC NUTRITIONAL SUPPLEMENTS FOR EXERTION

An "ergogenic supplement" is any substance, method, or technique that improves or is thought to improve performance, with the exception of training. More specifically, an "ergogenic nutritional supplement" is any non-medicinal substance or molecule that is not yet traditionally added to dog food but is very similar to a nutrient. This term therefore encompasses the concepts of safety, effectiveness, and improvement in performance and/or the recovery process under specific conditions.
Ergogenic supplements are frequently administered to sporting animals in order to activate a specific type of metabolism and consequently obtain better performance. This supplementation is based on the assumption that the endogenous production of the nutrient involved is insufficient and is a limiting factor to muscular activity.

Nevertheless, the mere presence of a nutrient in a metabolic system does not justify an artificial increase in its exogenous supply. The best example of this is probably ATP, which is still sometimes administered orally or parenterally but has no value in these routes other than commercial.

Below is a critical review of these non-essential nutritional factors, some of which may be of interest, in light of current scientific knowledge.

Vitamins in megadoses

As mentioned in the more general chapters on nutritional needs and their fulfillment, sporting and utility dogs may benefit from an increase in the amount of certain vitamins in the daily portion.

This is true of most B vitamins, all of which play a role in energy or protein metabolism. Of fundamental importance in the synthesis of red blood cells, which carry oxygen to the muscles, vitamin B12 (cyanocobalamin) is worth special attention. Increasing the amounts of this vitamin during periods of intense exercise or general fatigue can help the body fight athletic anemia and restimulate the appetite (with the daily recommended dosage being 40 mg per kilogram of body weight).

We will not further describe the interest of vitamins E and C, already discussed at length, as antioxidants that help prevent the harmful effects of oxidation on the cell membrane during exertion. Owners must be very attentive to the amount of these two vitamins in the food when the dog is in a period of training or competition.

Efficiency of different ergogenic nutritional aides for dogs available on the market

PRODUCT	ACTIVITY				Daily Dose (/kg)	Harmless
	Brief Exertion	Intermediate Exertion	Long Exertion	Recuperation		
L. Carnitine	+	++	++++	++	50 mg	Yes
Aspartic Acid	0	+?	+?	?	?	?
Arginine	0	+?	+?	?	?	Yes
Sodium Bicarbonate	+	0	0	?	400 mg	Yes
Dimethyl-glycine	++	+	0	?	1.5 mg	Yes
Inosine	0	0	0	++	10 mg	Yes
L. tryptophane	+?	+?	+?	0	5 mg	?
Ascorbic Acid	+	++	++++	+	100 mg	Yes
Methylsulfonylmethane	0	0	0	0	-	?
Vectorized Superoxide dismutase	++	++	+++	++	20 mg	Yes
Probiotics	+	+	+	0	?	Yes
Octaconasol	0?	0?	0?	?	?	?
Gamma oryzanol	?	?	?	?	?	?
Bioflavinoids	?	?	?	?	?	?
Chondroitine Sulfate	+	++	++	Prevention	50 mg	Yes

Carnitine

Carnitine is a non-essential amino acid that ensures the transport of fatty acids through the mitochondrial membrane to the site of metabolic oxidation. Carnitine therefore limits muscular activity during aerobiosis (exertion lasting over two minutes). At this time, we will not review all the known physiological and metabolic roles of this substance, which for example has curative properties in the case of dilated cardiomyopathy in Boxers.

One of the more recent applications of carnitine relates to the study of how to improve athletic performance. During non-exertion, the body apparently synthesizes carnitine easily from other amino acids (lysine and methionine) in the presence of cofactors including iron, niacin, and vitamins B and especially C.

A number of studies demonstrate the effectiveness of adding carnitine to the daily portion, in terms of the body's physiological response during extended exertion and the improvement of the body's recovery capacity.

An amino acid, carnitine exists in two biological forms: L-carnitine and D-carnitine. Only L-carnitine is physiologically active, while D-carnitine is an inhibitor of L-carnitine. In terms of nutritional value, L-carnitine is therefore preferred to the racemic mixture of both forms, which in fact has no physiological interest.

It appears that carnitine can be a limiting factor in dogs under certain conditions, for example during extended exertion at semi-maximum intensity, during which glucose could be easily used instead of free fatty acids in the blood, even though these are available.

L. carnitine concentration of some food sources (in mg/100 g of bulk matter)

Food	L.Carnitine
Mutton	210
Lamb	78
Beef	64
Pork	30
Rabbit	21
Chicken	7.5
Cow's Milk	2.0
Egg	0.8
Vegetables	0

In any case, it now seems clear that L-carnitine plays an important role in energy metabolism by acting on the following:
– the entry of fatty acids into the mitochondria;
– the oxidation of short-chain and medium-chain fatty acids;

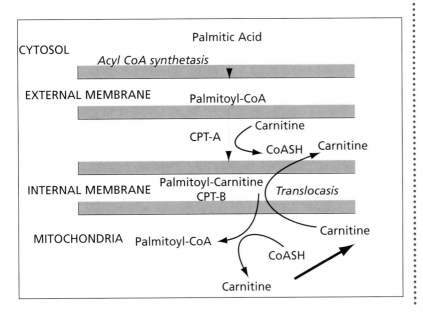

– the oxidation of fatty acids in the peroxysomes;
– the ratio of linked coenzyme A to free coenzyme A;
– the elimination of excess acetylcoenzyme A, which is toxic;
– the production of energy from the cetone bodies, pyruvate, and amino acids, including branched-chain amino acids; and
– the regulation of ammoniemia.

As for the nutritional dosage of L-carnitine for sporting dogs, 500 mg/10 kg of body weight administered orally appears optimal, based on field studies conducted on sled dogs. Finally, the relatively high level of in L-carnitine in mutton must be mentioned and may explain the significant empirical use of this type of meat in the diet of sled dogs.

Dimethyl glycine

Dimethyl glycine (DMG) is the active principle in pangamic acid, also known as vitamin B15, in which it is combined with gluconic acid. Involved in the metabolism of methyl group molecules, DMG is used as a nutritional supplement for athletes in order to reduce the lactic deficit and delay the sensation of fatigue by:
– improving the storage of phosphagens in muscles;
– decreasing lactate production; and
– reducing post-exertion lacticemia.

Place of dimethyl-glycine in the metabolism of methyl molecules

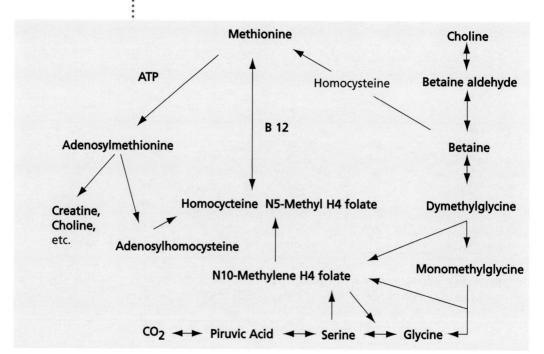

DMG supplementation has improved performance in horses. Nevertheless, the results obtained are contradictory, in part because the chemical preparations of pangamic acid on the market vary, making it difficult to repeat and interpret tests. A certain degree of caution is always necessary, since some ingredients in unpurified products may be harmful (dichloracetate and d.gluconodimethyl aminoacetate). In addition, the very status of pangamic acid as a vitamin is under discussion in the United States, where the Food and Drug Administration has discouraged its use until commercial mixtures are clarified. Still, interesting results, in terms of increasing the anaerobic threshold, can apparently be gained by administering a purified DMG supplement to canine athletes.

In an Australian study of sighthound athletes, Gannon compared the racing times at 510 and 720 meters without and with oral DMG supplementation (0.8 mg/kg, twice a day), or with DIPA (diisopropyl ammonium dichloracetate) supplementation (1.5 mg/kg, taken daily). The times for the shorter distance were approximately 31 seconds and improved by 0.1 to 0.2 second with DMG and by 0.13 to 0.3 second with DIPA. For the longer distance, the average time was 45 seconds, with an improvement of 0.1 to 0.3 second with DMG and 0.12 to 0.3 second with DIPA. No difference was observed at 200 meters, thus confirming that DMG and DIPA do not affect phosphagens. Since the same improvement in performance was obtained for 30 and 45 seconds, DMG and DIPA appear to promote the oxidation of pyruvate from muscle glycogen rather than the oxidation of blood glucose.

Although interesting, this observation allows no other scientific conclusions, since data involving training in particular are not given. Still, we may conclude that DMG can be given daily, in an oral dosage of 1.5 mg/kg during anaerobic or aerobic/anaerobic exertion.

Inosine

An inotropic substance and a precursor of AMP, ADP, and ATP, inosine is a cardiotonic with specific properties, given the existence of myocardial receptors specific to this substance. Studies of the metabolic activity of inosine supplied exogenously to myocardial cells show that inosine:

– stimulates glucose collection;
– activates the process of phosphorylation;
– promotes the flow of pentoses, normally very limited in myocardial cells;
– catalyzes lactic dehydrogenase toward the normal course of the Krebs cycle, thereby preventing anoxia due to the accumulation of lactic acid;
– activates the oxygen supply to the myocardium by acting on the 2,3-diphosphoglycerate in red blood cells; and

– intensifies the activity of the respiratory chain by increasing the number of mitochondrial walls.

In a recent experiment, Sarret demonstrated that administering inosine orally at a dosage of 10 mg/kg in the ten days preceding an event does not improve endurance in dogs but does increase the recovery capacity of a non-trained animal.

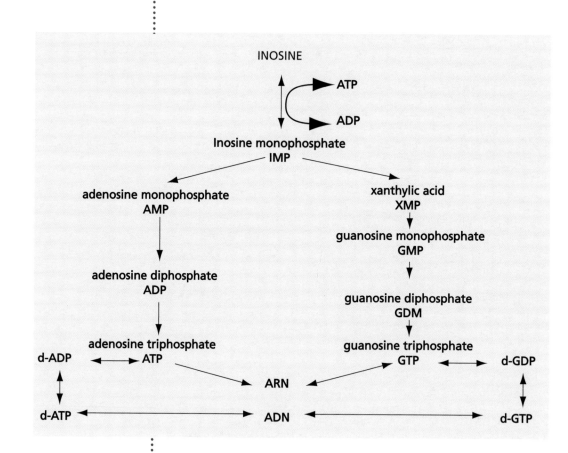

Tryptophan

The stress of exertion affects cerebral serotonin (5-hydroxytryptamine, or 5HT) in terms of the synthesis and activity of this neurotransmitter involved in the regulation of many physiological functions.

Its precursor is an essential amino acid, tryptophan, of which only the L form is active. In terms of tryptophan transfer to the encephalon, it appears that exertion increases the supply of tryptophan to the brain and is regulated by catecholamines. Therefore, it appears that overall sero-tonin metabolism is increased by exertion, depending on the type of activity.

Physical performance is known to be closely linked to the onset of fatigue and physical pain. Given that serotonin affects nociception through its influence on the enkephalin-endorphin system, a recent study analyzed the effects of tryptophan supplements in the diet (at a dosage of 5 mg/kg) on endurance and the sensation of fatigue. An improvement in both areas was observed when L-tryptophan was administered. No specific data is currently available on dogs.

Methylsulfonyl methane

MSM is a terminal metabolite of dimethyl sulfoxide (DMSO) which has been lauded as:

– an anti-stress substance beneficial in post-injury recovery;
– a source of bioavailable sulfur; and
– a substance with anti-inflammatory properties.

Some probably overzealous individuals even claim that for muscle pain, MSM is more active and effective on the hind legs than the forelegs. We will end our commentary here, since this molecule, if marketed, is of no interest and carries no guarantee of safety.

Superoxide dismutase

A newcomer on the athletic nutrition "market," superoxide dismutase (SOD) is an enzyme that generates the hydrogen peroxide used by gluta-tione peroxidase to reconvert reduced glutathione. It is abundant in the red blood cells and the muscle cells. An oral SOD supplement appears beneficial, as long as it is not destroyed in the dog's stomach, which is characterized by a particularly acidic pH. Currently, the UMES is con-ducting several studies focused on demonstrating the interest of a nutri-tional supplement of "vectorized" superoxide dismutase, a natural com-pound found in melons which, because it combines with the gliadins in melon, is not destroyed in the stomach and can therefore be absorbed nor-mally. In a daily dosage of 15 to 20 mg per kilogram of body weight, SOD may be a major factor in preventing the oxidative stress of exertion.

It is nevertheless interesting to note that the degree of biological activ-ity of SOD is closely correlated with the amount of dietary copper, itself greatly depreciated due to reduced digestibility when food is enriched with calcium. Excess calcium may therefore decrease the activity of SOD, making it necessary to adapt the amount of copper in the diet.

Probiotics

Probiotics are products of bacterial or fungal fermentation, usually lactic, and can provide animals with potentially beneficial nutrients including amino acids, B vitamins, and enzymes. Certain strains of probiotics are effective in improving digestibility and growth indices in "production" species. Probiotics are beginning to be used successfully in dogs (Paciflor ND), and bring about:

– the bioregulation of intestinal microflora (the rapid germination of these lactic bacteria in the intestine allow microflora to "occupy the terrain" and "stifle" the development of pathogens);
– an increase in nitrogenous retention, leading to the improved assimilation of dietary proteins;
– the production of enzymes beneficial to digestion;
– the production of organic acids that function as antibacterial agents against pathogens; and
– the stimulation of local and then general immunity in the animal.

Since they do not colonize the intestine, probiotics must be administered daily.

Octacosanol

Octacosanol is an alcohol that contains twenty-eight carbon atoms and exists in very minute quantities in vegetable oils, especially wheat germ oil. It is thought to exert a potentializing action on vitamin E and for this reason has been recommended as an ergogenic supplement given daily throughout the training period. No data involving dogs is available.

Gamma oryzanol

Gamma oryzanol is an ester of the ferulic acid in triterpenic alcohols. It has been proposed as a natural antioxidant for preventing the alteration of the cell membrane during anaerobic exertion. No data involving dogs is available.

Bioflavonoids

Bioflavonoids are also natural antioxidants. They are not essential nutrients but enhance the effectiveness of vitamin C. It appears that a smaller amount of vitamin C in the diet is therefore acceptable for dogs in periods of stress, as long as the diet is enriched in bioflavonoids. Here again, no scientific data involving dogs is available.

Chondroitin sulfate and glycosaminoglycans

Polymerized derivatives of glycuronic acid, a basic component in cartilage, these non-dietary elements have for some time been the subject of considerable study in dogs. Roughly speaking, chondroitin sulfate and glycosaminoglycans are molecules which are integrated in the cartilaginous matrix, where they are renewed continuously from an intra-articular supply in the synovial fluid and an extracellular supply circulating in the blood.

Initially used as "markers" of cartilaginous degeneration in diseases caused by physiological stress, chondroitin sulfate and glycosaminoglycans are beginning to be used to prevent or treat degenerative joint diseases (osteochondrosis, arthrosis, etc.). The following substances have produced positive results: chondroitin sulfate, polysulfated glycosaminoglucans, and certain natural, more complex "blends" derived from mussels (Perna canaliculus) or shark cartilage.

Frequently prescribed by veterinarians for aging dogs (at the beginning of what is traditionally called the "adult 2" phase), these molecules are

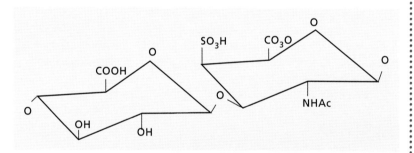

Chemical structure of chondroitine sulfate

especially beneficial for sporting and utility dogs, given the considerable impact of joint trauma.

Some of the substances discussed in this overview are undeniably beneficial for sporting dogs (L-carnitine, dimethyl glycine, probiotics, SOD, chondroitin sulfate, and antioxidant vitamins).

As for others, even though they may be derived from natural products, we believe they fall outside the domain of nutrition and should at least be tested for safety before being marketed. For these substances, the boundary between nutrient and unknown, potentially harmful drug remains ill-defined.

THE BASES OF PHYSICAL TRAINING

When we begin to talk about canine sports and how certain types of performance can lead dogs to behave like real athletes, it is important to be clear about properly designed and adapted physical training programs. In its basic definition, "training" is defined as the "physical, technical, tactical, intellectual, and moral preparation of an athlete through physical exercises." When applied to dogs, this definition refers to a set of exercises commanded by the owner in a psychological atmosphere of trust in order to preserve the "play" aspect and maintain the dog's motivation.

An animal's physical capabilities depend on numerous physiological and psychological factors that have a great range of influences depending on the sporting activities in question. Aptitude tests, still rare for dogs but quite common for humans, only take into account a small number of these factors, and the results obtained often provide only partial information as to the subject's abilities. Let us point out that there is no universal aptitude since aptitudes must always be considered for a given activity or category of activities.

Generally, training is associated with a certain number of catabolic processes such as the breakdown of substrata in the energy supply or other cellular components, followed by an intensification of the anabolic processes, which manifests itself in an increased production of the molecules that were mobilized or destroyed during the work itself.

We believe that physical training implies that the organism is exposed to an intense work load of such length and frequency as to determine a measurable affect, and thereby an improvement in the functions undergoing the training.

To obtain such an affect, it is necessary to submit the organism to an overload: a load that is greater than the one encountered in everyday life.

The term "training" is currently used in a variety of fields and most often refers to a process that, through physical exercise, aims at reaching a higher level based on planned objectives.

A more precise notion of "sports training" entails all physical, technical, tactical, intellectual, and moral preparation of the athlete through physical exercise. Though limited, this notion also implies a subsequent potential for gradual improvement and development. When adapting this notion to Sporting dogs, in addition to the program's strictly physical aspect, it should include a human-dog relationship that maintains the "play" aspect for the dog in the effort demanded.

The principes of training

OVERVIEW

Contrary to what is still frequently practiced in canine sports, not just any activity constitutes training. In fact, the load applied during training not only requires a certain intensity, but also a sufficient duration of application.

As a result, two principles must absolutely be respected when establishing a training program:

– knowing the primary source of energy used during a particular activity

– using the principle of overloading, set up a program that will best develop the animal's particular use of this energy source

To maintain the effectiveness of training, it will be necessary to increase the load as performance is gradually improved. The influence of training on heart rate demonstrates this necessity quite well: regular training at a given level determines a gradual decrease in heart rate observed during the exercise (in humans as well as in dogs).

Little by little, the heart rate stabilizes at a level that can no longer be lowered by continuing the training. On the other hand, after a period of training at a higher level, the original level of performance can be obtained at an even lower heart rate. This is also a general principle, stated by Astrand, that can be observed during training of a certain number of functions, "Training at a given level determines a certain level of adaptation and to obtain further improvement, it is necessary to increase the intensity of the training."

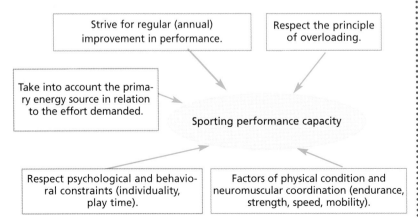

**The main
principles for
training
Sporting dogs**

Still, it should be noted that it generally takes several years for a high-level athlete (human or animal) to reach optimal results. Though we do not currently know exactly which quantitative and qualitative modifications come into play at the level of the organism's different functions to determine this slow and progressive improvement, an appropriately managed training program should take this into account and therefore be designed with several seasons in mind.

Finally, one last aspect that should be considered is the animal's psychological state. In this respect, the idea should be stressed that training doesn't have to be a struggle in order to be effective, because it must maintain the dog's motivation and desire to perform well. Consequently, in many cases, the best solution is to choose a leisure activity that involves a certain amount of physical work, even if this type of training is not very intense and is difficult to quantify.

Psychologically, dogs will more readily participate in a 10-kilometer (6 1/4 miles) race than repeat the same 1-kilometer stretch (5/8 mile) ten times or the same 100 meters (330 feet) 100 times. They will also prefer to follow a path with some variety than to work in a closed environment.

It is also this respect of a balance between work and play, even the most scientific in design, that will make a dog owner a good trainer and will lead the animal (or group of animals) to better performance. Respecting these basic principles will allow functional and useful training methods to be implemented.

PRINCIPLES FOR STRUCTURING TRAINING PROGRAMS

The Principle of Increasing Training Loads

The principle of increasing training loads (gradually) is based on an increase in the volume and intensity of loads in the training process. For beginners, increasing the volume works in conjunction with increasing the intensity, but the work load should be increased very slowly. On the other hand, for animals that have already been well trained, this increase can be done in larger increments, while taking into account the fact that this method can cause significant physiological changes that need to be monitored.

The Principle of Continuous Training Loads

The term "continuous training load" refers to a regular set of training sessions that lead to continued improvement in performance until a maximum level (determined by genetic factors) is reached. In such a case, if for one reason or another, training is interrupted (due to an injury, for example), there will be a drop in performance that is as rapid as the increase had been during the previous training sessions.

Extremely rapid improvement of performance is lost just as quickly when training stops for an undefined period, unlike gradually improved performance, which is slower to disappear.

The Principle of Periods in Training Loads

The canine athlete cannot remain in the same condition throughout the year. As a result, periodic modifications should be made in alternating training sessions and recuperation periods in the volume and intensity of the work demanded, etc. By proceeding this way, it is possible to reach optimal condition at the right moment, while still not disregarding the principle of continuous training loads.

For this reason, a training program should be divided into three periods: preparation (training), competition (maintaining the condition), and transition (un-training). A structure based on this principle, while still rarely encountered in canine sports, allows dogs to:

Principles for planning training cycles

– avoid over-training
– reach points of performance not otherwise reached
– work throughout several successive seasons

The Principle of Variation in Training Loads

The principle of variation in training loads can play a special role when several physical factors intervene within the same discipline: strength, great speed, endurance, coordination, etc. Different types of training loads will affect the body in very different ways, as the amplitude and duration of recuperation differ depending on the type of training.

For example, intense endurance training in dogs calls on the reserves of glycogen in the muscle (as well as calling on the fats in the body), which makes a significant rest period necessary for the body to regenerate these energy reserves and return to its initial performance capacity.

If, instead of rest, another metabolic function is demanded of the organism (very

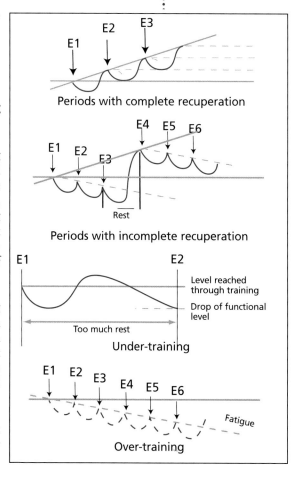

Periods with complete recuperation

Periods with incomplete recuperation

Under-training

Over-training

Mechanism of "overcompensation"

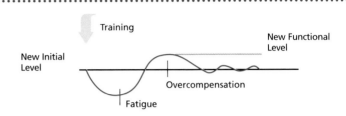

brief and intense effort calling upon the creatine phosphate and ATP reserves), the body is better able to manage this new load than it would be to repeat the first action. Consequently, carefully organizing and alternating different training loads will allow more volume and intensity in a session.

The Principle of Carefully Organizing Training Loads

This principle is fundamental when a single form of training is intended to improve several different performance elements:

– at the beginning of the training session are exercises that require the animal to be in a psycho-physical station of relaxation (coordination exercises, speed exercises, explosive strength, or maximal strength) to be effective

– then come the exercises that are effective when done with incomplete recuperation (endurance-strength exercises)

– the session is finished with exercises that encourage the development of endurance

The Principle of Effective Stimuli in Training Loads

The principle of effective stimuli in training loads implies that the training load must exceed a determined threshold for there to be improvement in the animal's performance capabilities. This threshold of course depends on the dog's previous level of training.

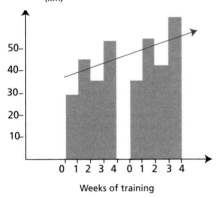

Weekly training distance (km) — Training load increase

Weeks of training

An average-level sled dog should cover 200-250 km (125-155 miles) per month, according to the 4-week progressive overload cycles (for "speed" races)

Training methods (overview)

THE SPECIFICITY OF TRAINING

It is important to stress that every training program should develop the system or systems that dominate the physical activity or sport for which it is preparing the dog.

Nevertheless, let us note a systematic flaw in this principle of specificity: The general training of every individual, regardless of age, sex, or weight, should entail:

– training the system for carrying oxygen (which allows it to adapt more easily to specialized training required by the distance in question)

– muscular training specifically involving the muscles of the legs and back (if possible)

– training intended to maintain joint mobility (which improves the metabolism of the joint cartilage and encourages coordination of movements).

Where the function of transporting oxygen is concerned, Astrand makes a distinction between the factors that affect the heart and central circulation and those that affect the peripheral circulation. In the case of central circulation, the most effective and least tiring training will involve the greatest amount of muscle mass possible. Improving peripheral circulation only requires training the muscles directly involved in the test or activity one wishes to improve.

In addition to these general considerations, the specificity of training is based primarily on recognizing the primary energy source used in the sport in question. Clearly, we only currently have partial information of this type concerning Sporting dogs and it must be developed in the future for each of the sporting disciplines practiced.

Based on current knowledge, the effort of sled dogs or hunting dogs is similar to that of human marathon runners (a traction component should be added for sled dogs), whereas the exercise demanded of Greyhounds appears to be similar to the 400-meter run by human athletes.

Training Muscle Strength

Training techniques for muscle strength have been defined for many years for humans, particularly following the work by Delorme and Watkins, but they remain undefined for dogs. This being the case, strength and endurance should be developed first in the type of static or dynamic activity that one wishes to improve.

Despite the relative imprecision, it seems to be possible during very short periods of work (15 to 30 seconds) to intensely solicit muscles without calling into play the anaerobic processes that cause a significant increase in the level of blood lactates.

As a result, for animals exerting effort that calls into play their muscle strength (traction efforts, for example), choosing an intermittent form of training with a high work intensity (ballast) for a very short period and very short rest periods will primarily call on muscle strength without sig-

Influence of intermittent exercise on intramuscular tests of ATP and creatine-phosphate

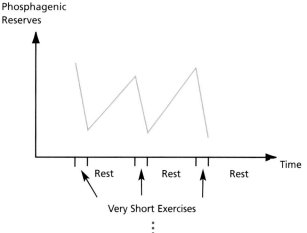

nificantly increasing the amount of oxygen consumed and without involving lactic anaerobic metabolism.

Anaerobic Strength Training

In this case, we are improving the functioning of the processes that depend on the breakdown of energy-rich phosphorous compounds (ATP and creatine-phosphate) and on lactic anaerobiosis (transformation of glycogen into lactic acid).

Improving alactic anaerobic muscle function is possible, according to Astrand, with very short exercises (10 to 15 seconds maximum), broken up with periods of rest that should not be too short. This way, we avoid too much glycogenolysis in the muscle, which allows it to restore its ATP and creatine-phosphate supplies through the aerobic system.

While not wanting to set any hard and fast rules, we can suggest that the maximum rest periods separating the exercises be a minimum of 2 to 4 minutes each.

Training lactic anaerobic processes can be done effectively for one minute and separated by periods of 4 to 5 minutes of rest. The main problem involved in such a method is that it can be psychologically difficult for the animal and quickly lead to discouragement and a refusal to perform. Indeed, owners must always keep in mind the idea of motivation or playing games, without which no results will be obtained. This is why such an intense type of training should not be used more than a few weeks (3 or 4) prior to the beginning of a competition.

Aerobic Strength Training

The goal here is to solicit the oxygen transport system as much as possible. There are two main training principles in this regard:

– one involves continuous courses and consists of having the animal run relatively long distances without interruption. Whether the run is slow or fast, the aerobic system dominates in providing the energy.

– Astrand again prefers a fractioned method here, which makes up the second principle: the athlete (human or canine) is asked to exert a relatively intense effort for 3 to 5 minutes, followed by rest or light exercise for the same period, and so forth and so on. Asking a dog to do a very moderate intensity exercise (walking or trotting) between periods of real work eliminates the lactic acid produced more quickly in these conditions than in periods of rest, as Gisolfi and Gollnick have shown.

Nonetheless, it is likely (though not exactly proven in humans) that the ability to work for a long time at a strength determining oxygen consumption that is close to its maximum value is primarily due to exercises involving long periods of continuous work (endurance training).

The capacities for storing glycogen in the muscle (and also in the liver) and particularly the ability to mobilize and use plasmatic free fatty acids indeed play a significant role in prolonged work by dogs. And even if we do not yet have a means for appreciating the dog's oxygen consumption, the trainer or owner is still able to judge the intensity of the work done.

In conclusion, to summarize the most practical aspects of the topic we have just covered, it seems useful to have four types of exercises in a training program intended to develop all forms of strength in the animal. A greater specificity will lead to accentuating one of these forms, based on the previous paragraphs:

– Strengthening the tendons and ligaments and developing muscle strength should entail very intense phases of activity that last a few seconds.
– Anaerobic strength will be improved by a series of periods of intense activity of about 1 minute in length and periods of rest or moderate exercise of 3 to 4 minutes.
– Phases of exercise with an intensity that is slightly less than the maximum aerobic strength (theoretically—and ideally) 4 to 5 minutes long will develop aerobic strength.
– The aptitude for endurance effort is linked to periods of more moderate intensity or activity lasting 45 minutes to 1 hour.

Can certain methods for training human athletes be used with dogs?

Many improvements in human sporting performance over the last few decades can be attributed to improved training methods used by trainers and athletes, whether these improvements are judged by performance, aerobic energy capacities (endurance), or anaerobic energy capacities (sprints). It should be noted that animal sports with horses or dogs have certainly not undergone such a transformation...

Based on this information, one might wonder if certain training methods used by humans can be used with animals. Since the vast majority of canine sports are entirely or partially based on racing, it is conceivable that some aspects of human training could be used with animals.

INTERVAL TRAINING

As its name implies, and as we have already mentioned earlier on, interval training is a series of exercises that are

Percentage of training time to be devoted to three energy sources in different types of races in humans

| Type of Race | Length of Performance | Percentage of training time to devote to | | |
		Anaerobia Alactic	Anaerobia Lactic	Aerobiosis
Marathon	135-180 min	-	5	95
10,000 m	30-50 min	5	15	80
5,000 m	15-25 min	10	20	70
3,000 m	10-16 min	20	40	40
1,500 m	4-6 min	20	55	25
800 m	2-3 min	80	15	5
400 m	1-1.5 min	80	15	5
200 m	22-25 sec	98	2	-
100 m	10-15 sec	98	2	-

broken up by periods of recuperation (light exercise). By applying the previous paragraph, this system is primarily characterized by transforming the fatigue caused by intermittent work into an increased intensity of the work provided.

Of course, the interaction between the different energy metabolisms varies with the intensity and type of activities performed, in the working period as well as in the recuperation period.

Nonetheless, this type of training clearly has its advantages:

– it allows repeated use of intramuscular reserves of phosphagens, which serve as a stimulus for increasing the system's energy capacity
– the participation of anaerobic glycolysis is minimal. Fox showed that man can also provide an intermittent effort with an intensity two and a half times greater than that of continuous effort before reaching identical levels of lactic acid accumulation
– executing longer periods of work with several repetitions encourages the system for carrying oxygen

Interval Training Terminology

– Work Period: part of the training that consists of providing intense work for a certain amount of time (for example, a dog race for 100-300-500…meters) (330, 660, 1/3 mile…)
– Recuperation Period: Period of rest between each work period and between each set of repetitions (walking, slight trot)
– Set: group of periods of work and recuperation (for example, six races of the same distance and the necessary recuperation periods)
– Repetitions: number of periods of work contained in a set

Determining the Variables

While this training method sounds great in theory, incorrectly adapting a program to a dog can prove to be quite problematic. In fact, according to the energy systems that need to be improved, the work period can be:

– longer in length and lower in intensity
– of medium length and medium intensity
– short in length and greater in intensity

There are several methods for calculating adequate intensity during a work period for humans. Here we shall only cover those that seem to be immediately or gradually adaptable to dogs.

One of these methods is based on the observation of variations in heart rate during the work period and can be used regardless of the type of activity. The higher the heart rate, the greater the intensity of the exercise.

The intensity of the work program can therefore be determined by a "target heart rate" (THR) to be reached during endurance training sessions. This rate is calculated as a percentage of the maximal reserve heart rate (RHR), as defined by Karvonen or the maximal heart rate (Max HR). The maximal reserve rate corresponds to the difference between the maximal heart rate and the heart rate at rest:

RHR = max HR - HR at rest

Interval training for endurance purposes would impose a target heart rate that represents 80 to 90% of the heart rate, to which is added the heart rate at rest or 85 to 90% of the maximal heart rate. This last data should of course be confirmed for dogs, but such a principle seems simple to apply. It only requires taking the femoral pulse before and immediately after effort or initially implementing an ambulatory means of monitoring the animal's heart rate.

A second method allows the number and intensity of work periods (repetitions) imposed during each session to be determined. It can also be used regardless of the type of activity. Regardless of the work time, we can conclude that when the intensity is too great, the animal cannot (or will not) perform a certain number of repetitions, the exercise is biologically too difficult.

**Repetition
Method Principle**

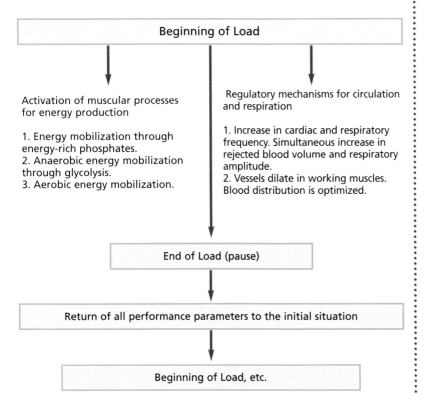

Number of Repetitions

The total training distance determines the number of repetitions for a work period. A total distance of 2 to 4 km seems minimal if one is looking for real biological improvement. If, however, a distance of 200 meters is chosen, at least 10 repetitions will be necessary.

Recuperation Periods

The evolution of heart rate after a work period remains an excellent indicator for determining whether the dog is physiologically able to begin a new work period or another set. The trainer must then check the dog's heart rate regularly (during the recuperation period) by counting the femoral pulse for 6 to 10 seconds.

Of course it is still difficult to set specific standards for dogs, given the diversity of breeds and sports in question. We can, nevertheless, group the variations observed during effort based on the work done with sprinting Greyhounds, sled dogs, hunting dogs, and dogs trained on a treadmill (unpublished data).

But it is not always possible to use the heart rate as an indicator because of certain practical difficulties (a large number of dogs being trained at the same time, for example). Fox suggests a few simple rules for organizing interval training in humans with work periods determined by a work-recuperation ratio. The training method is then facilitated. Taking the heart rate at the end of a recuperation period still allows us to know if the intensity of the work should be increased, reduced, or left as is.

Finally, the type of activity required during a period of recuperation should be taken into account:

– "passive" recuperation (rest or slow walk)
– "active" recuperation (fast walk or trot)

Variations of cardiac frequency in dogs during exertion

Type of Animal	Distance Run (m)	Time (min)	Cardiac Frequency Average (beats/min)		Number of Animals
			Before	After	
Greyhounds	440	0.5	105	197	12
Sled Dogs	12,000	30	100	134	176
Hunting Dogs	14,000	120	84	130	32
Dogs on a Treadmill	60,000	240	102	190	6

Passive recuperation should be reserved for training programs intended to improve alactic anaerobiosis and aerobiosis, since moderate effort partially hinders the muscular rebuilding of phosphagens and can lead to an accumulation of lactic acid during the next work period.

CONTINUOUS TRAINING

This method consists of having the animal work with relatively long distances in an uninterrupted course, calling on its aerobic metabolism.

Continuous Slow Course

Still referred to as endurance training, or aerobic strength training, this type of work requires covering long distances (2 to 5 times the distance of the course test) slowly (at 70% of the heart rate or 80% of the maximal heart rate). This way, an ultra-marathon runner can cover distances of more than 1,000 kilometers (620 miles) per month and Alaskan sled dogs can cover 2,000 to 3,000 kilometers (1,250 to 1,850 miles) per month.

Continuous Fast Course

In this case, the speed is greater (90% of the maximal heart rate), and fatigue occurs sooner, so less distance is covered. For example, a dog racing in a competition measuring 8 kilometers should cover 10 to 12 kilometers (6 _ to 7 _ miles) at a constant, high speed, or 5 to 7 kilometers (3 to 4 1/3 miles) 2 or 3 times.

The total distance covered per session per week is an important overloading factor in endurance dogs. At this level, according to Costill, the

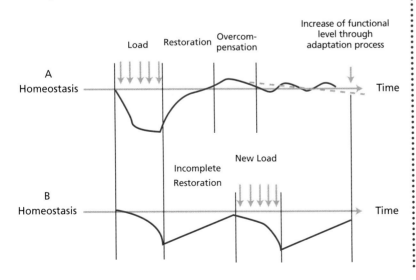

Hypothetical functioning of the muscular system's restoration and adaptation processes after complete restoration (A) and incomplete restoration (B)

total monthly distance should be broken down weekly and into cycles of four weeks each. In each of these cycles, the greatest distance should be covered in the second and fourth weeks, with gradual overloading (about 10%) from one cycle to the next.

Fractioned Course

This training methods only differs from the interval training method in:

– the distance to be covered during the work period
– the degree of recuperation between the repetitions

The distance to be covered is directly related to the distance of the competition, with the recuperation between each course being more complete than with interval training. There are two possibilities:

– the dog covers half of the distance of the competition at a speed that is equal to or greater than the speed used in the competition, if possible. The total distance covered represents 1.5 to 2 times that of the race, broken up by periods of complete recuperation.

Such a method develops the aerobic and anaerobic capacities in the first case and the aerobic capacities in the second case.

It can also be done, though this is more difficult with dogs, in the form of a series of maximum speed sprints (as is the case with racing Greyhounds).

Which training method should be used for the various canine sports?

The answer depends primarily on the ability of each to develop the various types of energy metabolism.

Designing an appropriate training program therefore requires understanding the biological and physiological consequences of each type of effort in dogs, which is rarely the case... Individual differences also mean that training for high-level canine sports requires repeated functional exploration during the season, and this alone will guarantee good biological adaptation to performance.

Changing Training Based on the Season

Regardless of the goal being sought, it is important for a Sporting dog to be trained regularly. In fact, it is possible to reach a reasonable level of ability, strength, or endurance in a month's time, but this affect disappears when training ends. This is even more important to acknowledge, since the effort needed to maintain a certain degree of physical conditioning is much lower than that needed to reach the level in the first place.

It is therefore in the trainer's best interest to initially devote more time to training the dog, so that later he must simply "maintain" the advantages the dog has acquired, by putting the animal through a limited number of weekly sessions.

Certain canine sports require training several functions (strength, technique, motivation, aerobic and anaerobic strength, endurance, etc.). It is then useful and sometimes even necessary, given time constraints for these functions. This brings us back to specific training, which—let us stress again—must be maintained (even at a reduced intensity) when training a new function.

Only high competition requires that training be maintained all year long, particularly for the oxygen carrying system. In fact, from one season to the next, the maximal oxygen consumption can vary considerably and only relatively intense training throughout the year can avoid a sharp decline in performance. Annual training can then be broken down into three phases: off-season, pre-season, and season.

OFF-SEASON TRAINING

The dog must at least remain moderately active and the owner should make an effort to maintain the animal's weight as close as possible to the dog's standard. The general training program for the off-season would then integrate:

– exercises that develop or at least maintain muscular endurance and strength
– a program of low-intensity courses once or twice a week
– a maximum amount of games so the animal can relax and have fun

PRE-SEASON TRAINING

This starts 2 to 3 months before the first competition and involves increased intensity, duration, and frequency of the exercises demanded (most often courses). It is during this period that the increases in energy capabilities are obtained. It should therefore involve the programs discussed in the previous paragraphs.

SEASON TRAINING

It is generally believed that competition (if it occurs at least on a weekly basis) is enough to maintain the increased energy capacity obtained during pre-season training. One to two weekly sessions are then sufficient to maintain the level of conditioning in order to avoid discouragement during a crucial period.

The Problem of Warming Up Prior to Competition

It is certainly not impossible for a human or animal athlete to set a record without first warming up. Karpovitch's work has even shown that there is no difference between performance with or without warm-up. On the other hand, more recent publications have shown the usefulness of such warm-up exercises prior to competition. Warming up by increasing the body temperature (and therefore muscle temperature) allows for:

- an increase in enzyme activities, and therefore improved energy metabolism
- an increase in blood flow and in the availability of oxygen
- a decrease in contraction and reaction times

On a practical level, we shall restate Fox's recommendations for warm-up exercises that can be done with dogs. The animal should first be made to stretch by:

- mobilizing its limbs by extending and flexing, adducting and abducting
- hyper-extending the hind legs and the dorsal-lumbar region
- mobilizing the animal's head by rotating it

This allows for:
- increased flexibility in the joints (improving motor skills)
- avoiding muscle tears
- preparing the animal with regard to dorsal-lumbar injuries

The warm-up period should finish with having the dog perform low-intensity movements from the sporting activity for which it is being prepared, which:

Influence of muscle temperature on certain biological parameters following exertion

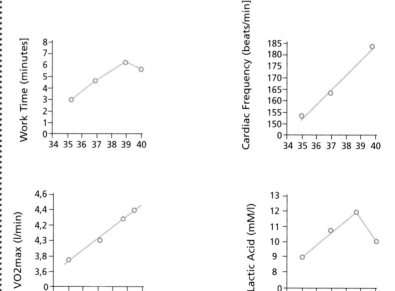

Muscle Temperature (°C)

– ensures optimum physiology
– improves neuro-muscular coordination

Cooling Down After Competition

The period immediately following competition is still too neglected by dog owners, though it is common practice for human athletes to return their metabolism to its normal level using "cool-down" exercises: low-intensity exercises performed immediately after competition.

Based on everything we have stated, there are two very important, purely physiological reasons supporting this practice:

– the lactic acid accumulated in the blood and muscles is eliminated more quickly during an active recuperation period, which results in the animal's having less of a sense of fatigue—which can be further reduced if this period of active recuperation is followed with a light massage.
– The heart muscle continues to pump, which prevents an accumulation of blood in the extremities.

Un-Training

The period following the end of training is important to consider. In fact, most of the affects of training disappear shortly after the end of training (4 to 8 weeks).

To effectively conserve the affects of training, it is necessary to train the dog regularly throughout the year. In this respect, one of the most important affects that can be maintained seems to be the ability to perform sub-maximal work with the least amount of lactic acid accumulation:

– by maintaining at least one training session per week
– by taking the animal to a high-altitude from time to time

We therefore strongly discourage completely stopping training, especially for endurance sports (drop in heart flow, maximal oxygen consumption, oxidative mitochondrial enzyme concentrations by groups of tissues).

Regardless of the case, respecting the fundamental principles of training that we have just put forth causes (sometimes significant) metabolic and physiological changes to the body that should be taken into consideration.

Recuperation and Over-Training

After physical training, fatigue and even more or less significant exhaustion appear as a function of the work load. Fatigue in itself precedes exhaustion and by doing so is sort of a protective mechanism that allows us to avoid completely using up the body's energy reserves.

Though the limits of fatigues can be physiologically expanded though the adaptive affects of training, the subsequent rebuilding also increases. From this we can understand that the training load and the subsequent rebuilding are closely linked and have a reciprocal affect on each other, which makes it necessary to really understand and appreciate the state of every dog being trained.

FATIGUE AND ITS ORIGINS

Recognizing the animal's limits is the basis of all kinds of prevention, and also all kinds of success in the field of canine sports. Fatigue is a biological state that follows excessive work or effort that is too long or too intense, resulting in a drop in performance and a localized or general sensation of malaise for the animal.

Physical fatigue can occur during an endurance-type effort (hunting, sledding, etc.). In this case, it is generally secondary to a poor regulation of the energy supply and responds quite well to improvements in training techniques and diet in preparation for effort.

Fatigue occurring in relation to a sprint- or resistance-type exercise (Greyhound racing, ring, etc.) generally manifests itself after effort in the form of cramps, sprains, or muscle stiffness. This state can only be improved by the quality of the warm up and the progression of training sessions in their intensity and their volume.

Physiologically, the phenomenon of fatigue originates from the following:

– exhaustion of energy reserves
– decrease in enzyme activities such as ATPase myosin
– disturbance of hydro-electrolytic metabolism

PHYSIOLOGICAL MEANS OF RECUPERATION

Rebuilding During Effort

Given that ATP is the energy source for muscle contractions, the entire energy restoration process collaborates in its renewal and maintenance at a constant level. As long as the instantaneous re-synthesis of ATP is possible, the muscular work can continue.

On the other hand, once effort becomes very intense, the production of energy is maintained by lactic anaerobiosis, which inevitably reduces the work time and can even bring about a complete end to the effort. Rebuilding during muscular work is primarily done during aerobic effort for intensities of medium or moderate courses that last a long time.

Rebuilding Immediately After Effort

In all short-duration, high-intensity exercises (for example, Greyhound racing), calling upon alactic anaerobiosis, lactic anaerobiosis, and aero-anaerobiosis, the rebuilding of organic and cellular functions is done once the effort has ended. The oxygen debt contracted at the beginning of the exercise is paid back and the initial situation is reestablished in about thirty minutes.

Rebuilding After Effort

During effort that lasts a long time, there is a gradual drop in energy reserves, which is only very rarely a limiting factor, and also a breakdown of protein structures on a cellular level (enzymes, co-enzymes, etc.). Once the effort has ended, these structures can be rebuilt, which can take several hours or several days.

Active and Passive Means of Recuperation

It is necessary to clearly distinguish active recuperation (cool down, walking, or slight trot) from passive recuperation (inactivity, massage, etc.). In fact, even very slight muscular work increases muscular irrigation by about 6 times, which is particularly important for eliminating metabolic waste. A massage—even a very effective one—cannot therefore be a back-up method for active recuperation (Greyhounds, ring, agility).

OVER-TRAINING

Following a series of bad recuperations, various physical and psychological signs of over-working can appear in dogs. These are signs of over-training, and there are many causes:

– increasing the amount and intensity of training loads too quickly
– too much psychological pressure for the dog (owner is too eager)
– using training methods that are too exclusive
– too many competitions with recuperation intervals that are too short

The rhythm of training sessions should allow the phenomenon of overcompensation to be used to an advantage. Training cycles should therefore be organized after a period of complete recuperation, with the next cycle in the phase of overcompensation from the preceding cycle.

In humans, there are two types of over-training: Basedowian (sympatho-tonic) and Addisonian (parasympatho-tonic). Basedowian over-training is characterized by a preponderance of excitation processes, sometimes with marked over-excitation. Addisonian over-training has a preponderance of inhibitive functions, physical weakness, and a lack of will.

Organizing training by intervals

1. Know the energy metabolism to be improved.

2. Determine the exercises to do during work periods.

3. Design the program for each session.

4. Respect the principle of overloading.

In dogs, such a dichotomy is difficult to pinpoint with current knowledge. In this species, the signs of over-training, as we know them today, tend to be Basedowian (sympatho-tonic):
– fatigues easily
– excitation
– disrupted sleep
– drop in appetite
– loss of body weight
– normal temperature regulation, but slight chronic hyperthermia
– tendency for tachycardia
– abnormal hyperpnea with training load
– delayed recuperation (time for heart rate to return to rate at rest)
– auditory hypersensitivity

When a dog presents with some or all of these symptoms, a certain number of therapeutic steps can prove effective in one to two weeks:
– considerable reduction in specific training; maintain only daily sessions of one hour of slow trotting
– change the animal's environment, if possible
– regular light massages
– "stress" diet (high-energy, high-protein)
– possible medical treatment

Certain canine sports (sledding, Greyhounds, ring) have now reached a level of competition and professionalism (in the most noble sense of the term) that it is necessary for owners to pay very close attention to their training methodology.

The practice of training energy capacities, the sources of which are known, is subject to a group of rules and principles common to all types of activities. They should be applied while respecting the specificity of the goals in question and while keeping in mind the fundamental importance of the recuperation process.

THE EFFECTS OF PHYSICAL TRAINING ON DOGS

A well-designed training program not only improves a dog's physical capacities and performance, but also decreases his susceptibility to the many pathological conditions associated with athletic activity and the sometimes difficult environment of working dogs.

Training brings about certain modifications in the body which can be grouped roughly in three categories:
– metabolic modifications in various body tissues;
– systematic modifications in the cardiovascular and respiratory systems; and
– other effects, not yet well-known in dogs, relative to the distribution of musculoskeletal mass and hormonal balance, for example.

Metabolic changes

Generally speaking, the main quantifiable effect of regular training is to decrease the variation in many physiological factors each time the animal exerts effort. This phenomenon involves factors as important as heart rate, hematocrit, creatin kinase, and lactates. When training is focused on aerobiosis (endurance), a gradual deviation in metabolic function toward the improved oxidation of fat can be observed. Thus, a well-trained dog not only digests better but also makes better use of the fat in his diet. All of this arises from the body's tendency to improve its energy output. Based on this concept, trainers can develop a simple way to roughly gauge the effectiveness of a specific training program, as described below.

During physical effort, the muscles need energy to contract. This energy comes from chemical energy, which is broken down and transformed into mechanical energy (muscle movement). The output of this transformation is far from 100%: Just as a car's motor heats up as it runs, much of the chemical energy broken down during physical effort is lost as thermal energy that accumulates as heat in the body. The overall energy output of an untrained dog never surpasses 17%, with 83% of the initial chemical energy lost as heat. This causes a significant increase in the dog's rectal temperature (during intense effort, rectal temperature may rise from 38.5°C to over 42°C (69.3°F to over 75.6°F). Through training, energy output can be increased to 25 to 27% and, for an equal amount of effort, rectal temperature will therefore rise less.

Trainers can easily gauge the effectiveness of a physical training program by giving the dog a standard exercise repeated at regular intervals (weekly, every two weeks, etc.) and taking the dog's temperature before and after effort. As the dog's physical capacity improves, his body temperature differential (post-effort temperature – pre-effort temperature) should decrease, thereby indicating the desired improvement in energy output by the muscles.

Hematological factors relative to the blood's capacity to carry pulmonary oxygen to the muscles (hematocrit, red blood cell count, hemoglobin content) are also modified by training. All increase during the most intense phase of training and become stabilized during the phase of strict competition.

These variations are accompanied by an increase in the dog's total blood volume. In fact, it has been shown that blood volume increases 13 to 15% after only two months of pure endurance training.

These erythrocyte-related factors (involving the red blood cells) are excellent indicators of the degree of cumulative stress from training and the necessary adjustment to the protein content in the dog's diet. In fact, they enable early detection of the onset of athletic anemia, which generally appears late in the training period or early in the competition period in overtrained animals with a protein deficiency in the diet.

Magnesium and iron are among the blood mineral factors that are interesting to monitor. The body requires more of these minerals during physical effort and therefore training. A drop in the levels of magnesium and iron in the blood can lead to post-effort tetanic spasms (low magnesium level) and an increased risk of athletic anemia (low iron level).

At the cellular level, the factors involved in aerobic metabolism undergo a certain number of significant changes that may be observed after the start of an endurance training program:
– an increase in the myoglobin content of muscle fibers. Myoglobin, a pigment similar to hemoglobin in the blood, stores intramuscular oxygen and improves oxygen diffusion to the mitochondria, the sites of intracellular oxidation;

Consequences of training on hormonal metabolism

Hormone in question	Change under exertion	Effects of training On homeostasis	On response to exertion
Catecholamines	↑	↓	↑
Insulin	↓	↓	↕
Glucagon	↑	↓	↑
Growth hormone	↑	?	↑
Corticoids	↑	↓	↑
Thyroid hormones	=	↕	=
Androgens	↑	↑	
Estrogens	↑	↓	↑
Endorphins	↑	=	↑

– the gradual transformation of "fast" muscle fibers into "slow" muscle fibers. The opposite is impossible. For example, a sprinter can, over time, improve his aerobic capacity and work toward covering medium or long distances, while the reverse is not possible;

– an improvement in fat and glycogen oxidation through an increase in the number and size of mitochondria in striated muscle fiber and an increase in the enzymes involved in the Krebs cycle or the respiratory chain;
– an increase in intramuscular triglyceride (lipid) reserves, in the release of fatty acids by adipose tissue during effort, and in the transport and breakdown of these fatty acids by enzymes in the muscle cells; and
– an increase in the antioxidant capacity of enzymes in the muscles, allowing muscles to better (but not always sufficiently) fight the consequences of the release of free radicals and the subsequent stress on cell membranes from oxidation.

Anaerobic metabolism in dogs is also improved through training, both in terms of non-lactic anaerobiosis and lactic anaerobiosis. This improvement is illustrated by:
– an increase in phosphagen reserves (ATP, creatine phosphate);
– the more effective activation of enzymes during lactic anaerobiosis; and
– a higher tolerance of lactate accumulation in the muscles and blood.

Cardiovascular and respiratory changes

Like all skeletal muscles, the heart adapts to changes in physical activity level. The canine heart is relatively large and has a considerable volume. Its weight, expressed as a percentage of body weight, ranges from 0.75 to 0.80%, compared to only 0.5% in humans. Racing Greyhounds undoubtedly hold the record, with a relative cardiac weight 1.2 to 1.4% their body weight. A dog's maximum heart rate during physical effort ranges from 310 to 340 beats per minute, while maximum heart rate in humans is only 170 to 210. Richer in "slow" muscle fiber, the human heart has less contractile strength but uses energy more efficiently than the canine heart.

Endurance training brings about a significant increase in heart volume in dogs (similarly, hares have a larger heart

Modifications observed after a sub-maximum or maximum training plan

Maximum Training	Sub-Maximal Training
↑ VO2 max	# VO2 max
↑ blood output	↓ Use of muscular glycogen
↑ O2 brought to muscle	↑ Oxidation of fatty acids
↑ Production of lactates	↑ Anaerobic threshold
↑ Cardiac output	↓ Oxygen loss
↓ Sympathetic activity	↑ Cardiac output
	↓ Cardiac frequency
	↓ Blood output
	↑ O2 extraction by the muscle

volume than rabbits), with a growth in the volume of the ventricular cavity and a higher volume of systolic discharge. In subjects who do not participate in endurance training, the ventricular cavity is of normal size but has a thicker wall. The increased myocardial vascularization caused by training can be useful in predicting possible ischemia.

It has long been known that the heart rate is particularly low in trained subjects (especially those with endurance conditioning). In fact, with regular training the body can maintain a given cardiac output, both at rest and during effort, by lowering heart rate and increasing the volume of systolic discharge. This reduces the energy and oxygen consumption of the myocardium. However, maximum heart rate does not seem to be influenced by training. At the most, it is slightly lower in dogs with endurance conditioning, probably because of factors related to body constitution.

Contrary to popular belief, pulmonary ventilation is almost unchanged by training. Only a slight decrease in respiratory rate is observed because of the improved efficiency of overall ventilation.

The concept of maximum aerobic power

Maximum aerobic power is defined as "a subject's maximum oxygen consumption ($VO2max$) during muscular activity at sea level." By comparing a subject's maximum aerobic power to his body weight, we can evaluate his capacity for movement. When we calculate maximum oxygen consumption in relation to weight and in units of time (ml of oxygen per kilogram per minute: $mlO2/min/kg$), or more specifically per kilogram of lean body mass in relation to muscle mass, blood volume, or other similar factors, we can examine the relationship between the functioning and the extent of the systems involved.

Determining maximum oxygen consumption provides information about:
– the maximum possible contribution of aerobic energy (produced in dogs by the oxidation of fats) per unit of time; and
– the functional capacity of circulation, since we know there is a very strong correlation between maximum cardiac output and maximum aerobic power.

During prolonged exercise, a strong correlation can be observed between maximum oxygen consumption and the amount of work produced (maximum aerobic capacity). The level of oxygen consumption the subject is able to sustain is a percentage of maximum consumption, which decreases the longer exercise lasts.

Average VO2 max values in dogs

Type of Dog	Physiological State	VO2 max (ml/min/kg)
Common	Untrained	60-80
Hunting	Trained +	100-110
Hunting	Trained ++	130-145
Sled Dog	Trained +++	150-180

Training exercises developed for humans are now being adapted to dogs. Submaximal exercise is used in order to develop the functional capacity of the entire system of oxygen transport:

– direct determination of the oxygen consumption of a dog running on a treadmill and wearing a mask for measuring air flow and collecting exhaled air in a bag or directly in an analyzer;

– research on a strong correlation between a specific physiological factor and the VO2max (heart rate, respiratory quotient, lacticemia); and

– a telemetric system for measuring the exchange of respiratory gases.

Recently, thanks to the joint scientific efforts of the UMES, the physiology laboratory of the National Veterinary School in Lyon, the sports physiology laboratory of the University of Auvergne, and the Société Cosmed, a telematic system was adapted for measuring the exchange of respiratory gases in working dogs. Very roughly, this system ("K4") includes a face mask designed especially for dogs by the UMES and equipped with a turbine flow meter and a polarographic oxygen electrode for the instantaneous measurement of the oxygen concentration of air inhaled and exhaled by the dog. A transmitter sends the data to a computer, while a cardiac telemetry system simultaneously provides a reading of the heart rate during effort. Transmitting distance is approximately 800 meters (1/2 mile), and the total weight of the system in working order is no more than 800 grams (1 _ pounds).

Thanks to this system, the concepts of maximum aerobic power and maximum oxygen consumption—the basis of many human studies and currently a significant limitation in developing the field of canine sports physiology—will soon be better defined for dogs and might be used routinely in the future.

Evolution of oxygen consumption (VO2) and CO2 production (VCO2) as a function of time (growing intensity test, stop at 6'40) [example on Cosmed K4 material]

COSMED s.r.l.
P.O. BOX 3, 00040 Rome, Italy
tel: +39-6-9315492; fax: +39-6-9314580
http://www.cosmed.it; E-mail: information@cosmed.it

COSMED

	Last name: LOUPS First name: C	
ID code: 01	Test number: 1	Barometric press. (mmHg): 760
Sex: M	Test date: 06/05/98	Temperature (degrees C): 19
Age: 2	Test time: 11:32	STPD: 0.875
Height (cm): 167	N. of steps: 99	BTPS: 1.117
Weight (Kg): 27	Duration (hh:mm:ss): 00:09:20	UN (g/day): 12.0
HR max (bpm): 217	BSA (m^2): 1.1	FEV1 (l/s): 0.00
LT: --:--:--	VD (ml): 70	

In any case, well-designed endurance training for dogs will:

– considerably increase a dog's VO2max and therefore his maximum aerobic power; and
– thereby indicate the need to increase the amount of fat in his diet (for higher energy output and to increase work time before the onset of physical fatigue).

Other effects of training

In addition to modifying the various functions involved in energy metabolism as a whole, training also modifies a certain number of other organic and functional structures.

Musculoskeletal organs

The musculoskeletal organs are strongly influenced by activity level. The weak point of the "bone + ligament + muscle" grouping is the area where tendons or ligaments attach to bone. This area is strengthened considerably through regular exercise. An increase in muscle mass caused by the thickening of the fibrillae also occurs, but there is no increase in the number of fibers per muscle.

A well-designed training program also strengthens the joints and cartilage.

However, it is important to note that in growing puppies, intense training inhibits bone growth (in length and circumference) and increases bone density. For this reason, heavy training must never begin too early

Determination of oxygen consumption in a dog during exertion

in a dog's athletic career, and the following minimum ages must be respected: eight months for small breeds, ten months for medium-sized breeds, and twelve months for large breeds.

Endocrine system

Training affects the hormones in many ways which are still highly debated because of the difficulties encountered during study. Although hormones play an important role in regulating energy metabolism, it is best for the time being to take some hypotheses and results with a grain of salt. We must remember that training is far from being the only variable to consider (others include the precise conditions in which physical effort occurs, circulatory modifications in each organ, stress, the level of energy and water reserves, etc.).

In addition to causing many hormonal modifications, physical conditioning tends to alter a dog's body mass by:
– decreasing the total amount of fat;
– increasing lean muscle mass; and
– decreasing total mass in the adult.

Nevertheless, these long-term physiological effects of training must be considered in light of certain factors that influence them to some extent. These factors are discussed below.

Factors influencing the effects of training

The biological effects of training mentioned above depend mainly on three variables:
– the intensity of training sessions;
– the frequency of sessions and program length; and
– the genetic limitations of the particular dog.

Training intensity

Whether training is continuous or in intervals, it is training intensity that determines the improvement in physical condition. Therefore, in more intense training, biochemical modifications and changes related to the musculoskeletal organs mentioned above are more pronounced. The only exception to this phenomenon appears to be a decrease in heart rate, which depends instead on the frequency of sessions and program length.

Frequency of sessions and program length

The most significant effect of these two aspects involves the heart rate during exercise: The longer the training program and the more frequent

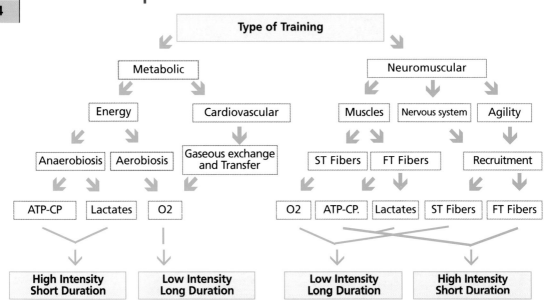

Type of Training

- Metabolic
  - Energy
    - Anaerobiosis
    - Aerobiosis
  - Cardiovascular
    - Gaseous exchange and Transfer

ATP-CP | Lactates | O2

High Intensity Short Duration | **Low Intensity Long Duration**

- Neuromuscular
  - Muscles
    - ST Fibers
    - FT Fibers
  - Nervous system
  - Agility
    - Recruitment

O2 | ATP-CP. | Lactates | ST Fibers | FT Fibers

Low Intensity Long Duration | **High Intensity Short Duration**

the sessions, the smaller the rise in heart rate during the same exercise over time. However, conducting several training sessions in one day is useless and can even impair physical performance, and eventually affects aerobic capacity, heart rate, and the concentration of hemoglobin in the blood (onset of athletic anemia).

Genetic limitations

An animal's genetic makeup invariably limits his physiological and functional capacities, if these capacities are indeed used properly. For example, it is estimated that the distribution of muscle fibers ("fast" or "slow") is genetically determined at 95%, and that this figure is approximately 82% for lactic anaerobic capacity and 86% for maximum heart rate.

The fundamental conclusion to the information presented in this chapter is the need to customize the training program to the dog. This program will be influenced by
metabolic and neuromuscular factors that are best determined beforehand if a training program is to be effective. Of course, this chapter only lays the groundwork. Hopefully, the future will bring an increased standardization in the training programs for sporting dogs.

Practical Concerns in Physical Training

Since it is not the veterinarian's role, in our opinion, to interfere with the professional dog trainer, we hope that the reader will consider the items presented in this chapter as simply informative. Between theory and practice, there is often a world of difference. For this reason, it is important to recognize that the trainer's experience is irreplaceable, even though he must remain aware of the need to further develop certain concepts or training methods. It is therefore not our intention to take the trainer's place, but rather to provide everyone with basic information that might be helpful.

Sled dogs

Sled dog training has roughly three goals:

– to get the dogs in optimal physical condition, based on the musher's goals for his racing season (sprinting, mid-distance, or long-distance);

– to ensure that the dogs understand what is expected of them and will respond immediately to the driver's commands with a conditioned reflex, and

– to eventually select the best canine athletes for the team, based on their physical condition and behavior, as well as their hardiness at work. Reaching this compromise is often difficult, since maximal performance is often accompanied by fragility.

Training
without snow

The realization of these goals depends on the degree of competitiveness sought by the musher, whether for:

– recreational sport, in which the overall well-being of the person working in cooperation with his dogs is more important than performance. Here the musher is first and foremost a handler, and his role in training and selecting dogs is secondary (since he wants all his dogs to participate);

– competitive sport, in which the musher is primarily the team trainer and must also choose from among several dogs when the time comes; obedience work remains a key element of training.

In the early twentieth century, sled dogs were utility animals, and training was limited to obedience, since any dog harnessed to a sled has a strong natural tendency to want to pull it. Dogs were conditioned by extending work time more or less gradually.

After World War II, sled dog racing truly began to develop, and people started seriously training teams of dogs for the sport. Training was focused on developing speed and began in October, after the first snowfall. Not until the 1960s did mushers realize the need to train dogs even before the arrival of snow, using automobile frames, and begin using interval training. Finally, since the early 1980s, training programs have been based on physiological guidelines, and the most competitive mushers keep their dogs in condition year round, primarily by using automatic training systems and beginning heavier training in early autumn.

OBEYING THE MAIN PRINCIPLES OF TRAINING

Each of the following principles must be adhered to strictly. If not, the efforts of many days of work with the dogs may be lost.

Gradual changes

The first training sessions in which the dogs pull an harnessed object should not cover more than 2-3 km (1 1/4 to 13/4 miles) with stops in between. Distance should be increased very gradually over the first three months.

Team training on a treadmill

Regular sessions

Early in the season, three or four sessions per week are necessary; later on, five weekly sessions should be conducted,

– never with more than two consecutive rest days; and
– never with more than four consecutive work days.

Focus

Training should be focused on developing the qualities needed for the target event:

– speed and resistance for sprinting races in large teams;
– speed and power for sprinting races in small teams; and
– endurance and recovery speed for long-distance races.

Mutual trust

The human-dog relationship must be built on complete mutual trust, since training by force can lead only to mediocre performance. The dog should enjoy pulling the sled; if he does not, he will quickly become discouraged and refuse to move.

PRACTICAL TRAINING METHODS

Non-harnessed training

Non-harnessed training is practiced primarily without snow and includes:

– off-leash walks (note, however that Nordic dogs have a strong tendency to run away);

– the training track (allows eight to twenty dogs to trot at 8 to 15 km/h (4 1/2 to 9 1/3 miles); very popular in the United States);

– running semi-loose on a playing field with supervision due to the risk of interteam conflicts;

– the treadmill, still seldom used because exercising several dogs simultaneously requires a very expensive treadmill designed for horses; and

– swimming, especially for dogs with signs of a limp who are undergoing "occupational" therapy.

Harnessed training without snow

A bicycle can be used for working one or two dogs but is always fairly dangerous. A "kart" (with three or four wheels, weighing 50 to 300 kg (110 to 660 pounds) depending on the number of dogs harnessed) is preferable or, where permitted, a "quad," a sort of motorcycle with three or four wheels. The optimal weight for a kart is:

– 50 to 80 kg for a team of three dogs (110 to 175pounds);
– 70 to 100 kg for a team of six dogs 155 to 220 pounds); and [
– 100 to 150 kg for a team of ten dogs (220 to 330 pounds).

Harnessed training in snow

The training sled should be heavier and sturdier than the racing sled (20 kg versus 6 to 10 kg) (44 pounds versus 13 to 22 pounds), and it should be equipped with runners that are less likely to be damaged by an uneven surface (rocks, tar, etc.).

Training program

A good training program should:
– cover the entire year;
– include various stages and be designed for several seasons;
– be adapted to the target race;
– be based on the desired level of competitiveness; and
– take into account from the start each person's availability.

A training program for one season (in the northern hemisphere) would therefore be distributed roughly as follows:

1) Rest period from May to July or September, according to geographical location;
2) Conditioning period from July or September to November;

3) Pre-competition period in December;
4) Competition period from January to April; and
5) Tapering off period in April and May.

Rest period

The rest period is essential for maintaining the dogs' spirit over a series of racing seasons. This period should be active and involve non-harnessed training methods and play. One hour of activity per day prevents dogs from gaining too much weight and losing muscle tone.

Conditioning period

The conditioning period begins with harnessed training without snow. For this activity, the choice of terrain is of utmost importance—it should be neither too uneven nor too flat, with a surface that is not too harsh on the paw pads.

Roughly speaking, a team of three or four dogs covering 7 to 9 km (4 1/3 to 5 2/3 miles) can begin harnessed training in October, while teams preparing for races or legs of 70 km (43 _ miles) or more should begin as early as July.

The dog's physical capacity develops most markedly during the first twelve weeks. For this reason, training should be especially gradual during this period, with a "step backward" every once in a while in order to avoid physiological overload.

It should be noted that in early autumn, the ambient temperature may be a limiting factor in certain countries. If so, the trainer should choose the best time of day (usually daybreak) and avoid training in temperatures above 15°C (27°F). When training in temperatures above 8°C (14°F), dogs should be given water at least every 8 km (5 miles).

During the conditioning period, interval training is strongly recommended and can consist of several minutes of running alternated with passive rest periods of equal duration. The duration and number of work periods should increase over the season in order to help the dogs develop their VO2max.

Speed type training with 6 dogs: Training distances

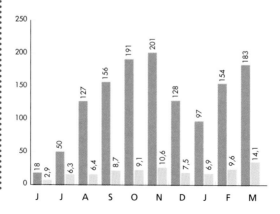

Average/Training Distance
Monthly Distance

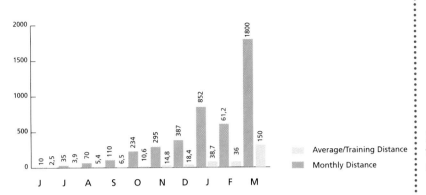

Average/Training Distance
Monthly Distance

**Iditarod type
training: Training
distances**

Pre-competition period

During this period in December:

– interval training continues;
– preparatory training for competition is introduced (stops are eliminated, and dogs should be "forced" to obey voice commands in order to maintain a constant speed). Distance should never be more than two-thirds that of the target race nor impose excessive psychological pressure on the dogs;
– training in snow is introduced (trainers can take advantage of sessions sponsored by clubs or federations); and
– the team can participate in one or two small "training" competitions.

In certain cases at this stage (such as when preparing for a long-distance race), it is possible to conduct training sessions focused purely on endurance by covering long distances at a relatively moderate pace.

Competition period

During this period, training consists simply of maintaining the dogs' physical conditioning, since each competition is in itself a training session. At this stage, the number of training sessions conducted between two weekends of competition is reduced to two or three. When preparing dogs for a significant competition, trainers can increase rest time during the two weeks preceding the event and then increase the psychological pressure on the dogs during the event. After this, a "rebound" effect leading to a period of decreased performance is to be expected.

THE IMPORTANCE OF OBEDIENCE TRAINING

Training the dogs to obey is undoubtedly the musher's most difficult task, given the number of dogs in the team, the independent nature of Nordic dogs, and the absence of direct contact between human and dog during races. At the very minimum, each dog in the team must be able to:

Magnetic sign used
in positioning dogs
in the team during
each training session

– tolerate having the harness harnessed and removed;
– pass or cross the path of other teams as well as other dogs running loose,
– tolerate unusual situations (yelling crowds, motorized vehicles); and
– understand the commands for "go," "slow down," and "stop."

Only lead dogs are trained to understand other commands, particularly the well-known "Gee" (turn right), "Haw" (turn left), and "On by" (go straight). This takes a great deal of time and combines obedience training with commands developed in other sports.

Serious training should not begin until a dog is one year old. Dogs peak at three to six years old and can continue running until they are ten to twelve years old. A sound training program can guarantee a dog's success and longevity.

Scandinavian pulka

Although it is placed in the same category as sled dog racing, Scandinavian pulka racing has some differences that must be addressed in training. For one thing, the pulkaist (a cross-country skier) must train himself at the same time as he trains his dog or dogs.

Generally speaking, 80% of the training for this sport is practiced on a bicycle or using a "ski-joring" (a coiled leash harnessed to the skier's belt), while only 20% is conducted with the dog harnessed to the pulka. The overall training program is similar to that for sled dogs, with a predominance of interval training. Sessions with the pulka are short and conducted at maximum speed (with 500-meter repetitions [1/3 mile]).

A good training program includes a total of 220 to 250 hours of running per year for the dog, or over four hours per week with a maximum of over one hour per day in December.

For a competitive pulkaist, the most difficult task is to develop the dog's rhythm, given the technical difficulty of this activity performed in cooperation with the dog.

Kart racing and canicross

Compared to sled and pulka racing, preparing dogs for these activities conducted on natural terrain presents no special requirements, in terms of developing a practical training program. The basic guidelines and their practical adaptation are similar, except that for canicross the owner must run alongside his dog in order to fine tune his own physical conditioning.

Number of hours of training per week

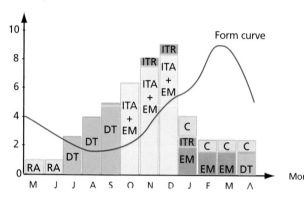

RA = AR = Active Response

DT = Distance Training

ITA =AIT = Aerobic Interval Training (minimum 2 hours)

EM =ME = Maximum Endurance (Intervals of 6-10 minutes)

ITR = RIT = Resistance Interval Training (Intervals < 3 minutes)

C = Competition

Sighthound racing

Still today, sighthound athletes too often receive non-specific training focused only on increasing muscle mass and endurance, which is not the sighthound's main strength. For this reason, it is necessary to develop training methods designed especially for this canine athlete by striving to select the most adaptable and effective methods used by human sprinters, despite the technical difficulties that may arise.

BASIC CONSIDERATIONS

From a physiological standpoint, a sighthound race can be broken down into four successive phases:

Departure
In the starting box, the dog must react as quickly as possible to an audible signal (the arrival of the lure) and then to the immediate opening of the starting gate. Reaction time to this signal depends on the animal's neuromuscular capacity and is improved very little through training. Still, it must be maintained through departure repetitions with various stimuli (auditory or visual).

Attaining running position
Sighthounds require less time than humans—only two or three strides—to attain running position, which consists of passing from departure "position" to running position. This requires a technical effort that is difficult for the animal to learn but that the trainer can attempt to perfect through repetitions of box departures in the absence of other competitors.

Acceleration
This phase begins when the dog reaches running position and contin-

ues for 30 or 40 meters (100 or 130 feet). During acceleration, the dog strives to attain the highest possible speed as rapidly as possible. In humans, top sprinters can attain running position and accelerate faster than average athletes. For the dog, this means moving to the head of the pack at the first turn; thus the importance of preventing the traumas caused by lateral impact and aggravated by centrifugal force. These injuries can be very harmful to the animal.

A dog's acceleration can be improved through muscle strengthening and "pure speed" exercises. This speed work, difficult to conduct with dogs, can consist of running back and forth between two people standing some fifty meters apart on sandy ground in order to prevent orthopedic injury to the dog. Some American trainers have straight tracks with starting boxes and a lure for working on acceleration.

Maintaining speed

Speed is developed through "speed endurance" training, consisting of repetitions at maximum speed lasting approximately ten seconds. Speed almost always decreases in the final meters of a race, a phenomenon more pronounced in dogs of average quality.

Based on the physiology of exercise, we know that during very intense activity lasting under ten seconds, the muscles involved receive energy through non-lactic anaerobiosis. For activity of a longer duration, lactic anaerobic glycolysis and, to a lesser extent, aerobic glycolysis, occur in sighthounds. The accumulation of lactic acid in the muscles leads to a decrease in muscle contraction strength and therefore in running speed. This is why training at maximum speed ("pure speed" exercises) must be conducted without lactic acid in the muscles, to the extent possible. Trainers must therefore carefully juggle exercise and recovery time in order to avoid the accumulation of lactates.

TRAINING PROGRAM

From available data, it appears that each sighthound has a physiological performance limit that is determined genetically. The goal of a good training program is thus to attain this limit and strive to keep the animal there.

Working the cardorespiratory system

In light of the dog's low (but still existent) oxygen consumption while running, and especially in order to help the body make up for this oxygen deficit during recovery time, the following exercises are recommended:
– walking or trotting 7 to 8 km (4 1/3 to 5 miles) per day at a slow speed (4 to 5 km/h) (2.5 to 3.1 mph). The dog can trot alongside his owner or on a treadmill or rotating training system, if available; or
– swimming, a highly developed activity for Greyhounds in the United States and Australia. Swimming can be very beneficial to the dog when done in two-minute intervals with five or six repetitions twice a week (in

specially designed pools in some countries, but a dip in the pond can work). Swimming is to be avoided in the forty-eight hours preceding a race.

Developing endurance

Endurance can be defined as an organism's ability to perform an activity without a decrease in overall efficiency (the goal is therefore to delay the onset of fatigue). Endurance training should work on all the ways a muscle can produce energy, but at different levels. In practice, trainers can strive to apply certain methods used by human athletes.

Based on studies of the musculature of different sighthound breeds and on limited scientific data regarding the typology of their muscle fibers, it appears that some breeds have a prevalence of slow-contraction muscle fibers (Afghan, Saluki), while others have a strong prevalence of fast-contraction muscle fibers (Greyhound, Whippet). For this reason, breed-specific training programs must be designed.

Whatever the breed, lactic endurance training should begin four to five weeks after work on the cardiorespiratory system is renewed. This is especially important, since in certain types of competition, multiple races may be held in a single day. Training on the track should begin with short distances (200 m) (650 feet) at maximum speed repeated three times per session and alternated with active recovery in order to develop lactic strength. Gradually (in three to four weeks), normal race distances should be used, and the number of repetitions increased (from three to six) and alternated with passive rest periods in order to improve lactic capacity (the body grows accustomed to the accumulation of lactates, which are eliminated more efficiently).

Developing strength

Strength is an organism's ability to overcome an external force (body weight and inertia for a sighthound athlete). It seems difficult, if not impossible, to apply to dogs the methods used by human athletes to develop muscle strength (working with maximum loads, working to the point of exhaustion or isometric contraction). Still, specific exercises must be used to develop muscular strength:
– running with a weighted jacket (500 g to 4 kg [1 to 8 _ pounds] for a Greyhound);
– a series of vertical jumps (as play and using a lure, for example); and
– running up hills or sloped embankments (very effective at distances between 50 and 100 meters (160 and 330 feet) at a 25% incline).

The optimum number of repetitions for these types of exercise is three or four, alternated with short rest periods (of approximately one minute), with two sessions per week during the first two months of annual training. Muscle strength conditioning should cease during the competition period.

Developing speed

"Speed" refers either to:
– reaction time to a signal, which actually involves only the dog's neuromuscular acuity; or
– maximum running speed, which for dogs means producing a high rate of efficient motion in order to reach full potential.

A dog may have good reaction time (rapid departure from the starting box) but a weak or inefficient rate of motion, or vice versa. That is why these two elements must be worked separately.

Maximum speed is attained in two phases:
– increasing speed (acceleration phase); and
– maintaining speed (maintenance phase).

The first phase involves the ability to overcome inertia in order to accelerate. In this phase, the dog's weight relative to his strength is most important.

The second phase involves achieving the best possible compromise between rate of motion and stride efficiency (length). Some dogs rapidly attain running position but cannot reach a high maximum speed, while others require a long time to establish an efficient "pace" and run in two different manners (short strides to accelerate, long strides to maintain speed). The best canine sprinters are those who constantly adapt their stride without significant modification in length or rate.

Working on a sighthound's speed boils down to repeating very short but very intense exercises. For example, a dog can complete a series of short sprints (100 m) (330 feet) in a straight line between two people (with two minutes of active recovery between each round trip). The only necessary precaution is to find soft ground in order to prevent any trauma when the dog accelerates or brakes (grass, hard sand, stopping in a pit of loose sand). These exercises conducted at maximum speed and repeated in six- to ten-minute blocks at least twice a week should be used only after a dog has reached adulthood.

Developing neuromuscular acuity

From a very early age, sighthound athletes need wide open spaces for running. In fact, as soon as a puppy reaches five or six months old, he can be started with a series of very short sprints (30 to 50 m) (95 to 160 feet) on soft ground, since his body is not yet fully developed. Off-leash running, running on uneven ground, and even sight coursing can also increase neuromuscular acuity in dogs.

Apart from adapting the running exercise to the type of ground, it is also important to work on developing the dog's reaction speed to the starting signal. Gains in time can reach 20 to 30 hundredths of a second for human sprinters; for dogs this means that a mere 80 cm to 1 m (30 to 40 inches) separate an excellent canine sprinter from a poor one!

For humans, the amount of time between "ready" and the moment the starting gun is fired is fixed. The same is not true in dog racing, where the time between the passage of the lure and the opening of the starting boxes depends on the track and the person controlling the lure. In training, the only way improve a dog's reaction time is to vary as much as possible the time between the departure of the lure and the opening of the box, to prevent the dog from concentrating only on the mechanical noise produced by the box just before it opens.

It is also important for sighthounds to be able to successfully negotiate the entry into each turn while running by using the front right leg for support. Since turns are made by cutting hard to the left, a "left-handed" Greyhound must instinctively modify his gallop as he enters or exits each turn. This makes him very unstable (given that two-thirds the weight of a body moving at 70 km/h (43.5 mph) is supported by the front legs) and therefore at risk of falling or injuring the toes. A "left-handed" dog can be made into a "right-handed" dog by winding an adhesive bandage (size 4 or 6) around the right metacarpus two or three times. The additional weight of the bandage on the front right leg permanently reverses the dog's gallop in two to four training races.

Other sporting and utility dogs

In this chapter dealing with the practical concerns of physical training, the reader may be surprised to find that training programs for many other sporting and utility dogs are not covered to the same extent as those for sighthounds and sled dogs. In fact, sighthounds and sled dogs are the canine models of sprinters and marathon runners, and all other disciplines require an effort somewhere between the two extremes. These two canine athletes are also the only ones on whom true research has been conducted and for whom physical training methods have therefore been developed.

In field trials, for example, dogs are conditioned before the competition period using methods that have remained unchanged since they were created in 1865! Without wishing to criticize in a negative manner, it can be said that hunting dogs, ring dogs, herding dogs, etc. most often receive instinctive, empirical physical preparation that is far from optimal for obtaining maximum performance. It is also true that the aspect of canine "obedience training" (discussed elsewhere) is heavily stressed in these disciplines.

Owners will find it helpful to refer to the data on sled dogs and sighthounds and can adapt the most appropriate methods to their dog's activity. Still, it is important to recognize that scientific research, particularly that directed at better understanding metabolic functioning in so-called "intermediate sports," is necessary before we can determine what might be good specific training programs.

Even in disciplines that rely heavily on dog's natural skills and obedience, optimal physical conditioning can always help improve performance and efficiency.

THE HUMAN-DOG RELATIONSHIP

Dogs and humans have been close ever since dogs were first domesticated. Ties developed between them, with humans providing food and warmth, and dogs helping in hunting, guarding the home, and protecting the flocks.
The rich relationship between humans and dogs must be based on applying some basic observations.

Knowing the dog

Any kind of training requires a knowledge of canine morphology and physiology. Dogs may or may not be physically able to perform the task at hand, and their behavior can influence the way an exercise is carried out.

Therefore, knowing the dog means first and foremost knowing the canine species and how it is organized.

THE CONCEPT OF PACKS

A single look
is enough

Before dogs were domesticated, they lived in packs, like today's wolves. A pack consists of a large number of individuals living together, sharing the same territory and often the same food. Each individual is a part of this "society" and has a specific status based on his position in the hierarchy.

THE CONCEPT OF HIERARCHY

Groups cannot survive in anarchy, where each individual does whatever he pleases. A pack of wolves is governed by a complex hierarchy in which each member is both dominant and submissive, except for the "leader," who is dominant over the entire pack.

Dogs are still strongly influenced by these constraints and will behave either submissively or dominantly toward whomever they meet, whether or not of their own species.

PREDATORY INSTINCT

As hunters, dogs have a certain degree of hunting instinct based on breed. Hunting techniques therefore vary greatly depending on type and even on the individual breed (a Dachshund does not hunt in the same manner as a Brittany Spaniel).

Whether developed or toned down, the predatory instinct still pervades the entire canine species.

TERRITORIAL INSTINCT

Whether living alone or in a group, dogs occupy a defined area they consider to be their territory. They exhibit complex observation skills and guarding behavior in order to monitor the comings and goings of strangers.

Two additional concepts related to the dog's environment are important. When in the presence of a hostile individual, a dog faces one of two situations. When the individual reaches escape distance (several meters), the dog tries to escape by running away. When the individual reaches critical distance (several dozen centimeters to approximately one meter) and the dog has been unable to escape, he exhibits active defense behavior—attack.

THE CONCEPT OF PLAY

Sometimes leading to conflict, play is a means of easing the tension that may arise between individuals.

It is also a good way to redirect a dog's urge to run away, since dogs expend energy by frolicking and engaging in other forms of play.

Socialization of the dog

INNATE POTENTIAL

Dogs have innate potential (the natural aptitudes of their breed) that can be developed through external influences and stimulation. It is therefore preferable to choose a dog whose parents exhibit certain aptitudes, since genetic makeup influences character.

MIMICRY

Puppies spend a great deal of time observing other dogs. Through mimicry, they learn to copy the movements and behavior they see.

Note, however, that a puppy's development is primarily physical and physiological: From birth to four weeks, his senses develop in the following order: taste and touch, smell, sight, and finally hearing. Only after the puppy reaches six to seven weeks old does the phase of socialization begin, during which he learns to recognize friendly and unfriendly species.

PLAY

Through playful interaction with other puppies and adult dogs, the puppy learns to recognize the communication signals particular to dogs. He thus assimilates the social cues specific to the canine species.

Communication between humans and dogs

All relationships are built on communication between the two parties involved. By getting to know his dog, an owner can come to understand all his perceptible signals (postures, sounds, etc.). It is through these signals that dogs communicate with people.

As for how humans communicate with dogs, there are several principles to discuss.

MEANS OF COMMUNICATION

The means of communication can be both human-related and object-related:

– Signals from a distance and signals in proximity (petting, contact with the owner, etc.) are very well perceived by dogs.

– Often, dogs can better perceive vocal intonation than specific words, since dogs can understand only approximately one hundred different words. Stressing certain sounds or syllables can help the dog differentiate between two words that are similar phonetically ("Fetch the ball" and "Catch the ball," for example).

– To better control the dog, owners should use objects such as collars, leashes, tethers, leads, etc., to communicate their wishes to the dog. All these items should be considered tools for the owner and may vary depending on the dog.

Communication can also be improved by outside observers, who can provide important complementary information.

PUTTING COMMUNICATION METHODS INTO PRACTICE

Dog training is punctuated by rewards and reprimands. They allow the trainer to keep the dog alert and attentive to the task at hand, with rewards signifying a job done well and reprimands signifying improper behavior.

Reprimands must be administered as soon as improper behavior occurs, but the strength of reprimands may vary. For example, a reprimand can be exaggerated in order to upset the dog and increase his motivation, since a dog who is upset will usually try even harder to please his owner.

In order to simply guide the dog during training, owners can of course use physical connections (collars, leashes, tethers) or vocal intonation. Physical connections and vocal intonation are similar to real rewards and reprimands but are not as demonstrative.

CONSISTENCY

It is very important that commands to the dog be logical. The same words and gestures should always be used.

The number of commands should be limited: If the owner gives several commands in rapid succession, the dog will not know which to respond to and may not obey any.

These basic principles should be incorporated into gradual training, in which the trainer increases the difficulty of exercises while laying the groundwork for a specific athletic program.

SOCIABILITY TESTS

In the last decade or so, there have been many activities world-wide focused on better integrating dogs in urban life. All have been based on defining and putting into practice tests to help the owner evaluate and then develop the dog's ability to behave appropriately in society.

Historical synopsis

In 1974, the Animal Advisory Committee was founded in Great Britain. Its role is to integrate the dog into daily life through owner education, prevention, and law enforcement. Since the early 1990s, British law has stipulated that animal-related issues must be handled by a specialist. Since then, 93% of the local governments have employed Dog Welfare Officers. Since the law was passed, there has been a considerable improvement in the management of animal-related issues in urban settings.

In the United States, the Canine Good Citizen Test has existed since the early 1990s. The purpose of this test is to identify and reward dogs trained to be good members of the family and of society as a whole. All dogs who pass the Canine Good Citizen Test receive a certificate from the American Kennel Club. The aim of the Canine Good Citizen Test is to show that man's best friend, the dog, can be a respectable member of the community when trained to behave well in the home, in public places, and in the presence of other dogs. The program is designed for all dogs, both purebreds and mixed breeds. Other countries have followed these initiatives: Germany, for example, has the Obedience Test, and France has the Certificate of Sociability and Utility Aptitude.

Sociability tests

Most of today's tests are derived from the Canine Good Citizen Test, in which the dog must demonstrate his trust and self-control in a series of situations:

Test 1: Allowing a stranger to approach

A stranger approaches the owner and his dog in a completely natural manner, shakes the owner's hand, and speaks to him. The dog must show no signs of aggression or fear.

Test 2: Sitting and being petted

The dog is on a leash, sitting at his owner's feet. A stranger must be able to pet the dog's head and body and walk around the dog and his owner without the dog showing fear or aggression.

AMERICAN KENNEL CLUB'S

CANINE GOOD CITIZEN TEST

owned by

IS A CANINE GOOD CITIZEN
and has been awarded this certificate
on ―――――19
*in recognition of
successful completion of the
American Kennel Club*
CANINE GOOD CITIZEN TEST

Test 3: Examination and grooming
The judge inspects the dog, combs or brushes him, and examines his ears and forelegs. The dog must fully accept this handling.

Test 4: Following on a leash
The dog should walk on one side of the owner, at the owner's preference. They must turn left and right and change direction. The owner commands the dog to sit at least once during the exercise and then at the end. The dog is not required to be perfectly in line with his owner, and it is not necessary for him to sit automatically as soon as he stops.

Test 5: Walking through a crowd
The dog and his owner walk past a group of people (at least three). The dog must show no fear or aggression and should not become overexcited. The owner is allowed to speak to his dog but may not pull on the leash.

Test 6: Sitting, lying down, and staying on command
The dog must sit and lie down at his owner's command, even if the dog is slow to obey or the owner must repeat the commands several times. The dog must also stay (while sitting or lying down, at the owner's discretion) when the owner walks about 6 meters away from him.

Test 7: Coming
The owner walks about 3 meters away from his dog and then calls him, using a signal and encouragement if he wishes. The dog must go to his owner when called.

Test 8: Sociability toward other dogs
Two people with their dogs, separated by approximately 10 meters, walk toward each other, stop, shake hands, and converse. Then they walk approximately 5 meters away from each other. The dogs should show only general curiosity toward each other.

Test 9: Reactions to distractions
The dog must remain calm when confronted with disturbing situations, such as when a book is dropped or when someone runs in front of him. He can show natural curiosity or become slightly startled but should not panic or try to run away.

Test 10: Supervised separation
A person takes the dog by the leash while his owner walks away. The dog is held for three minutes. He is not required to maintain his position, but he must not cry, bark, howl incessantly, or show anything except slight agitation or nervousness.

These tests demonstrate the dog's behavior in the types of situations he may encounter in an urban setting. There is no scoring; dogs either pass or fail the test.

In some countries, dogs must pass this test to be eligible to begin a career as sport dog.

SPECIFICS OF SPORTING AND UTILITY TRAINING

The way in which a particular characteristic is developed in dogs and how dogs are taught the behaviors related to athletic performance traditionally fall under what is known as "dog training." Nevertheless, to help readers make a clear distinction between the goal of "physical fitness" and training, from the purely technical and behavioral standpoint of training, we decided to separate these two complementary aspects from the overall concept of preparing a dog for sport or work.

The information provided below is only a guideline for how dogs should progress. In no way do we wish to replace professional trainers, nor do we claim an extensive knowledge of their various areas of expertise.

Schutzhund, ring, and related disciplines

In these disciplines, described in detail elsewhere, the dog learns to express his natural aptitudes in the areas of obstacle jumping, obedience, defense and attack, and tracking.

These dogs are trained beginning at the age of three months. From this age until around six months, puppies are introduced to tracking and jaw holds. They are taught the basics of practical obedience, as well as the call to attention, and are habituated to city life.

Puppies from six to nine months are introduced to the series of exercises that will be their work program. They learn to bite the arm pad, then the leg pad, then the pant leg of the attack suit, developing their speed and holding technique and changing holds from the left or the right leg. They also learn to resist threats with the stick and must not fear the attacker's gunshots.

Specific training begins at the age of nine months and lasts until dogs are at least two years old.

JUMPING AND CLIMBING EXERCISES

The high hump (hedge) is generally not a problem for dogs, who enjoy this exercise. As soon as dogs are able to sit still, they will jump the hedge by themselves; they need only be properly placed on the starting marks.

The hedge is raised gradually from a height of 80 cm and can later be placed in front of a ditch.

Training for the long jump begins with the placement of a hurdle in front of the ditch that the dog already knows well. As soon as the dog can jump a length of 3 meters, the hurdle is placed in the middle of the ditch until the dog can jump a length of 4.5 meters (the current record is close to 7 meters).

Finally, the vertical fence is actually a climbing exercise that requires that the dog mount the apparatus and pull himself to the top with his front legs. This exercise is taught last so the dog does not develop the habit of mounting the obstacles during jumping exercises.

OBEDIENCE EXERCISES

We will not discuss in detail here the specific training for various dog obedience exercises, as these exercises form the basis of any obedience school training. Heeling should be practiced on and off leash. Retrieving thrown objects is taught through the technique of compulsory retrieval: on sight (the object falls out of the owner's pocket) and out of sight (the dog is sent out at the owner's command when the owner notices the loss of a personal item). The dog learns to hold the object in his mouth, then move without dropping it, then fetch the object, retrieve it, and drop it at the owner's command. A discipline such as country trials requires that dogs be able to swim for water retrieval.

The dog is also taught gradually to walk on command, sit at a distance, stay, and refuse food.

Defense & attack and bitework

In defense work, the handler with his dog on heel walks up to the attacker and shakes his hand while initiating conversation. The attacker then walks away, turns around, and attacks the handler. The dog must actively defend his owner, stand guard when the attack ceases, and finally resume his position on heel. This exercise has many variations, depending on the discipline. It must be noted that most dogs become conditioned to the attacker's uniform and would not defend their owners in real-life situations of aggression. Attacks are highly varied, with the attacker approaching head on or fleeing, using a gun or stick for protection (split bamboo that will not injure the dog but makes a noise that frightens him).

The dog must learn to return to heel or stand guard when attack ceases. Overall, training a dog to resist attack is technically complex and should combine decision-making, strikes, and jaw hold techniques. By gradually and methodically teaching the dog to bite the attacker's pivotal leg when his other leg is relaxed, the dog learns to make good decisions during attack. Gradually, the dog learns to grab the attacker's arm when the attacker waves the stick in front of his legs and to grip the attacker's inner arm near the body when the attacker shifts his upper body away. Initially, jaw holds are practiced with a large cloth arm pad until they are secure and firm.

Interrupted attacks are the most spectacular and demonstrate total control of the dog. Once he is released, the dog literally throws himself to

one side at a distance of less than one meter from the attacker as soon as he hears his owner's whistle. This exercise is taught to the dog last, since it is very difficult to learn. In training, the owner stands beside the attacker and leaves his dog at the starting point, normally 20 meters away. He releases him to attack and then commands him forcefully to come 3 meters before reaching the attacker, then alternates "bite" and "stop," and eventually joins his dog back at the normal starting point. Among the other exercises taught according to discipline are tracking, barking, and escorting the offender, as well as guarding an object.

Obviously, behavioral and physical parameters constantly overlap in these disciplines, which are based on an extremely strong human-dog bond. This makes training essential, to the detriment of the physical preparation of trainers which is too often neglected.

Hunting : example of the field trial

Hunting in general, and more specifically the field trial derived from it, are yet other working and sporting disciplines in which training has been the subject of numerous works, while improving dogs' physiological endurance and recovery abilities has been neglected. Generally speaking, field trials give dogs the chance to do nearly perfect, incredibly spectacular work: demonstrating obedience, tracking like clockwork, remaining as still as a statue when game is flushed and the shot is fired, coming immediately, going down when the arm is lifted or the whistle is blown. First and foremost, "down" is a form of "come" and is the key of the training process. It allows the trainer to get the dog to obey, to behave properly when game is flushed, and respect game. Dogs learn this easily: While repeating the word "down," the owner holds the dog on a leash, presses the dog's back down with one hand, and uses the other hand to hold the dog's head to the ground between his front legs. The exercise is repeated three or four times in a row, twice a day, for about two weeks. The hunt is truly effective only when the dog thoroughly explores the designated area by making regular loops in front of the hunter. At first, the dog should always be released against the wind to help him learn to use his nose. From "down" position, he is released on the command "go" and takes the direction the owner indicates by extending his arm. The owner should then take several steps in the opposite direction and signal with his arm for the dog to return and set off in another direction. With time and practice, the dog's work improves and eventually becomes more instinctive.

While the ability to point is innate to the many breeds of hunting dogs, maintaining the point, sometimes for several dozen minutes, is not as easy to teach dogs. The owner must praise the dog as soon as he deliberately assumes this very characteristic position, at first leashing the dog before flushing game so the dog will understand that he must not chase the game. Long, daily practice is necessary to achieve the level of perfection required for competition. To place in a field trial, for example, a dog must point a bird for a specified amount of time. He must hunt steadily, widely, and elegantly and, once in pointing position, he must remain motionless

Shepherd dog: executing a "right" order

while the birds are flushed and the shot fired. Training for this type of obedience is done by giving the command "down" when the birds are flushed and when the shot is fired, an exercise which must be repeated dozens of times before a satisfactory result can be obtained in competition. Once this training is complete, physical conditioning and proper physiological preparation of the dog are what will make the difference.

Shepherd dog: executing a "right" order when the dog is on the other side of the herd

Sheepdogs

A friend to livestock farmers, sheepdogs also provide important assistance. For these dogs, sporting competition is an added bonus. As young as possible, before training for any specific kind of work, dogs must learn the basic obedience elements of come, sit, and stay at a distance.

Next, through training to the herd at an age ranging between 5 and 18 months, the dog can express his herding instinct and "announce" himself. This is a simple, gradual familiarization with the animals in the herd, so the dog learns not to fear them. Training for herd work begins next, with the dog being placed with the herd daily off leash. Some twenty docile sheep are necessary for this phase of training, during which the dog is taught at a distance to tell his right from his left and to carefully follow the herder's arm signals. Only when these commands are well understood will the herder send the dog to the other side of the herd. The dog must then be taught to "push the sheep" and back up when he is too close to them, these elements being the basis of his work. Additional training is necessary for certain professional activities and to achieve an appropriate level for sporting competition. As part of this additional training, the dog can be taught many exercises and maneuvers, including:

Shepherd dog : learning the " push " order

– pen work: gathering, patrolling, driving, keeping the herd in a group and stationary;

– road and path work: guiding, stopping at the head of the herd, driving back, guarding one side when a vehicle crosses or passes;

– pasture work: moving without gathering, guarding a riverbank;

– mountain work: patrolling, guarding a pass, keeping the group together during milking;

– restraining pen work: pushing, guarding, holding back, packing together, climbing on the back of sheep to get the first one moving, sorting.

A sheepdog must be trained to be useful in herding. This training is best highlighted in competitions and demonstrations, where the remarkable work of these dogs never fails to amaze the audience.

Water rescue

Training a Newfoundland for water rescue also requires long, painstaking work that obviously begins by getting the puppy used to water at a very early age. Pure obedience exercises begin by the age of three months, and specific rescue exercises begin when the dog is around one year old: moving over slippery rocks, gesture commands, etc.

Water work is divided into two parts, involving:

– The dog, who learns to retrieve objects and tow his owner, then divers he does not know, and finally sailboard floats and boats;

– The owner-dog team, who strive to form a tight partnership.

The Newfoundland's love for his owner and for the water, combined with the concept of play, are the basis of training and later rescue work that all can appreciate, based on certain recent events.

Canine search and rescue teams

Given the importance of search and rescue work, the (unfortunate) frequency of searches (missing persons, avalanches, wreckage, etc.), and the desired level of operational perfection, it is not surprising that training a search and rescue dog is a long and painstaking endeavor, regardless of the specialty.

First, the dog's learning largely determines the success of the team. Unlike hunting dogs and Greyhounds, search and rescue dogs have no instinctive drive related to their work. It must be noted that the issue of the ideal age for training search and rescue dogs is still under debate:

- young puppies can be trained better, but it is impossible to really tell if they have an aptitude for this type of work;

– the working skills of adult dogs can be evaluated, but their future handler had no part in most of their basic training.

To do their work, these dogs must not only be physically and physio-logically sound, but also psychologically stable and very reliable for the handler. In addition, one must know the work of these dogs to understand that it is not automatic or based on a simple Pavlovian process (which would be dangerous in a work situation), but rather a reaction to elements that only the dog can detect in the search. For this reason, the handler is instead taught to read his dog based on the expression of a natural talent that can certainly be cultivated, refined, and practiced, but not "learned." Indeed, this explains why a search and rescue team is completely indivis-ible; the dog must always work with his handler and no one else. This is a contradiction to true training, which makes actions automatic by con-ditioning the dog's overall behavior. In a search, the handler's role is only to detect the external signal indicating that the dog has made a discovery. The dog must learn an objective signal (scratching - barking) to alert his handler to a human presence. Marking work must involve reinforcing the dog's fixation on the hot spot discovered, in which he naturally tends to lose interest quickly.

In tracking (searching for a person based on initial scent evidence), the dog is trained to distinguish a number of odors and select the initial scent from among others that might be fresher and more attractive. Physiologically speaking, training therefore occurs through the cortical integration of the primitive, purely sensory analysis of the sense of smell originating in the rhinencephalon. Only by repeating exercises in work-ing conditions will the dog be able to refine his olfactory acuity.

Disaster search requires that the dog be accustomed to a hostile envi-ronment. This means "taming" the dog in inhabitual conditions that are essentially frightening to him: noise, smoke, fire, darkness, crowds of res-cue workers. For all specialties, this must be complemented teaching the dog to accept the muzzle and winching harness, which are essential for other psychologically trying exercises: mid-air suspension during trans-port, rappel dropping, hoisting or carrying by helicopter, suspension, heights, etc., not to mention the helicopter and its turbines, which emit large quantities of ultrasound waves that are perfectly audible to dogs!

Apart from this habituation work, training involves a series of phases of increasing difficulty, during which the dog learns what is expected of him; play remains the basis for success (the animal searches in order to be later rewarded with play with his handler, thanks particularly to the toy that is his reward). At first, the handler stimulates his dog with this toy, then hides with the dog watching ("visible motivation"). Next, the handler is replaced by a stranger, and the hiding place is no longer visible from the starting point ("non-visible motivation"). Gradually and on his own initiative, the dog will search the designated area at the handler's command, "search – bark!" One, two, or three "victims" hide, sometimes together, in hiding places of increasing complexity, while the elements discussed above continue to be practiced. Practice also involves improving the accuracy of the dog's marking skills, on which the efficiency and speed of rescue-clearing operations will later depend.

All this work must be enjoyable for the dog and must elicit his enthusiasm and motivation for the exercise.

Explosives and drug detection

In drug detection, working conditions are highly varied (building, vehicle, train, boat, plane, etc.), and the number of drugs involved is constantly on the rise. Let us state once again that a drug detection dog cannot be drugged himself! While dogs, like humans, can suffer from withdrawal, the side effects caused by drugs would have a negative effect on the dog's work. There are four stages to training an effective drug detection dog. The length of each stage varies, depending on the dog:

– Stage one
The substance to which the dog should react is placed inside a PVC tube pierced with holes. It is too dangerous for a dog in training to be in direct contact with heroin or cocaine. For this reason, small rags that have touched these substances and absorbed their odor are used instead. For several days, the trainer plays with the dog using the tube, until the tube becomes the dog's favorite toy. The dog learns to associate the odor of the drug with his toy.

– Stage two
When the handler considers the dog sufficiently attached to the toy, he hides it out of sight from the dog in an easily accessible place that requires the dog to use his sense of smell to find it. Gradually, the hiding place is more difficult to find, even impossible to reach. During this stage, the dog is also taught to scratch when the trainer buries the tube in sand.

– Stage three

The tube is hidden out of plain sight without the dog seeing. The trainer leads the dog into the room, briefly encourages him to find his toy, and then releases him on the command "search!"

– Stage four

In the final stage, the trainer eliminates the tube so that the dog learns to search only for the drug, which he will now always associate with his toy.

In explosives detection, these four "levels" of training are found again, with some differences in the exercises based on:

. the substances detected (dynamite, plastrite, TNT, formex, hexolite, tetryl, etc.);

. the dog's marking technique (sitting or lying down, with no barking or scratching);

. the search, which must be conducted as calmly as possible, due to the sensitivity of detonators.

A dog's willingness to complete specialized searches comes from his desire to find his toy and play with his handler. Because of the psychological pressure of this work, combined with its sometimes significant physical intensity, this discipline places considerable physiological stress on the animal.

Our objective in discussing some examples of the specific training programs used for working and utility dogs was to provide the reader a basis for reflection. The behavioral training for each discipline must be conducted by professional trainers and instructors with whom the veterinarian must work without interfering with the skills and knowledge of each but rather by fostering their complementarity. Discussing an exhaustive approach to the training specific to a particular purpose would require an entire book. This type of approach would have taken us away from the concept of complementarity between trainers and veterinarians and the developments necessary in canine sports medicine.

SPECIFICS OF ANIMAL BREEDING

A dog's origin and daily living conditions are both fundamental to his success. For this reason, breeders are not the only ones who need a good understanding of the data on genetic selection and breeding.

GENETIC SELECTION

Unlike in other large domestic animal species, in dogs there have not yet been any major breakthroughs in the methods and techniques of genetic selection. This is largely due to the fact that the dog's social and economic status is fundamentally different from that of so-called "production" animals in our developed societies. This difference has determined the main genetic direction of the canine species, characterized by desired morphological diversity and based mainly on esthetic criteria. At the same time, genetic selection in dogs has also been based on certain physical or behavioral aptitudes, leading to the well-known "beauty/work" dichotomy and producing the various working breeds, from which the sporting breeds are descended.

Today as in the past, canine sires and dams bred for sport are chosen based on their performance. The goal of the geneticist is to strike the best possible balance between hereditary genetic potential (additive genetic value) and exhibited performance (phenotype). This type of approach is possible only within the framework of sporting trials that are strictly regulated. Nevertheless, without underestimating the value and experience of some breeders, it is not yet possible to develop a group of dogs within a breed based on their genetic value. Consequently, selecting the best canine athletes for breeding is still approximate and often too empirical.

Much remains to be done in order to establish effective tools for the genetic selection of sporting, working, and utility dogs. In direct selection (focused on improving a work objective), the first problem that arises is that it is often difficult to measure athletic performance fairly (or objectively), accurately, and reliably enough (in a manner that can be repeated).

Timed sighthound racing is the ideal setting. Still, several variables in selection can be found in this activity:
– the best time achieved in the various races of a single event; and
– the average time of these races.

In ring competition, there are more variables:
– score, depending on the judges' scoring sheet or another scoring scale;
– ranking; and
– gains involving the level of competition and performance (system used for sporting horses).

Indirect selection criteria (involving performance) may include "performance-tests" conducted under standard conditions or leg length in

Selection Process and Genetic Progress

Phenotypic Value
of Reproducers

Additive Genetic
Value of Reproducer

Additive Genetic
Value
of Descendents

Genotypic Value
of Descendents

Phenotypic Value
of Descendents

sighthound athletes when it is positively correlated with the dog's speed or the angulation between bony segments during the event.

According to Jean-François Courreau, an expert in sporting dog genetics at the E.N.V.A. (École Nationale Vétérinaire d'Alfort), current work is moving toward a genetic Selection Index system established through the sophisticated mathematical evaluation of several of a dog's performances.

It is thus clear that the sporting or working dog, unlike other large, domestic animal species, has not yet undergone a major change in terms of the empirical methods and techniques for genetic selection. Logically, the genetic selection of sporting animals should be focused on improving the performance level within a population (average phenotypic value) by improving the genotype and, more specifically, the average additive genetic value. We will not discuss in detail the work already conducted in this field, since it demonstrates the low degree of heritability of certain performance characteristics today (apart from the "attack/jaw hold" component in the Malinois Belgian Sheepdog). The traditional selection strategy, which is logical (selection based on ascendance, peer group, and

Repeatability and inheritability (± standard error) for different hunting qualities in Finnish Spitz (according to Vangen, 1989)

Character	Repeatability	Inheritability
Search capabilities	0.31	0.07 ± 0.03
Finding birds	0.14	0.11 ± 0.03
Marking birds	0.16	0.04 ± 0.02
Barking	0.28	0.02 ± 0.02
Holding birds	0.23	0.18 ± 0.04
Following birds	0.22	0.10 ± 0.03
Overall Impression	0.15	0.09 ± 0.03
Total Score	**0.19**	**0.11 ± 0.04**

Inheritability for different ring competition qualities in the Belgian Malinois (according to Degauchy, 1993)

	Inheritability
Heel on Leash	0.03
Heel of Leash	0.09
Defense of Handler	0.00
Long Stay	0.28
Food Refusal	0.00
Attack	0.54
General Outlook	0.06
Total Score	**0.17**

descendence) and commonly used by breeders (but not always strictly or consistently), must give way to a true genetic evaluation of performance.

Performance modeling must therefore be the first step toward evaluation and must develop through a mathematical representation of the genetic and non-genetic factors that influence the characteristic being studied in order to create a performance index. A preliminary study with this aim has been conducted in France (at the E.N.V.A.) in order to propose a genetic evaluation of racing Whippets. In this study, various environmental variables were introduced in a performance model (dog track, natural ground, race distance, lure, year, gender, age, size of the dog, and speed category); some of these variables were shown to have a significant effect on performance. For example, the "distance" factor is defined by a specific increase in the speeds obtained at 225 meters (^{a} 1/7 mile), or 0.4 m/s.

Measurements of characters and types of selection (according to Courreau, 1991)

MEASUREMENTS	of objective character	of other character(s)	
of the candidate	←------↑---------↑--→		Mass-related
of relatives	←---↑----------↓--→		Genealogical
	Direct	Indirect	Selection

In coming years, it should be possible for veterinarians to provide trainers with reliable models for estimating the genetic value of sires and dams in terms of sporting or working performance. Indeed, the typological distribution of muscle fibers (slow-contraction or rapid-contraction) appears to be fixed at birth and perfectly correlated with the type of exercise involved. The same is probably true of a biological variable such as hematocrit level, for which the value often approaches 60 in Greyhound racing strains even in untrained dogs.

Flow diagram of the factors which influence performance (Tavernier, 1991)

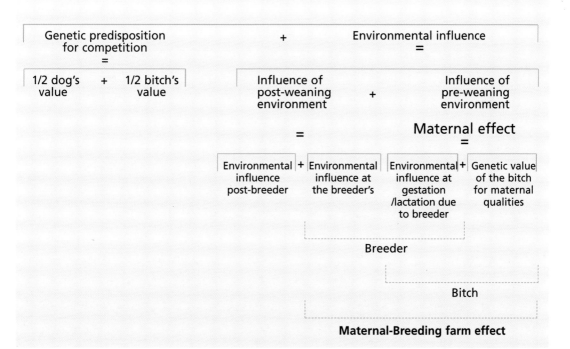

PERFORMANCE IN COMPETITIONA
=

| Genetic predisposition for competition = | + | Environmental influence = |

| 1/2 dog's value | + | 1/2 bitch's value | | Influence of post-weaning environment | + | Influence of pre-weaning environment |

Maternal effect
=

| Environmental influence post-breeder | + | Environmental influence at the breeder's | | Environmental influence at gestation /lactation due to breeder | + | Genetic value of the bitch for maternal qualities |

Breeder

Bitch

Maternal-Breeding farm effect

HOUSING FOR WORKING DOGS

The Double-Box / Pen System

The combination of an internal box and an outer pen is currently the system with the best results, except in the case of pack dogs.

Alone in their pens, dogs can get bored and develop tics and bad habits, adopting certain telltale behavior (constant surveying of the pen, licking their wrists, gnawing, self-mutilation, etc.) that is detrimental to their health and their activity (weight loss, etc.).

The other extreme is also dangerous, since the more dogs there are in the same shelter, the greater the risks for contamination and conflicts. A good compromise is two dogs per pen.

L = length
W = width
H = height at withers
S = surface area
≥ = greater than or equal to
(*) Andersen standards (3 m2/2.5 cm at the withers) are inapplicable in practice

Aerial view of a box-yard type dwelling for two dogs

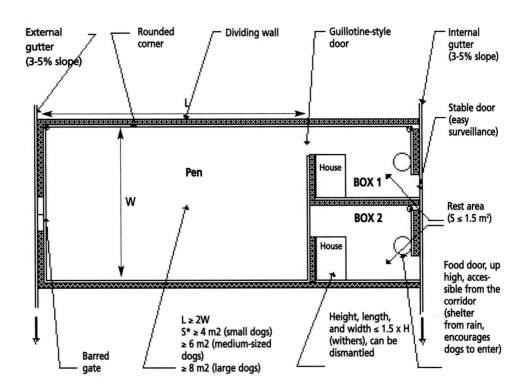

External gutter (3-5% slope) — Rounded corner — Dividing wall — Guillotine-style door — Internal gutter (3-5% slope)

Stable door (easy surveillance)

Pen

House

BOX 1

W

BOX 2

Rest area (S ≤ 1.5 m²)

House

Food door, up high, accessible from the corridor (shelter from rain, encourages dogs to enter)

Barred gate

L ≥ 2W
S* ≥ 4 m2 (small dogs)
≥ 6 m2 (medium-sized dogs)
≥ 8 m2 (large dogs)

Height, length, and width ≤ 1.5 x H (withers), can be dismantled

Living space depends on the temperament of each dog, since it is based on the dog's "flight distance" (the distance the dog flees when faced with a stranger) and the dog's "critical zone" (when breached, the area in which the dog feels compelled to attack or submit).

It is also necessary to provide the dog with a private area (a box and a dog house) where it can feel safe from aggression. Modern dog houses are designed with this in mind, so the dog can actually hide from view.

As a general rule, the length of the pen should be at least twice its width. It should be at least 4 m2 (43 square feet) for small breeds, 6 m2 (45 square feet) for medium-sized breeds, and 8 m2 (86 square feet) for large dogs.

We recommend a design with the following advantages:

– The box provides shelter from the elements and the yard allows for physical exercise (and a relaxing atmosphere).
– A partially covered yard provides an area sheltered from sun and rain at the entrance to each box.
– The dogs can see outside and watch neighboring pens.
– Two adjoining pens can be separated from the others if a contagious disease that is transmitted through the air is suspected (respiratory infections such as kennel cough, for example).
– Evacuation of liquids is created with an inverted slant at the division between the box and the yard. This design allows owners to alternately clean the yard while the dogs are in their boxes, and to clean the boxes while the dogs are in the yard. We recommend allowing the cleaned surfaces to dry completely before allowing the dogs to reenter the area. This helps to prevent dermatitis on the dogs' feet which can be promoted by excessive humidity in the pads.
– Ability to heat the boxes.
– Food and water protected from inclement conditions and contamination. Food and fresh water can be distributed directly from the main corridor without having to enter the boxes.
– Easy control of parameters for atmosphere.

Respecting the Dogs' Comfort

Separation between two pens
Vertical bars are preferable to woven dividers to avoid damage to teeth and nails.
It is also possible to use Plexiglas or thick glass (like that used for shelters at bus stops) to separate two adjoining pens.

The dividing walls should be at least as tall as the dog standing on its hind legs to avoid direct contact between two neighboring dogs and projections from one pen to another during cleaning.

Designs Dogs Enjoy

Most dogs like to spend time on the roof of their dog house, if it's flat. This becomes a favorite spot from which the animal can survey its surroundings, satisfy its curiosity, and dispel its fears.

Shady Area

A retractable roof provides a shady area by reflecting some sun rays in the case of extreme heat.

Boxes

It is best if the separation from the yard is airtight and insulating so the boxes can be heated more economically.

Since warm air has a tendency to rise, it is logical that the greatest heat loss will be through the roof. For this reason, it is also a good idea to provide an opening for fresh air at the bottom of the boxes (ventilation ducts) and an evacuation duct for used warm air near the top of the boxes (extraction ducts). This also allows the heating system to be adapted as necessary.

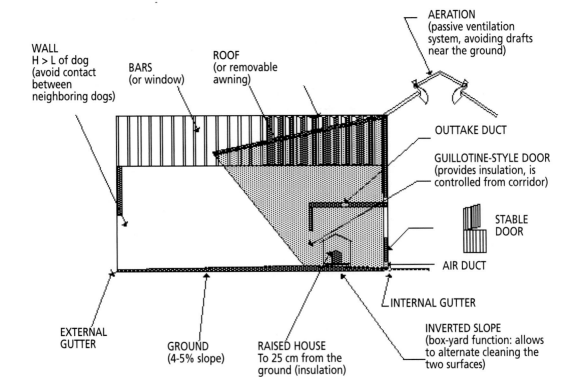

WALL
H > L of dog
(avoid contact
between
neighboring dogs)

BARS
(or window)

ROOF
(or removable
awning)

AERATION
(passive ventilation
system, avoiding drafts
near the ground)

OUTTAKE DUCT

GUILLOTINE-STYLE DOOR
(provides insulation, is
controlled from corridor)

STABLE
DOOR

AIR DUCT

INTERNAL GUTTER

EXTERNAL
GUTTER

GROUND
(4-5% slope)

RAISED HOUSE
To 25 cm from the
ground (insulation)

INVERTED SLOPE
(box-yard function: allows
to alternate cleaning the
two surfaces)

Dog Houses

Dog houses are areas where dogs can feel particularly safe and at home. The materials used should protect them from temperature changes (heat, cold, rain, freezing temperatures, wind, etc.) and be easily broken down and disinfected (plastic, resin, wood treated to resist water, etc.). The entrance should be smooth, safe, and encircled with rustproof metal to prevent gnawing. Dog houses should be insulated on the floor (20 to 30 cm) (7 3/4 to 11 3/4 inches), walls, and roof to facilitate cleaning and avoid conductive heat loss.

The dimensions of the dog house depend, of course, on the size of the occupant. It should be more than one and a half times the dog's height at the withers in all 3 dimensions.

The Owner's Comfort

Distribution of Food

Installing "stable" doors allows you to simply open the upper flap and check on the dogs or distribute food and water without having to enter the boxes.

Dogs Entering and Exiting

A "guillotine" door system allows you to release the dogs into their yards in the morning by sliding the doors up from the corridor. Distributing food then draws the dogs back into their boxes, at which point you can close the door behind them as they go down for the night. This system also allows a fast evacuation of the dogs in the event of a fire.

Cleaning

A 2 to 4 degree slant leading to collection gutters is generally enough to facilitate the draining of urine, rainwater, and cleaning products.

Controlling the Atmosphere in the Boxes

Air Flow

Controlling the air flow allows you to control the quality of the air circulating through the boxes by avoiding the accumulation of irritating or unpleasant gases, limiting the risks of contamination and altering the temperature.

During passive ventilation, the total surface area of air intake ducts must be about twice that of areas through which the air exits.

Humidity

It is rare to find hygrometry that is too low in breeding situations since the air exhaled by dogs already contains water vapor. The ideal measurement in a kennel is about 65% humidity.

Guillotine-style
door system

If you do not have a hygrometer (they are difficult to maintain and calibrate), it is easy to check for bad smells and condensation on the walls and windows. The presence of water droplets on the walls indicates excess humidity, which can lead to mold and certain respiratory and skin diseases (such as mycosis).

To help avoid such problems, limit the use of water during cleaning, avoid wetting porous or permeable materials and wash the pens when the sun is shining.

Temperature

Each dog has its own neutral heat zone, based on its age and breed. This means that there is a given range of temperatures in which the animal does not need to expend energy to regulate its own internal temperature. Therefore, to optimize a dog's performance and to avoid needless wastes of energy, the goal is to provide an average temperature in its box that is between 15 and 20o C (27 to 36°F) by limiting daily temperature changes to less than 2o C (3 to 4°F) if possible.

Puppies have a high amount of body surface compared to their weight and are therefore very sensitive to changes in temperature.

Lighting

The influence of daylight in the heat cycles of certain females (cats, mares, sheep, etc.) has long been known as well as its relationship to psychology and mood in humans. In dogs, no work has actually provided any probing information in this area, however it can easily be extrapolated that a minimum of 12 to 14 hours of light is necessary per day for well-balanced dogs.

Darkness also encourages the proliferation of several harmful elements (germs, fungi, most insects and rodents).

It is therefore advisable to supplement natural daylight hours in winter with electric lighting in the boxes for a few hours after dusk.

Stress

Dogs need an environment that is rich and varied to keep them alert.

The absence of stimulus can lead to boredom and behavioral problems such as dermatitis from licking (usually a wrist), bulimia, or potomania (excessive drinking).

The other extreme can also be dangerous. Too much stimulation can cause hormonal problems and nervous disorders such as weight loss, diarrhea, behavioral problems, reproductive difficulties, poor socialization, etc.

A compromise must therefore be established somewhere between the complete absence of stimulus (idleness is the root of many problems) and asking too much of the dog (which overwhelms the animal).

This balance can be found in the regularity of meals, visits, relaxation time, and maintaining the dog's area, but also in the choice of audiovisual stimulation.

Even if sound perception in dogs (65 to 15,000 Hz) is not comparable to that of humans, the diffusion of these waves can play a role in the socialization of puppies. Reducing external noises and the stress felt by the people caring for the dogs can involuntarily improve the dogs' well-being, too.

A knowledge of the colors dogs see can also help in the choice of paint. Though it is now well established that dogs see blues and greens in red light better than humans do, and that they see better in darkness than humans do, nothing has been shown as to what effect the color of wall coverings in their boxes may have on behavior in kennels.

A minimum amount of light is necessary for vision to develop in young dogs.

REPRODUCTION AND BREEDING

Breeding success is generally the reward for prior familiarity with the various technical factors of canine reproduction (environment, hygiene, psychological balance, birth site, etc.).

Sexual physiology: a review

Anatomical particularities of the genital apparatus in male dogs

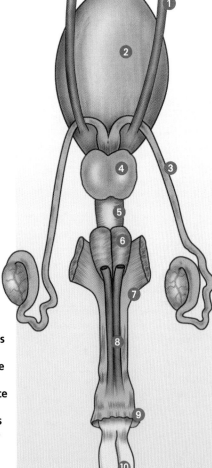

1. Ureter
2. Bladder
3. Vas deferens
4. Prostate
5. Ureter muscle
6. Bulb of penis
7. Ischiocavernosus muscle
8. Retractor muscle of penis
9. Inside of prepuce
10. Elongated portion of glans
11. External orifice of urethra.

This review is limited to the special characteristics of dogs that are important for understanding and mastering the different stages of canine reproduction.

THE MALE

Special anatomical characteristics

The genital anatomy of the male dog is characterized by the following:

– In dogs with a nervous temperament (Boxer type), the os penis can fracture during mating or rough semen sampling techniques, or when an attempt is made to separate a couple that is "locked together." The prognosis of these fractures is uncertain.

– The erectile tissue enables the partners to lock together during mating and stimulates the vaginal contractions that help spermatozoa move up toward the uterine horn.

– The bulbocavernous muscle extends to the perineum. Manual stimulation of this muscle can facilitate ejaculation in a stud that is difficult to sample.

– The convergence of the urinary and genital tracts explains why an infection of the prostate or bladder can affect semen quality (modification of the pH, the presence of calculi, etc.).

Special physiological characteristics

The onset of puberty occurs at different ages in dogs, depending mainly on the adult size of the breed (from six months in toy breeds to eighteen months in large breeds) and corresponds to the beginning of sperm production. Since fertility decreases with age earlier in large breeds, the fertile period of large dogs is shorter.

It is a good idea to verify that the testicles drop into the scrotum in the weeks following birth and to monitor their presence regularly until puberty.

During this pre-pubescent stage, the breeder should also check for the abnormal persistence of the frenum of the prepuce, which will prevent an adult from mating.

In addition, the use of anabolic growth stimulants is strongly discouraged in pre-pubescent males in order to avoid the risk not only of stunted growth but also of permanent sterility.

Ejaculation in dogs is long (sometimes over a half hour) and occurs drop by drop in three distinct phases that are easily recognized and well-defined:

– the urethral phase: semen is translucent and serves as a lubricant;
– the spermatic phase: semen is milky in appearance and contains spermatozoa; and
– the prostatic phase (the longest): semen is clear and diluted to a volume corresponding to the length of the female genital tract.

The number of sperm produced depends on:
– the size of the breed (a Neapolitan Mastiff produces over two billion sperm per sample!);
– the age of the stud;
– mating frequency (the supply of sperm is renewed every four days, on average);
– the length of abstinence periods (the first semen analysis after an abstinence period of several months is rarely satisfactory, especially in large breeds); and

– the dog's hormonal balance. On average, fertilization is thought to be likely when there are at least 150 million normal, motile spermatozoa in the ejaculate.

Spermatozoa are very sensitive to changes in the environment. Their survival time in the external environment is shortened by a drop in temperature, contact with a spermicidal substance, or rough handling (the needle of a syringe). They can, however, survive for approximately five days in the female genital tract but remain fertile for only about forty-eight hours after emission.

THE BITCH

Special anatomical characteristics

Monitoring heats, supervising mating, and artificially inseminating a bitch requires a review of the following anatomical characteristics:

A vulva that is too narrow (Collie) or is blocked (Picardy Shepherd, see photo), or the presence of hair can make natural mating difficult.

Vagina length in the female dog makes vaginal palpitation of the cervix impossible.

Because the urinary tracts converge in the vaginal cavity, it is difficult to accurately interpret a vaginal smear, a reagent strip, or the resistivity of vaginal mucus.

The presence of compact stools (fecalomas) in the rectum during delivery limits the size of the birth canal through which the fetuses must pass.

Anatomical particularities of the genital apparatus in female dogs

1. Ovary
2. Oviduct
3. Uterine horn
4. Intercornual ligament
5. Body of the uterus
6. Cervix
7. Vagina
8. Vaginal folds
9. Urethra
10. External orifice of urethra
11. Clitoral fossa
12. Vestibular glands
13. Vestibule of vagina
14. Hymen
15. Bladder.

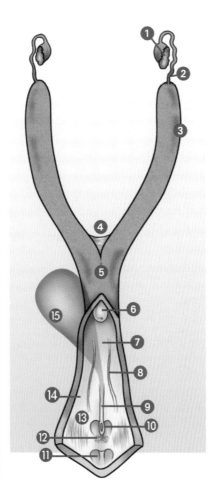

Special physiological characteristics

As soon as the onset of puberty which, as in males, occurs later in large breeds than in small breeds, the female genital apparatus begins to function in cycles.

Bitches have a monoestrual sexual cycle (a single ovulation period per cycle) with spontaneous ovulation (meaning that ovulation cannot be induced by an external stimulus).

Each phase of the cycle may vary in length (see diagram). Only the postestrual phase, corresponding to the periods of gestation and lactation, is relatively stable (120 +/- 20 days). Heats cover the proestrual and estrual phases and last an average of three weeks but vary in length depending on the date of ovulation, which itself varies from one bitch to the next and even from one cycle to the next in the same bitch. For this reason, a bitch who ovulates twelve days after the first discharge of blood in one cycle will not necessarily ovulate at the same point in the next cycle. Approximately 20% of bitches ovulate earlier or later (see Determining ovulation period, below).

Each breed has special characteristics that are helpful to know prior to conducting reproduction and selective breeding.

– Unlike in most other species, the ovaries of female dogs begin secreting progesterone several days before ovulation. The level of progesterone in the blood then rises gradually, whether the bitch is fertilized or not. Progesterone level is therefore a sign of ovulation but not of gestation (see figure).

**Sexual cycle
in the female
dog**

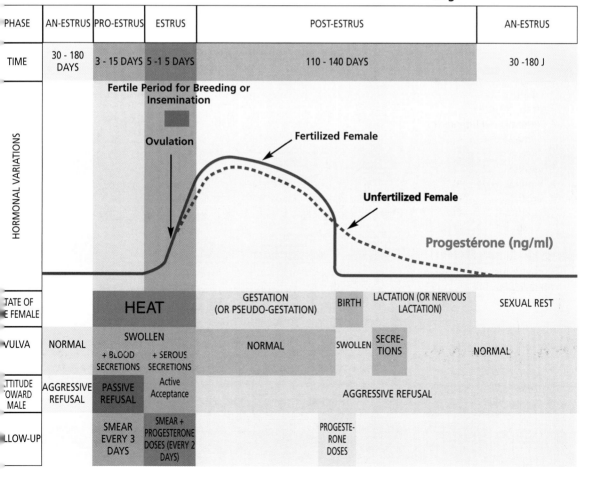

PHASE	AN-ESTRUS	PRO-ESTRUS	ESTRUS	POST-ESTRUS	AN-ESTRUS
TIME	30 - 180 DAYS	3 - 15 DAYS	5 -1 5 DAYS	110 - 140 DAYS	30 -180 J

Fertile Period for Breeding or Insemination

Ovulation

Fertilized Female

Unfertilized Female

Progestérone (ng/ml)

TATE OF E FEMALE		HEAT		GESTATION (OR PSEUDO-GESTATION)	BIRTH	LACTATION (OR NERVOUS LACTATION)	SEXUAL REST
VULVA	NORMAL	SWOLLEN + BLOOD SECRETIONS	+ SEROUS SECRETIONS	NORMAL	SWOLLEN	SECRE-TIONS	NORMAL
TTITUDE OWARD MALE	AGGRESSIVE REFUSAL	PASSIVE REFUSAL	Active Acceptance			AGGRESSIVE REFUSAL	
LLOW-UP		SMEAR EVERY 3 DAYS	SMEAR + PROGESTERONE DOSES (EVERY 2 DAYS)			PROGESTE-RONE DOSES	

**Interpreting
a Pap-Smear**

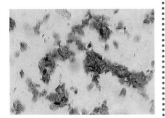

Estrus

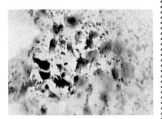

Pro-estrus

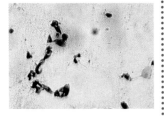

An-estrus

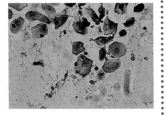

Met-estrus

Ova are released in an immature stage known as the oocyte phase. They generally become fertile in forty-eight hours. Given that spermatozoa remain fertile for forty-eight hours, breeding dogs consists primarily of increasing the chance of fertilization by synchronizing the meeting of gametes "in their prime" for optimal fertility and prolificacy.

–The period during which the bitch accepts the male generally occurs around ovulation and is frequently accompanied by a posture reflex (Liebenberger's sign) characterized by a lateral change in tail carriage after stimulation of the vulva. This sign may be used by the breeder but should nevertheless be interpreted with caution in certain bitches who accept males outside the ovulation period (German Shepherd in particular).

ENVIRONMENTAL FACTORS

As with most other species, many psychological and physical factors can interfere with canine reproduction.

Psychological factors

Any type of stress impairs reproductive performance in bitches. The best example is undoubtedly the hierarchical stress that governs dominance among males and among bitches.

Physical factors

In dog breeding it is not rare to observe problems with libido and therefore fertility in dogs exhibiting certain characteristics that may be the result of poor daily health practices. Weight loss or obesity may be observed. In bitches, obesity can lead to adiposogenital dystrophy, a disorder characterized by normal cycles but heats that are so subtle as to be undetectable by both breeders and studs.

Determining ovulation period

When the chosen stud is not always available, and since it is customary that the bitch be brought to the male for mating, it is important to choose just the right moment, in order to maximize the chance of fertilization and thereby avoid unnecessary travel and expense.

Ideally, mating or insemination should occur in the forty-eight hours after ova are released, in order to increase the chance that most fertile ova and spermatozoa will attain the "meeting place" (the oviducts). Ova remain fertile for two days after maturation; thus the possibility of superfecundation by two different sires. Given the short survival time of spermatozoa, breeders do have a certain safety buffer.

CHOOSING THE BEST TIME

To determine the ovulation period in a bitch in heat, the breeder can combine several methods of varying accuracy.

Mating conducted approximately twelve days after blood is first discharged and repeated two days later is still a practical formula for the breeder.

The lightening of vulvar discharge following the discharge of blood generally indicates the end of proestrus but is not a reliable sign of ovulation.

Accepting the male or teaser dog and Liebenberger's sign (a lateral change in tail carriage) are not signs of ovulation, either.

The resistivity of vaginal mucus generally decreases just after ovulation, indicating the end of the period of estrogenic impregnation and therefore the rapid renewal of vaginal cells. Measuring this factor provides a diagnostic tool that is unfortunately too late too be of use in breeding.

By monitoring the color of vaginal smears, breeders can correlate any change in the appearance of the vaginal cells with hormonal variations, particularly with regard to estrogen.

THE LEVEL OF PROGESTERONE IN THE BLOOD :
A SIGN OF OVULAR RELEASE

Traditionally, ovulation is considered to have occurred when the progesterone level exceeds 15 ng/ml. Consequently, mating or insemination should occur within the following forty-eight hours, given the maturation time of ovocytes and the fact that mating or insemination will be repeated in two days.

This fairly accurate indication of ovular release can help breeders not only to increase the success rate of mating and insemination but also the prolificity.

Through careful, consistent use of both the vaginal smear and the progesterone level, breeders can monitor the heat cycle quite effectively, in a way that is economically profitable (by increasing fertility and prolificity and decreasing needless travel for unproductive mating).

Natural mating

After selecting the parents and verifying their reproductive fitness, the breeder presents the bitch to the stud for mating.

Mating begins with a short phase of sniffing and courting behavior that increases the partners' arousal. The erection caused by the rigidity of the os penis and blood flow to the erectile tissue enables insertion of the penis. This insertion causes vaginal contractions in the bitch that promote sperm movement, maintain erection, and keep the pair locked together during prostatic ejaculation. This phase must last at least five minutes but can last over a half hour.

In most cases, if the time is right (peak in LH, or lutenizing hormone) the two partners do quite well by themselves.

Despite the progress in diagnosing ovulation, it is safest to always repeat mating forty-eight hours later.

Although the risk of superfecundation is lower in female dogs than in cats, it is recommended that the bitch be kept away from other males until all signs of estrus have disappeared.

If, for any number of reasons, natural mating between the two selected partners is impossible, the breeder may take the alternative route of using artificial insemination.

Artificial insemination

Artificial insemination is any technique leading to reproduction that would have been impossible without human intervention. Therefore, simply taking a semen sample from a stud and immediately introducing it into the female genital tract, an activity often called "mating intervention" is a technique of artificial insemination using "fresh semen".

INSEMINATION USING FRESH SEMEN

Indications

This technique is used when the breeder has two partners that are not able to mate for various reasons.

Results

Artificial insemination using fresh semen should be as successful as natural mating (approximate 80% gestation rate).

INSEMINATION USING REFRIGERATED SEMEN

Indications

This technique is used mainly when two partners are separated by a certain distance. It saves the owner of the breeding bitch from having to pay for travel and lodging in the location where the stud is kept.

Results

The success rate is comparable to that of natural mating, although each handling of the semen can decrease sperm vitality.

Osiris type flexible probe

Taking semen sample from the stud

INSEMINATION USING FROZEN SEMEN

Indications

This technique presents numerous zootechnical indications:

– It enables genetic exchanges between two countries separated by health restrictions or great distance.

– It allows the genotype of a good stud to be preserved for an unlimited amount of time and to be used even when he is not available or after his death.

– It enables breeders to take a step backward when the genetic selection techniques adopted by a breed club have led to a genetic impasse.

– It allows breeders to save certain endangered breeds and conduct the recombination of breeds that are limited in number.

Results

One sample is generally sufficient for a single bitch but is sometimes not enough for a second insemination.

Gestation follows insemination using frozen semen only 30 to 50% of the time. Prolificity is also decreased by approximately 15 to 20% relative to natural mating.

Intrauterine insemination through the cervix using a rigid catheter to place sperm in the uterus seems to improve these results, which are nevertheless encouraging.

Diagnosing gestation

The fertilization of ova by spermatozoa leads to the formation of eggs that must migrate and undergo several divisions before attaching themselves to the uterine wall. In bitches, this implantation does not occur until fifteen to seventeen days after fertilization and leads to the formation of embryonic vesicles visible by ultrasound beginning in the third week (eighteen days, at the earliest).

After the third week, experienced hands can sometimes detect a "beading" in the uterus through transabdominal palpitation, as long as the bitch is not too overweight and the abdominal wall is relaxed. Between weeks five and six of gestation, the uterus reaches the same diameter as an intestinal loop. It is therefore difficult at this stage to distinguish a pregnant uterus from an intestinal loop containing hard stools. Generally, the "window of palpitation" therefore occurs from twenty-one to thirty-five days of gestation, depending on the breed.

Radiography is not useful until late in gestation, when the fetal skeletons have developed, making the fetuses radio-opaque (after the forty-fifth day).

Storage of the straws

Abdominal palpation

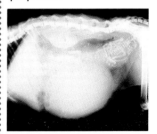

X-ray at end of gestation

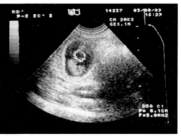

Diagnosing gestation through echography

Monitoring delivery

Monitoring the perinatal period begins with a prenatal visit to the veterinarian which should occur in the eighth week of gestation and include:

– a gynecological examination of the bitch in order to detect anything that could obstruct delivery.

– One or more abdominal radiographs during this period make it possible to count the fetuses more accurately than by ultrasound. This test also allows the veterinarian to detect any abnormalities that might cause dystocia.

– A possible uterine ultrasound, so that the veterinarian can check by sight the heartbeat of the puppies and thus their vitality.

THE PRECURSORS OF DELIVERY

In the week prior to delivery, the bitch usually exhibits a decrease in appetite, constipation, and swelling of the mammary glands. These signs are nevertheless not always apparent, especially in primiparas, who sometimes do not get their milk until the day of delivery.

Then the vulva swells and loosens due to estrogenic impregnation, which sometimes produces false heats in the bitch in the three days preceding and following delivery.

Rectal temperature drops by 1°C in the twenty-four hours before birth (Ammantea's sign). The breeder can use this sign to his advantage as long as he takes the temperature of the pregnant bitch morning and night in the four days preceding the expected delivery date. A drop of 1°C from the average of the four preceding days indicates that delivery is imminent.

This temporary hypothermia is accompanied by a drop in the level of progesterone in the blood. These two tests indicate that the fetuses are mature and that birth can occur naturally or by cesarean section with no risk to the newborns. Note that medical induction of delivery is in dogs dangerous.

Finally, the discharge of cervical mucus indicates that delivery is imminent and precedes the first contractions by a number of hours (twenty-four to thirty-six, maximum).

Losing the plug (cervical mucus) is a sign that labor has begun.

NORMAL DELIVERY

Unless specific risks were detected during the prenatal visit, it is generally not necessary for the breeder to intervene during delivery. The following details are no cause for alarm, unless a particular stage is abnormally long.

Gestation in bitches varies from fifty-eight to sixty-eight

Chronology of prenatal observations

Tool by which gestation can be dated	Number of days after fertilization	Observations (average breed)
Ultrasound	18	Embryo vesicles
	22	Visible embryos
	28	Heartbeats
	30-35	Head and trunk differentiation
	43	Vertebrae
	47	Skull and ribs
X-ray	45	Beginning of mineralization of bones (skull, spinal column, and ribs)
	50	Shoulder, humerus, femur
	54	Radius, tibia
	56	Pelvis

days. Variations are due to the discrepancy between the date of mating and the date of actual fertilization. The first signs of delivery appear on average sixty-three days after fertilization. A gestation time of sixty-five days is cause for suspicion; seventy days is frankly abnormal.

The first contractions involve the uterus and are often undetectable externally apart from nervousness in the bitch, who frequently inspects her flanks and generally seeks out a quiet, secluded area where she can prepare a comfortable bed unless she already has a whelping box. Still, it is not uncommon for the bitch to seek out human comfort. Anorexia (loss of appetite) is common during this phase, sometimes to the point of vomiting. This preparatory phase lasts an average of six to twelve hours but can last as long as thirty-six hours in primiparas.

The entry of the first puppy into the birth canal produces visible contractions in the abdominal muscles (Ferguson's reflex) that complement uterine contractions and should lead to the rupture of the first amniotic sac in less than three hours. The amniotic sac holding the puppy may appear in the vulva at this point (no more then twelve hours after the water breaks). If the amniotic sac has not been torn in its passage through the birth canal, the mother generally tears it herself in the minute following expulsion. She bites through the umbilical cord and licks the newborn's chest, stimulating him to take his first breaths.

It is important to verify that each puppy has nursed from the first milk (colostrum).

Each puppy is generally followed by his afterbirth, usually ingested by the mother, within fifteen minutes (except during intense contractions). The expulsion of blood clots during delivery occurs to a much lesser extent in female dogs than in cats (mode of placentation). The puppies follow each other at intervals lasting from several minutes to a half hour. A delay of over two hours between two puppies indicates an abnormality such as primary uterine inertia (associated with fatigue, hypoglycemia, or hypocalcemia) or secondary uterine inertia due to an obstacle (such as transverse presentation, two fetuses in the birth canal at the same time, or blockage of the birth canal). Medical or surgical intervention is necessary in these cases.

POSTNATAL CARE

One important precaution to take is to guide each newborn toward a teat when the mother does not do this automatically, in order that he may drink the colostrum (first milk) containing protective antibodies that give the puppy a so-called "passive" immunity, as opposed to the active immunity obtained through vaccination.

Since this is an area where too many cooks can spoil the broth, the breeder should simply take care of controlling the new mother's environment and let nature take its course, but be ready to intervene if necessary.

CONTROLLING KENNEL PROBLEMS

Dogs' good hygiene is often closely linked to their environment. This being the case, we recommend:
- Good sound insulation out of respect for the neighbors and also to temper noises (passing cars and people, alarms, other dogs barking, etc.) that would cause the dogs to bark.
- Good hygiene limits environmental pollution and also discourages insects and rodents.
Whether in the field or at home, owners of Sporting and Working dogs should take care to respect their environment and the people around them.

Noise

In France, noise is the most common cause of lawsuits involving dog kennels owners. Barking is the source of nearly 20% of the complaints involving neighborhood problems.

DEFINITION AND MEASUREMENTS

Noise is measured in decibels (dB) by a device called a sonometer. "Emergence" is the total of occasional noise and the level of ambient noise.

A dB are corrected decibels that take into account the length of the noise.

Measuring barking in A dB takes repetition into account in order to determine the cumulative length. The resulting noise must then be less than 30 A dB.

CAUSES AND SOLUTIONS

It is always easier and more economical to prevent barking than to fix it.

Preventing Barking

From the very beginning, the location and direction a kennel faces should take into account the way the sounds will travel (based on dominant winds), any possible echo that could occur (geography of the site), and factors that could cause the dogs to bark (noises, cars and people passing nearby, smells, and all external stimuli that could be detected by the dogs' keen senses).

Barking is often triggered by unusual events or as a last resort when threatening growls or whimpers prove insufficient.

To limit such occurrences, it is necessary to:

Relationship between the length of the noise and the value in A dB.

Length of Noise	Corrective Term in A dB
30 s to 1 mn	
1 to 2 mn	9
2 to 5 mn	8
5 to 10 mn	7
10 to 20 mn	6
20 to 45 mn	5
45 mn to 2 h	4
2 to 4 h	3
4 to 8 h	2
	1

- accustom dogs to a regular schedule of kennel maintenance, meals, and customer visiting hours;
- always have visitors accompanied by a staff member to whom the dogs are accustomed;
- limit visual, auditory, and scent stimuli from both outside and inside (such as the odors and noises of food preparation in the kitchen;
- keep confined dogs from seeing dogs in the play area (with a separating hedge);
- house dogs in compatible pairs and separate them in the case of repeated conflict;
- distribute meals individually and in sufficient quantities to prevent fighting over food, offering meals first to the noisiest dogs who, consequently, should be housed near the kitchen;
- keep to a minimum the time necessary for meal preparation and distribution (using dry foods, distributing food using a rolling cart); and
- at night, confine dogs to a windowless box.

The Fight Against Barking

If, despite all these precautions, bothersome barking persists, training and de-conditioning will be necessary, with the possible use of certain accessories used separately or with medication. There are currently two solutions for stopping undesirable behavior:
- pain (a painful stimulus)
- the surprise effect (using a "disruptive" stimulus)

These two principles are the bases for different types of anti-barking collars using ultrasounds, electric pulses and/or citronella spray.

Some ingenious breeders have invented an automatic system consisting of a barking sensor (microphone) and a valve that causes punishment to rain down from the sky (a stream of water or any other surprising "punishment") on offenders.

Once the de-conditioning has been achieved, it is enough to replace all these systems with fake equipment (a collar that is not loaded, a showerhead without a valve) to maintain the results of training.

Barking is the main sources of neighbors' complaints.

Some examples of sound intensities

Noise (Decibels)	30	60	80	100	120
Description	Soft	Annoying	Tiring	Painful	Dangerous
Examples	Hubbub	Noisy street	Truck at 10 meters	Jackhammer	Plane taking off

Odors

Odors are carried by tiny water droplets, evaporate with heat, and are dispersed by wind. Unpleasant kennel odors can thus be controlled by maintaining adequate humidity, temperature, and ventilation while of course limiting the source of odors related to food and poor hygiene.

Preventing unpleasant odors

– Providing highly digestible foods facilitates elimination and limits the amount of excrement produced.

– Collecting or vacuuming out the largest pieces of excrement prior to cleaning reduces the amount of water used and thereby prevents unpleasant odors from evaporating into the air.

– Waterproofing materials limits leaks that cause a constant build-up of humidity.

– When possible, rely on the sun to dry runs faster, especially since the sun's ultraviolet rays have considerable health-promoting qualities. This is why it is preferable to design south-facing runs.

– Use a high-pressure steam pump to completely remove encrusted organic residue. This kind of pump destroys most infectious agents, even in the tightest corners (including parasite eggs and bacterial spores), and leaves surfaces nearly dry after use.

– Clean runs one to two hours after feeding, since dogs generally defecate in the hour just after a meal.

– Clean more frequently in humid or stormy weather (when odors stagnate).

– Include a collecting pit of adequate capacity. (- Ensure the proper functioning of the upper-level exhaust system in covered parts of the kennel (pens, central hallway), since unpleasant odors (ammonia, methane, foul-smelling gases) tend to move upward.

The consistency, volume, and odor of stools reflect how adequate the food is for the individual digestive capabilities.

Runaways

Dogs can be prevented from running away by installing a peripheral fence around the kennel that will also prevent rodents from entering.

Insects and mites

RISK FACTORS

Attracted by the presence of dogs, stored food, stagnant water, and excrement and characterized by a life cycle linked closely to ambient temperature, these pests cause considerable problems, both for:

– the environment (flies, the transmission of zoonoses); and
– the kennel, as carriers of disease and parasites and through their own destructive habits (invasion of thermal insulation by beetles, tunneling through woodwork, etc.).

METHODS OF DEFENSE

Environmental Protection

To the extent possible, openings to the central hallway, whelping area, quarantine room, infirmary, and kitchen should be protected by mosquito nets with mesh no greater than 2 mm. Doors should be protected by strip curtains.

All useless sources of stagnant water (puddles, abandoned containers, etc.) must be removed or dried.

Finally, avoid unintentionally creating areas that promote the development of insects or mites.

The Fight Against Insects

Actinic lamps that zap insects electrically are perfect for closed areas. However, they are insufficient outside, where it is often necessary to use chemical insecticides.

Insecticides should be chosen based on their effective period and nontoxicity to dogs through licking or contact. Some substances, including pyrethroids and carbamates, are safe to use around warm-blooded animals.

These products can be used as preventive measures (before insect season) or once the problem exists and repeated as often as necessary.

The most common products used in breeding areas involve insect-repelling paints and pyrethroid-based, carbamate-based, or organic phosphorous-based insecticides. Certain products purport persistence of more than one year.

It is helpful to vary the products used, in order to keep insects from developing resistance to a certain product.

If these measures are insufficient, they can be supplemented with adhesive insect strips or homemade insect traps.

Protecting the Dogs

The geographic distribution of some diseases (for example dirofilariosis, leishmaniosis, piroplasmosis, ehrlichiosis …) depends on where their carriers proliferate (biotope).

In enzootic disease zones, it is therefore prudent to take certain basic precautions adapted to regional risk factors:
– Avoid still water
– Avoid dark colors, which attract and camouflage insects;

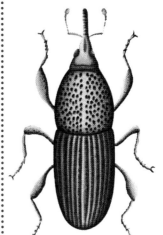

Weevils, with their needle-line rostra can attack sacks of food.

Insects multiply in the crust of excrement, thrive in dark, warm places, and dig tunnels in the insulation.

– Bring dogs inside their pens at dusk (when carrier mosquitoes come out);
– Be doubly cautious during the reproductive season of carriers;
– Protect dogs from bites, and
– As a last resource, keep in mind the possibility of antiparasitic vaccination (piroplasmosis) or primary chemoprophylaxis (piroplasmosis, Leishmania, dirofilariasis),

Rodents

Nuisances caused by rodents

Rodents are potential carriers of disease through their bites (Pasteurella, rabies, etc.), excrement (salmonella, etc.), urine (leptospirosis), their fleas (typhus, plague), or even their flesh (trichnosis). Of these diseases, only leptospirosis is still a problem for dogs in France.

Actually, the nuisances caused by rodents are centered around the depredation of thermal insulation materials (roof garrets, etc.), electrical equipment (fire risk, etc.); and walls (cracks, etc.).

In addition, the amount of stolen food is far from negligible, given that rats consume their own weight in food each day, on average.

Rodent Prevention

Naturally, cleanliness and the absence of leftovers are essential in effective prevention of infestation.

Next, identify local species (sewer rats, attic rats, mice, garden dormice, muskrats, etc.) in order to adapt prevention techniques to their way of life.

Actively Fighting Rodents

The best and simplest method is still, when possible, to use natural methods including cats, although this introduces the problem of contact between cats and dogs!

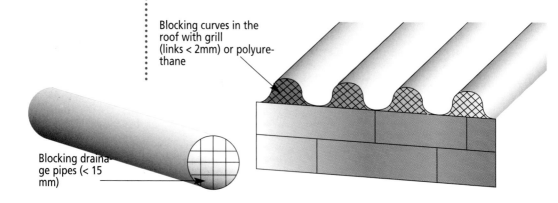

Blocking curves in the roof with grill (links < 2mm) or polyurethane

Blocking drainage pipes (< 15 mm)

Most rodenticides are poisonous anticoagulants that cause fatal internal bleeding in animals that ingest them. Since these products are palatable and toxic to most species (including human children!), they must be used with extreme caution. Note that they are also indirectly toxic to cats who eat poisoned rodents. Consequently, they should not be used when cats are employed to eliminate rats.

A final note: Every year, doctors and veterinarians treat cases of rodenticide poisoning. For obvious safety reasons, pest elimination is strictly regulated. To avoid error, it is obviously preferable to use the services of a professional.

Hygiene and Disinfecting Kennels

Following basic rules of hygiene is still the best way to prevent most pests. For this reason, kennel staff should first master the general principles of cleaning and disinfection and then learn how to select the most effective products for the purpose.

BASIC RULES OF HYGIENE

Definitions

Keeping a kennel clean is a constant struggle against the enemies (bacteria, viruses, mildew, parasites) that threaten dogs, food, drinking water, and buildings.

They can be combated through preventive or curative physical means (heat, ultraviolet light, high pressure, etc.) or chemical means (detergents, disinfectants).

Detergent and good old elbow grease are all you need to remove stubborn organic matter.

Cleaning is followed by disinfection, aimed at limiting the development of remaining germs (bacteriostatic and virustatic effects, etc.) or destroying most of the sensitive germs (bactericidal and virucidal properties, etc.).

Simply omitting one cleaning sequence (such as during a weekend break) can lead to the development of dangerous levels of disease-causing germs.

The Principles of Hygiene

Knowledge of the following principles allows you to understand that kennel hygiene is based on an actual battle strategy against clearly identified enemies.

– "An ounce of prevention is worth a pound of cure." There is no shortcut to good hygiene.

– Due to scratches and unevenness, an apparently smooth surface may have a much greater real surface area.

– Some physical factors, such as temperature (both cold and heat), humidity, and light (UV rays) can inhibit the spread of bacteria.

– It is best to proceed in three separate steps (detergent, rinse, disinfect) rather than using mixed products that may save time, but are never as effective.

– The repeated use of the same disinfectant may eventually lead to resistant germs that can develop with impunity. Effective hygiene therefore means alternating the products used. Of course, alternating products does not mean mixing them, because certain disinfectants are incompatible with each other. The same applies for detergents and insecticides, which are rarely compatible with disinfectants.

– Any good product should have instructions for use.

– Other disinfectants, such as household bleach, can be used at different dilutions based on the purpose.

– Most disinfectants are more effective in hot water. Remember this when choosing products exposed to cold. As a general rule, the lower the temperature, the longer the product application time.

– Disinfectants often have a very short effective period (less than six hours). This depends mainly on the excipient.

- Others are sensitive to light. It is therefore necessary to check their manufacturing date and avoid trying to save money by storing them for a long period (household bleach, even in a sealed container, loses its effectiveness after only three months of storage).

Examples of using bleach with 12 chlorometric degrees

Use	Dilution (minutes)	Contact Time
Disinfecting food	2 drops per liter of water	5
Dishes	2 cl per 10 liter bucket	5
Smooth surfaces	20 cl per bucket	5
Rough surfaces	1 liter per bucket	15
Gutters	Pure	15
Herbicide	Pure	Leave on

CHOOSING PRODUCTS

Choosing a Detergent

Unlike with disinfectants, one or two detergents can be selected once and for all and it should be avoiding making changes if they give satisfactory results.

If cleaning water flows into a septic tank, biodegradable detergents should be used, but not in conjunction with bacteriostatic products, which inhibit the natural decomposition of slurry.

Simply use **good sense** when making a choice, taking into account:
The nature of:

– The stain
– The water
– The cleaning
– The supports

For best results, it is therefore necessary to use your best judgement based on the:
– Temperature
– Mechanical action
– Concentration
– Time of contact

Choosing Disinfectants

The criteria for choosing disinfectants involve characteristics related to the product (range of effectiveness, lack of toxicity, cost, effectiveness on organic matter), the object being cleaned (resistance to corrosion), and the breeder's purpose (disinfection of the air or floor, for example).

Unfortunately, there are no universal disinfectants capable of destroying all disease-causing germs (given their forms of resistance).

FOOD HYGIENE

Although dogs are at low risk of toxi-infections caused by food (few types of bacteria can resist the high acidity level in a dog's stomach), certain hygiene precautions must be taken in the storage, preparation, and distribution of food.

– Food should be stored in its original packaging away from light, humidity, and air.
– Disposable shoe coverings should be required to enter the food storage area and there should be a step at the threshold to protect against crawling insects and rodents.
– The windows should be protected by mosquito nets, the walls covered with insect repellent paint, and the room equipped with an actinic lamp in the warm season.
- Large frozen pieces of food should not be thawed at room temperature (slow thawing allows bacteria to proliferate).

SANITIZING

This technique, commonly used in the breeding of "production" animals, consists of taking advantage of the temporary absence of animals in a room

Dry food is safe form of dietary hygiene.

to disinfect it and remove parasites as thoroughly as possible. The products available for this purpose are likely to be toxic to animals. Animals must be kept out for at least one week for a small room and two weeks for an entire building, based on the principle that the germs that survive disinfection will die from dessication, the lack of a living host, or simply from age. Here is one technique that can be used in the whelping area or quarantine room of a dog breeding kennel:

1. Dismantle and remove all accessories and utensils (doghouses, food bowls, etc.).
2. Collect or vacuum out all waste.
3. Clean floors and walls with a high-pressure pump (30 to 150 kg/cm3, for a flow rate of about 800 liters per hour) or, better yet, with a steam sprayer if there are parasite problems in the kennel.
4. Scour manually, using a stiff brush and detergent.
5. Perform first disinfection.
6. Remove insects overnight (make sure to separate this step from the preceding one because of the incompatibility between disinfectants and insecticides).
7. Vacuum out dead insects.
8. Bleach walls and ceilings with an insecticidal paint containing glue and kaolin.
9. The following day, disinfect the air with disinfectant dispensed from a thermal mister.
10. Repeat misting forty-eight hours before bringing animals back in. The above steps should be repeated two or three times a year.

Controlling problems in canine groups involves understanding the way sound, olfactory, chemical, or infectious pollution works, with the goal of respecting your neighbors and making your dogs comfortable.

TRANSPORTATION

With the increase in the number and frequency of national and especially international competitions, sporting and utility dogs must travel more often both inside and outside their native countries. For this reason, owners might find it helpful to consider the following aspects of transporting dogs.

On the road

From the simple individual kennel placed in a private car to the trailer designed to carry dog boxes to the pick-up truck or specially equipped van, there are now many systems on the market to help ensure the dog's comfort during road trips that are often fairly long.

In the examples mentioned above, the boxes must be large enough for each animal to stretch out and move around but not so large as to be dangerous during braking or sharp turns. The floor should always be dry and the ventilation adequate. A 25-kg (55 pounds) dog occupies a circle approximately 40 cm (15 _ inches) in diameter when he is curled into a ball resting but needs 80 to 90 cm (31 _ to 35 _ inches) of depth when stretched out.

However they are placed, dog boxes must be solid, easy to open but lockable, and firmly attached to the vehicle transporting them. When they are part of the vehicle, they should not open to the rear, since the vacuum created behind the vehicle when it is in motion takes up all the exhaust, which is highly toxic to dogs. Ideally, dog boxes should have no sharp angles inside and be made of a synthetic material that is easy to clean and disinfect completely, with a removable mat that is useful as long as the dog does not chew it up during the trip (a clean bed of straw can also be used, as long as it is changed daily). If the boxes are bolted to the van, a slight slope of 1 to 2% will allow the cleaning water to flow out.

During long road trips, dogs should be let out several times a day, ideally every two to three hours. When travel is stopped for the night, they can sleep for eight hours in their boxes with no problem. Dogs should be given water during stops, so it is necessary to carry a supply of fresh water (a 20-kg [44 pounds]dog needs 1 to 1.2 liters of water per day). Finally, out of respect for others, any excrement left on the ground should be collected and disposed of before getting back on the road. Apart from the obvious hygienic reasons, doing this always gives other people a good impression of dog owners!

Air transport

Regulations

The transport by plane of any live animal is precisely and strictly regulated based on the species involved. Dogs are also protected by the European convention of November 13, 1987 relative to the protection of companion animals, which stipulates that "no one may inflict unreasonable pain, suffering, or distress on a companion animal."

In addition, European convention number 65 relative to the protection of animals in international transport (effective December 13, 1968 and revised by member states November 7, 1989) lists the basic regulations to follow when transporting an animal in order to ensure the safety, health, and well-being of the animal during the trip. Chapter IV of this convention is focused on the transport of dogs and stipulates that:

– Bitches scheduled to deliver during the trip and bitches who gave birth less than forty-eight hours prior to travel are not eligible for transport.

– The cage must be large enough for the dog to lie down, must be waterproof and ventilated, and must contain bedding or another means of absorbing waste.

- Travel time must be as short as possible, including any connecting flights or layovers; each dog must be fed at least every twenty-four hours and given water at least every twelve hours.

These requirements are valid for any form of transport, whatever the means.

As for air travel in particular, the international regulation for the transport of live animals is revised and published each year by the International Air Transport Association (IATA) and can be found in Annex A of IATA resolution 620.

Airlines with specific IATA Regulation restrictions

Airline	Restriction
Air Canada	No dogs in Boeing 727 from 10/1 to 4/30
Air France	No wooden containers
Air Algeria	Accepts no responsibility
British Airways	No puppies under 10 weeks old
Dan Air	No wooden containers
Air Lingus	Mandatory metal muzzle
Lufthansa	Some blackout periods, call for information
Northwest Airlines	Accepts dogs only if temperature is > 10° F and < 85° F
Austrian Airlines	Accepts no responsibility
South African Airlines	Accepts dogs in cargo hold only
Saudi Arabian Airlines	Requires 2 health certificates per dog
Transworld Airlines	Accepts dogs only if temperature is > 10° F and < 85° F
United Airlines	See United States legislation

The owner of a dog who is to travel by plane must obey this regulation, in particular by:

– verifying that the dog is eligible for carriage by the airline, confirming the itinerary, reserving the animal's ticket, and filling out a "declaration of sender" form;

– obtaining information on the mode of travel and any rules specific to the requested airline;

– obtaining information from the consulate or appropriate authorities on governmental measures, particularly those relative to health, in the countries of origin, destination, and transit, if necessary;

– obtaining the required national documents, including veterinary vaccination and good health certificates, as well as any other proof or special permission required by some transit or destination countries, such as special import permits;

– using a kennel that is correctly labeled and, most importantly, complies with IATA regulation by at least allowing the dog adequate space to lie down; and

– preparing the dog adequately for the trip in order to prevent dehydration or underfeeding and to minimize the dog's stress.

If these rules are followed, the sender can in no case be accused of violating the law.

As for the carrier, before it agrees to transport a dog, it must ensure that:

– The dog's general morphological and physiological characteristics are acceptable (due to the increased risk for certain brachycephalic breeds or dogs with certain physiological conditions, such as pregnancy);

– The kennel complies with regulations, in terms of cleanliness and safety, both for the dog and for the people who will be handling it;

– The type of plane allows live animal transport and has sufficient space in the baggage hold or cabin;

– Waiting times are kept to a minimum for the dog, at both departure and arrival; and

– The required documents have been filled out correctly: reservation, declaration of sender, and health certificates.

If the carrier complies with all these instructions and the dog is still lost, becomes ill, is injured, or dies from natural or accidental causes during any phase of travel, the owner is warned that the carrier cannot be held responsible.

Preparing for travel

The IATA regulation covers not only general, theoretical measures, as mentioned above, but also a number of more specific, practical issues that each airline should discuss with the dog owner in order to optimize the transport conditions of the animal or animals.

For example, the space provided for the dog, whether in the cabin, in the baggage hold, or in the cargo hold, must be reserved and paid for in advance. The difference between these three types of air carriage involves the size of the dog, the price of the ticket, the animal's function, and the veterinary examination upon arrival: Dogs traveling in the cabin or baggage hold are considered as baggage and therefore cost more to transport but have a guaranteed reservation and a more flexible veterinary examination upon arrival.

Characteristics of DC 10 planes with lower or upper room and place for dogs (Lepiller, 1998)

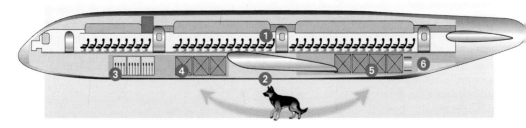

1. Main Level: human transport, ventilated, air-conditioned, Class B or E
2. Lower Level: animal transport, not ventilated, heated, Class D
3. Lower room (absent on DC 10 with upper room)
4. Lower front compartment
5. Lower middle compartment
6. Lower back compartment

DC 10 Planes	Characteristics of Compartments	Main Level	Lower Front Compartment	Lower Middle Compartment	Lower Back Compartment
Type 10/30 DC 10 with lower level	Class	B or E	D	D	D
	Volume (m3)	418,3	38,6	44,9	22,8
	Ventilation	Yes	No	No	No
	Change of 100 m3 of air	4.6/hour	Very slow*	Very slow*	Very slow*
	Temperature Control	Air-conditioned	Heat regulated	Heat regulated	Heat regulated
	Temperature in flight (Co)	22 (± 5.5)	12.5-18	12.5-18	12.5-18
Type 10/30 DC 10 with upper level	Class	B or E	C	D	CA● or D
	Volume (m3)	397.1	86.2	44.9	22.8
	Ventilation	Yes	Yes ▶	No	Yes ▶
	Change of 100 m3 of air	4.9/hour	21.7/hour ▶	Very slow*	98/hour ▶
	Temperature Control	Air-conditioned	Air-conditioned ▲ or heat regulated	Heat regulated	Air-conditioned ▲● or heat regulated
	Temperature in flight (C°)	22 (± 5.5)	Adjustable ▲ or 12.5-18	12.5-18	Adjustable ▲ or 12.5-18

▲ = if the plane is equipped with a circulation system
▶ = if the plane is equipped with a cooling system (optional)
● = except on models with a very long fuselage
* = exchange of air from leakage in the door joints, cannot be quantified

CONCLUSION: Lower front, center, and back compartments are heated as controlled by thermostats. They are all three, therefore, suitable for transporting dogs.

When several dogs travel as cargo, a person may be allowed to accompany them, as long as this does not violate governmental or airline regulations.

Finally, if the dog's trip involves several different airlines, he will not be accepted until each airline has confirmed its ability to carry the dog on the planned route. In this case, the initial airline must communicate the following information to the other airline or airlines:

– the number of the air waybill printed on the declaration of sender of live animals;

– the number, weight, and size of each container if more than one dog is involved;

– the names of the departure, connecting, and destination airports;

– the date of transport;

– the names, addresses, and telephone numbers of the sender and the recipient, if these are two different people;

– the equipment needed for unloading upon arrival; and

– if necessary, instructions for the care of the animals and for giving food and water.

Sedation and the dog's safety

It is extremely dangerous to administer sedatives to dogs before air transport: Tranquilizers decrease a dog's resistance to stress, and sedation always puts a dog at risk of behaving unpredictably, especially during the flight. Administering tranquilizers is therefore completely discouraged, except in extreme cases as determined by a veterinarian (such as for dogs who are very aggressive or paralyzed by fear). Whenever a dog is tranquilized, a detailed note should be attached to the container providing the generic name of the sedative, the dosage, and the method and time of administration.

Containers for dogs

IATA regulation stipulates the minimum standards for dog containers. Airlines must ensure that these standards are complied with, in order to avoid heavy fines. Containers should be made of fiberglass, metal, rigid plastic, soldered metal grids, wood (discouraged), or wicker (only for dogs weighing less than 3 kg) (6 _ pounds).

Dimensions are strictly regulated and must allow the dog to stand with his head carried normally, lie down naturally, and turn around in order to find the most comfortable position possible.

It is sometimes accepted or even advised to place more than one dog in the same air

Construction norms

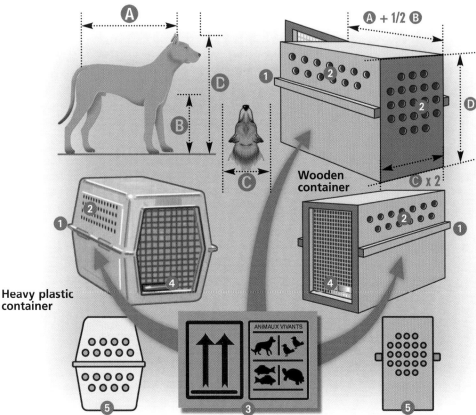

Wooden container

Heavy plastic container

1. Handle or spacer
2. Ventilation openings
3. Required labels: "Top" (arrows) and "Live Animals" (designed by the IATA)
4. Drinking trough accessible from the outside
5. Rear view.

transport container. Two adult dogs may travel in the same kennel as long as the weight of each dog does not exceed 14 kg (30 3/4 pounds), and three puppies from the same litter may travel in the same container as long as they are at least six months old.

Special permission for cabin travel

Permission to transport a dog in the passenger cabin of the plane either depends on the laws in force in the departure, transit, and destination countries or is left up to the carrier.

Young dogs or small dogs can travel in the cabin as long as their weight added to that of the kennel does not exceed 4 kg.

The kennel must be designed to fit under the seat and still comply with IATA regulation.

Some large dogs are allowed to travel in the passenger cabin outside a container, as long as they are muzzled:

– seeing-eye dogs;
– the canine assistants of deaf or physically handicapped people; and
– search and rescue dogs on official missions.

The IATA regulation for the air transport of dogs is restrictive but also ensures safety. Still, some aspects of this regulation are under discussion, given that an experimental study recently conducted by the UMES and Air France on the influence of kennel size on the amount of stress suffered by dogs traveling in the baggage hold has shown that large kennels (in compliance with the current regulation) can be more stressful to dogs than smaller ones.

Fiberglass, metal, or heavy plastic container.

Equipped with a solid frame, the container should be built to resist the animal's clawing and chewing.

One end of the container should be the main source of ventilation. It should consist entirely of smooth reinforced mesh, bars, or welded wire mesh attached firmly to the container.

The door, either sliding or hinged, can be the main source of ventilation. It should have a fastening mechanism designed to prevent accidental opening (some countries require that the door to dog and cat containers be locked and/or sealed).

Ventilation can be provided by a wire mesh on one side or at the end of the container. In addition, the opposite side must be entirely covered by openings 2 cm (3/4 in.) in diameter and spaced 10 cm (4 in.) apart, center to center. The two sides should have openings of this type from two-thirds the height, such that the open area equals 16% of the area of the vertical walls.

Note 1: Up to two adult animals may travel in a single container, provided they are of comparable size, weigh less than 14 kg each, and are accustomed to being together. Animals over 14 kg must travel in separate containers.

Note 2: Three young animals may travel in a single container, provided they are from the same litter and are six months or younger.

Note 3: Measurements A, B, C, and D for the dimensions of the container should be determined based on the largest animal. Container width should be established as follows:

2 animals C x 3
3 animals C x 4

Note 4: Height and length should be determined as for a single animal

Legally required dimensions for dog containers, based on current IATA regulations

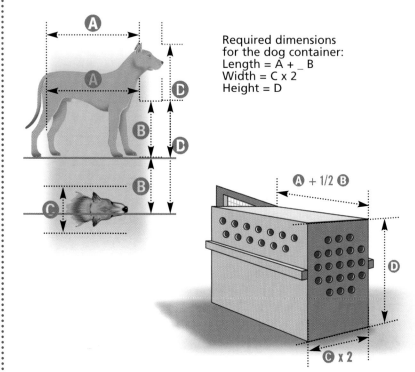

Required dimensions for the dog container:
Length = A + _ B
Width = C x 2
Height = D

A = length of the dog, from the tip of the nose to the base of the tail

B = height of the dog's elbow, from the ground

C = width between the dog's shoulders

D = height of the dog standing, with head held normally

IATA Live Animals Regulations

IATA LIVE ANIMALS ACCEPTANCE CHECK LIST

IATA
Live Animals
Acceptance
Check List

DISEASES AND DISEASE PREVENTION

As is already the case in human medicine and equine medicine, canine sports medicine requires a highly scientific approach in the areas of prevention and cures.

INFECTIOUS DISEASES

Sporting dogs and Working dogs are at risk for certain infectious diseases, especially viral infections, for the following reasons:
– Their lives are usually spent in the company of many other dogs.
– They are often in contact with dogs from other countries during competitions.
– The cumulative stress of training, working, and competing makes them less resistant to infectious agents because their overall immune systems are weakened, as is also the case for human athletes.
– They generally have more "ports of entry" for pathogens, since they may be subject to more minor cuts and bruises than other types of dogs.
Our goal here is not to cover infectious diseases in dogs, but rather to pinpoint certain illnesses that may be linked to breeding conditions and may therefore be contagious for other dogs in the group that could become infected or become carriers.

Leptospirosis

Leptospirosis results from infection with Leptospira microorganisms. It affects many species and can be transmitted to humans. In dogs, there are two main types (serovars): Leptospira icterohaemorragiae and Leptospira canicola. These diseases are endemic throughout the world and especially in humid areas and large populations of dogs. Leptospirosis shows various clinical symptoms depending on the serovar present. At first, the dog may have hemorrhagic gastroenteritis, which can be caused by either of the serovars mentioned above. This is a severe form of gastroenteritis: After an incubation period of five days, the dog is exhausted and prostrate with anorexia and polydipsia (increased thirst). It will have a high fever for two or three days, followed by an abnormally low temperature. Palpation of the abdomen is extremely painful.

The clinical stage that follows is five to six days long. During this period, digestive symptoms appear (bloody vomit and diarrhea), as well as hemorrhagic patches on the mucous membranes and skin, inflammation of the oral mucosa (which smell extremely unpleasant), and acute kidney failure (reduced quantity of urine, sometimes tinged with blood).

Nervous, visual, cardiac, and pulmonary symptoms may also be observed. This stage is followed by a coma, leading to death. Gastroenteritis may be present in a superacute form leading to death within forty-eight hours, after a period of hypothermia accompanied by vomiting and diarrhea, followed by a coma. There is also a less acute form lasting about two weeks, in which the dog may recover after the gastroenteritis phase.

A second form of leptospirosis known as icteric leptospirosis (infectious jaundice) also exists. It is caused exclusively by Leptospira icterohaemorragiae. The incubation period lasts between five and eight days, giving way to hypothermia, exhaustion, and abdominal pain. The dog becomes anorexic. The clinical phase follows, during which the mucosa take on the reddish-orange color characteristic of jaundice. Associated digestive symptoms are diarrhea and vomiting. This form leads to death in five to fifteen days.

A third form of the disease, leptospiral nephritis, is caused by Leptospira canicola. There are two forms:

– a fast form in which gastroenteritis predominates, and

– a slow form, which is usually not discovered until its final stage, uremia (a large increase in the urea concentration in the blood). The dog dies after falling into a uremic coma.

Leptospirosis is diagnosed by examining the animal. The symptoms are fairly characteristic. Laboratory analysis can reveal leptospires in the blood before the eighth day of the disease, and in the urine after this date. Diagnosis by testing for antibodies is not possible until after the tenth day.

Dogs may contaminate themselves or each other by biting, licking, or coming into contact with dead animals. River or pond water and objects soiled by urine may lead to indirect contamination. Leptospires enter the body via the mucous membranes or through wounds in the skin. Sources include the excreta and secretions of diseased animals, blood at the beginning of the infection, and urine for several months after the eighth day. Dogs suffering from less acute and chronic forms of the disease can be treated with certain antibiotics. Preventive hygiene includes avoidance of water contamination, destruction of rodents (which are vectors), and disinfection of the premises. Vaccines do exist, and confer fairly good immunity with a maximum duration of six months, so they should be used in high-risk areas with two injections each year.

Leptospires can be transmitted from dogs to humans, who then develop jaundice similar to that seen in the dog.

Parvovirus

Parvoviral infection is a contagious disease that appeared in the U.S. and Australia in 1978, and is now found throughout the world. It is caused by a member of the parvovirus family that is very resistant in the environment. Only canid species are affected.

This disease usually causes hemorrhagic gastroenteritis. After an incubation period of three to four days, the clinical phase begins. During this stage, the dog is at first prostrate and anorexic. Vomiting then occurs, followed shortly by bloody diarrhea. After four to five days, the stools become pinkish-gray in appearance, which is characteristic of this disease. In the superacute form of this disease, the dog becomes extremely dehydrated and dies within two or three days. In the acute form, the reduction in blood volume caused by diarrhea and vomiting and secondary bacterial infections cause death within five to six days. Animals that have not died by the fifth day recover. The disease is deadliest in young puppies aged six to twelve weeks, i.e., when the protection conferred by the mother's antibodies wears off. There is also a rare myocardial form of the disease that affects only one- to two-month old puppies that did not receive immunity from their mother. The disease usually leads to death after a short period of respiratory distress. Puppies that survive suffer cardiac after-effects. Finally, many dogs can be infected and show no symptoms.

Puppies are particularly at risk concerning parvovirosis

Dogs can be directly infected by contact with an infected dog. They can also be indirectly infected by contact with objects that have been contaminated by an infected dog's stools. The virus enters through the nose or mouth, then multiplies in the ganglia before spreading through the body via the blood between the second and fifth day. It is eliminated in the feces between the fourth and ninth days. Once the virus has been disseminated in the blood, it multiplies in the digestive tract and destroys cells there, causing an intestinal infection. The virus is excreted mainly in the feces, but also to a lesser extent in the urine and saliva. Young and old dogs are most susceptible to infection.

Diagnosis is practically impossible in a single animal, but is fairly easy within a population. In this case, the disease is highly contagious, affecting dogs six through twelve weeks of age with a fifty-percent mortality rate. Some animals suffer from hemorrhagic gastroenteritis. Those that live beyond the fifth day recover rapidly. Laboratory examination can confirm the diagnosis, either by detecting the virus in the stools, or by identifying antibodies specific for the disease in the blood. (The antibodies are present as soon as diarrhea appears.) It is possible to treat the symptoms to stop the vomiting and diarrhea, rehydrate the dog for about four days, and avoid secondary bacterial infections entering through the lesions caused by the multiplication of viruses in the cells of the digestive tract.

In breeding establishments, preventive measures are strongly recommended. Contaminated areas should be disinfected with bleach, and affected animals should be quarantined (although this is made less effective by the fact that the virus is so resistant in the outside environment, particularly on the coat). Puppies can be vaccinated against parvovirus beginning at the age of eight weeks.

Distemper

Distemper is a highly contagious disease affecting dogs and wild carnivores, and is caused by a paramyxovirus. It has been very rare since 1960, when a vaccine was developed. Distemper affects dogs of all ages, although different dogs have varying susceptibility. Dogs usually become infected by direct contact, inhaling the virus, which enters through the respiratory tract. After the virus enters the body, it multiplies in the tonsils and bronchi, then spreads throughout the body in about eight days. From this point, the disease can develop in three different ways. In about half of all dogs, the immune response developed after the infection is adequate and the virus disappears. These dogs recover after displaying only a few mild symptoms. In other dogs, however, the immune response is inadequate. These dogs have the characteristic symptoms of the disease. Finally, in a minority of dogs, apparent recovery takes place, but the dogs have nervous symptoms a month later.

The most classic form of this disease develops as follows. The incubation period lasts three to seven days, during which the dog displays no symptoms. Then the virus spreads through the dog's body and a fever of 40°C is observed, with a yellow discharge from the eyes and nose and sometimes small pustules on the abdomen. This stage lasts two to three days and is followed by a stage in which the dog seems to return to normal, except for persistent conjunctivitis. Next comes the clinical phase, during which occur most of the symptoms typical of canine distemper.

The temperature remains high (about 39.5°C), the mucous membranes are inflamed, a discharge appears from the nose and eyes, the dog has diarrhea, and coughing reveals the presence of tracheobronchitis.

The virus may be localized in various places: rhinitis, conjunctivitis, bronchial pneumonia (revealed by coughing and respiratory problems), gastroenteritis (causing diarrhea and vomiting), and keratitis (inflammation of the cornea) with ulceration are symptoms of complications due to the presence of bacteria. Later on, two types of nervous symptoms caused by the immune system's reaction to the disease may appear. If the symptoms appear rapidly, paralysis, convulsions, involuntary muscle contractions, and coordination problems while walking may be observed.

When the symptoms take longer to appear—up to several months— the dog will still have difficulty coordinating its movements, and this ataxia progressively becomes paralysis. Involuntary muscle contractions and vision problems also occur.

There are several courses the disease can take. The dog may recover completely, without going through the clinical phase; or it may recover incompletely and suffer nervous, respiratory, or dental after-effects.

Atypical forms of the disease also exist. There is a form that affects the skin and nerves, which causes a thickening of the nose and footpads, discharge from the nose and eyes, and persistent fever. This form progresses slowly. After a few weeks, encephalitis appears and leads to death. Another form of encephalitis (old-dog encephalitis) can affect old dogs, as the name implies.

At least four of the following six criteria must be met for a positive diagnosis of distemper: discharge from the nose and eyes, digestive symptoms, respiratory symptoms, nerve symptoms, and persistent fever, observed in a young dog. Laboratory tests will confirm the clinical diagnosis.

. Treatments include a specific treatment, consisting of administration of high doses of serum, and a more general treatment allowing the dog to fight secondary infections, as well as the digestive and respiratory symptoms. Preventive measures are the most effective way to protect a dog against this disease. In large populations of dogs, it is preferable to quarantine animals being brought in. The facilities should also be disinfected. Vaccines exist, and can be used after the age of eight weeks. Dogs should be immunized as soon as possible.

Infectious canine hepatitis

Also called Rubarth's hepatitis, infectious canine hepatitis is an infectious disease that is specific to carnivores and is caused by a virus that was isolated in dogs in 1933. The disease is found mainly in northern and central Europe and the U.S., affecting mostly young dogs between three and twelve months of age, and occasionally adult dogs as well.

The disease is caused by canine adenovirus 1 (CAV1), which can live for about ten days in the environment, but is destroyed by heat and ultraviolet radiation. It has superacute, acute, and subacute forms.

The superacute form affects puppies, which die within a few hours without displaying any particular symptoms. The acute form consists of an invasion phase during which the dog is apathetic and has a fever for about forty-eight hours; and a clinical phase during which digestive symptoms appear (diarrhea, vomiting, gastroenteritis, anorexia, and increased water intake), the size of certain ganglia increases, and optical symptoms such as conjunctivitis and corneal clouding ("blue eye") are seen. The dog usually recovers in six to ten days. More rarely, the disease leads to a coma and then death.

The subacute form has essentially the same symptoms, but they are less severe than in the acute form. The dog recovers within three or four weeks.

The prognosis is usually good, except in the superacute form. However, in some cases, corneal clouding may persist.

Infection results from contact between an infected dog and a healthy one, or by indirect contact (contact with contaminated objects or food). Nursing bitches can also transmit the virus to their puppies, which then develop the superacute form of the disease. The virus enters the body mainly via the digestive tract, but also via the respiratory tract. It affects only dogs and foxes, which can spread it through the environment by any blood or excreta deposited during the illness. Urine can spread the disease for several months after the animal recovers.

Once in the body, the virus first multiplies in the tonsils and various ganglia, then it may or may not spread. The fact that it can remain localized in certain areas explains why so many cases remain undetected..

. A specific treatment for infectious canine hepatitis consists of serum therapy, which is effective when administered during the first forty-eight hours of the infection. The second part of the treatment consists of treatment of the major symptoms: vomiting, diarrhea, and corneal clouding. Sanitary prophylaxis consists of isolation of animals introduced into a group, and a search for antibodies against the virus. Vaccines also exist, based on the CAV2 strain, which is related to CAV1 but does not cause infectious hepatitis.

Infectious Tracheobronchitis (Kennel Cough)

Kennel cough is a contagious respiratory disease characterized by a cough lasting up to several weeks. The syndrome is caused by bacterial and viral microorganisms, and is found mainly in large populations with dogs of various origins. It is also found in isolated animals, for example, after a dog show. The main bacterium responsible is Bordetella bronchiseptica, which often appears at the same time as a viral infection. The dog's general health is not affected. After an incubation period of about three days, the dog begins to cough and a purulent nasal discharge appears. Different viruses may cause the various symptoms. Canine parainfluenza virus may provoke a slight inflammation of the nasopharyngeal region and a cough lasting a few days. This virus is highly contagious. .

The Adenoviruses CAV1 and CAV2, after contamination through nasal passages, are responsible for harmless symptoms (cough and discharge). The disease can then be transmitted to nearby dogs. Finally, various mycoplasma may increase the effects of other microorganisms, although they alone do not cause symptoms.

The most common clinical symptom of kennel cough, tracheobronchitis, is uncomplicated. It causes a severe cough that is dry, harsh, nonproductive, and persistent.

The symptoms may disappear in less than a week or last several weeks in more serious forms of the illness. Associated symptoms are inflammation of the conjunctiva, sinuses, tonsils, and pharynx. Usually, the dog's overall health is not affected.

More rarely, in dogs with diminished immune response, a more serious form of the illness develops, leading to pneumonia and affecting general health (producing exhaustion, anorexia, and fever). This form develops slowly over several weeks.

Diagnosis is easier within a population than on a single animal. Kennel cough is usually suspected if a cough corresponding to the previous description is observed. Laboratory analysis of a sample of the nasal secretions can confirm which viruses or bacteria are responsible, thus indicating which treatment will be most effective. For isolated cases, other possible causes of the same symptoms should be investigated before concluding that the disease is kennel cough. The value of laboratory analysis in implementing treatment is limited.

The only effective medical treatment is an aerosolized antibiotic. If treatment is administered less than forty-eight hours after the appearance of the first symptoms, injection of serum specific for the principal

called a sporont. Inside the sporont, thousands of sporozoites form and infest the dog. Each sporozoite enters a red blood cell and becomes a trophozoite to complete the cycle.

Babesiosis is especially frequent in hot and temperate climates, in areas where ticks are abundant. It is more widespread during seasons in which ticks are active, and with certain lifestyles, as in hunting dogs. Highly-selected breeds such as Cocker Spaniels, spaniels, Yorkshire Terriers, and Dobermans are more susceptible than others. Puppies are more vulnerable than adults.

The incubation period, which corresponds to the period during which the parasites are multiplying in the dog's body, can last from two days to about two weeks. During this stage, no piroplasmids are present in the blood. After this stage, the parasites appear in the blood and symptoms appear almost simultaneously. In the acute form of this disease, the dog has a very high fever and is exhausted. The fever lasts an average of six to ten days. At the same time, anemia (pallor of the mucosa) is present due to the destruction of red blood cells as the parasites multiply inside of them. After several days of illness, hemoglobinuria arises and blood appears in the urine. Atypical clinical symptoms can be nervous, respiratory, digestive, cutaneous, or visual. The course of the disease is short: one week at the most. The dog becomes worse if untreated and falls into a coma leading to death. There is a chronic form of the disease, found mainly in adults, that can follow an acute form. The fever is not as high, or is absent, and the overall condition of the dog remains good. Anemia is always clearly present. This is a slow form of babesiosis, and complications may occur. The disease may last several weeks and end with the dog's death.

Diagnosis is made based on the presence of fever and anemia. The dog's lifestyle should be taken into account. Microscopic examination of the blood can confirm the diagnosis. A blood sample is taken from a peripheral area—usually the ear—and examined for the presence of Babesia in the red blood cells. The parasites are more difficult to find in the chronic forms of the disease, since there are fewer in the blood.

There are treatments specific for Babesia, of which the most frequently-used is imidocarb. Sometimes two injections at an interval of forty-eight hours are necessary, since there is a risk of relapse. In addition to this specific treatment, the symptoms of the disease can be treated, particularly the anemia (by means of antianemic agents, or blood transfusions in the most serious cases).

Prevention is still the best cure. The disease can be prevented by destroying all ticks as early as possible, and by using acaricide (anti-tick) treatments.

There is a vaccine for babesiosis, but it is active for a maximum of only six months and is only about seventy percent effective. The protocol for the vaccination consists of two injections three weeks apart, followed by a yearly booster.

Leishmaniosis

Leishmaniosis is a parasitic disease that primarily affects dogs and is caused by a single-celled parasite (Leishmania infantum) that is transmitted by a vector insect (the female sandfly) which lives mostly on the Mediterranean coast of Europe. This sandfly ingests leishmania from infested dogs and can transmit them to other individuals one to two weeks after ingestion.

There are several clinical forms of the disease in dogs: Veterinarians working in an infested zone should immediately suspect infestation when a dog presents with an ulcerated lesion on its nose (inoculation chancre) and becomes lethargic and gaunt (marked change in temporal muscles, making the afflicted dog look "old"). Other signs such as pronounced rib cage, and flaky skin on the back, nosebleeds, ocular inflammations, or kidney problems may not be constant, but should also point to leishmaniosis for dogs that have traveled in enzootic areas. To confirm diagnosis in a dog with suspicious symptoms (clinical symptoms and travel to applicable area), the veterinarian can detect the parasite using a microscope (studying lesions and punctures of ganglions or bone marrow), or by looking for evidence of its passage (searching for anti-leishmania antibodies in the blood).

As with most serious parasitic diseases (dirofilariosis, piroplasmosis, etc.), the best prevention consists in avoiding contact with a vector. There is currently no vaccine available, so certain precautions should be taken whenever a dog lives in or is traveling through an enzootic zone during competition: Avoid taking the dog out after dusk (because sandflies are more active at night) and use insecticides, especially on areas of the body that are particularly at risk (the nose). No treatment currently prevent a recurrence of the disease: Dogs can develop leishmaniosis throughout their lives regardless of how many times they have contracted it already.

Coccidiosis

Coccidiosis is a parasitic digestive disorder caused by the presence of microscopic, single-celled parasites called coccidia. There are several types of coccidia in dogs, such as Isospora (transmitted from one dog to another), cryptosporidia (can be transmitted by an intermediary mammal such as rodents, cats, cattle, etc.), and sarcosporidia (transmitted by consumption of flesh from a contaminated animal). Isispora coccidiosis is by far the most common in dog breeding.

The disease most often affects puppies during weaning and the stress and change in lifestyle for the young dogs are traditionally considered to be favorable factors for its development (mother's milk is a unfavorable factor for the development of coccidia). It manifests as fresh blood (red) or digested blood (black) in mucus and excrement, which will be diarrhea-like and yellowish. Suspicions of coccidiosis should be confirmed by a veterinarian through stool samples from afflicted puppies. It is preferable to perform this study one to two weeks after the first symptoms have appeared to avoid false negative results.

Coccidiosis is rarely serious, but can cause immunodepression problems that will be exaggerated through sports, considerably increasing the overall risk of infection. Prevention involves isolating maternity in a breeding situation, taking excrement samples twice daily in the yard, and by regularly and effectively disinfecting the environment (steam is very effective). Treatment should be early and complete, using sulfa drugs and related medicines and certain (anti-adhesive) dressings that prevent the parasites from attaching and penetrating the intestinal cells.

Specific examination of these parasites also stresses the importance of appropriate hygienic and sanitary prevention in the dogs' daily environment.

ELEMENTS OF PREVENTIVE MEDICINE

Most serious infectious and parasitic dog diseases can now be effectively prevented if the appropriate prophylactic measures are taken.

Preventing Ectoparasitosis

This is the prevention of external parasitic problems affecting dogs.

FLEAS

A flea is an insect with a wingless body that is flattened sideways. Ctenocephalides canis and Ctenocephalides felis are the fleas commonly found on dogs, and only the adults are parasitic. They are usually found in areas frequented by the dog: it has been estimated that at any given time, only ten percent of the fleas present are in the dog's coat. Fleas are quite prolific: the females lay many eggs (sometimes one or two thousand) within a few months. The eggs do not stick to the dog's coat, but fall to the ground and collect in rugs, wood floors, etc. Then they hatch, and the larvae undergo metamorphosis, molt to become nymphs, and when conditions are favorable, emerge as adults and become parasites on dogs, their definitive host. The adult flea pierces the dog's skin with its mouth parts and, after injecting some anticoagulant saliva, drinks the blood through its proboscis.

The presence of fleas is revealed by their excrement: tiny black pellets found on the animal, particularly in the dorsal lumbar region. The pellets consist of blood eaten and digested by the fleas. Fleas cause many diseases. Firstly, they are a direct pathogen, although usually not a serious one, merely causing an itch. However, a dog can develop flea allergy dermatitis (FAD), causing significant pruritis that leads to hair loss and even sores from scratching, localized on the top of the body (especially in the lumbar region). This is less common in cold seasons when fleas are not as active. Their indirect pathogenic role consists of transmitting pathogenic agents: bacteria (including the bacterium responsible for bubonic plague in humans) and digestive-tract parasites (transmitted when adult fleas are ingested).

In order to limit or prevent infestation, there are several methods of eliminating the fleas currently on the dog and where the dog lives. It is often useful to treat the animal preventively. .Antiparasitic sprays (pyrethroids) or "spot on" applications (direct application of very concentrated spray solution that then diffuses throughout the animal's body

Dog flea and flea larva.

and kills the fleas as they eat) are used for this purpose. This treatment must be repeated every month. Another method attempts to sterilize the fleas as they eat. This treatment is administered by giving the dog a tablet once a month.

TICS

Ticks are very large acarids (from two to ten millimeters long) of the Ixodidae family. They display a significant sexual dimorphism: the female's abdomen can expand greatly, while the male's cannot. Their bodies are reddish-brown and flat, except after eating, when they are globular. They are intermittent parasites that live strictly on blood, except for the males of certain species, which do not eat at all. The main species that is parasitic on dogs is Rhipicephalus sanguineus, the kennel tick, which is highly specific to its host. It attaches preferentially to dogs, and only dogs, at all stages of life (larva, nymph, adult). Ticks attach to a dog's skin, preferring the most delicate areas. They use their mouth parts to pierce the skin and inject a special saliva, which solidifies into a very strong attachment point. The tick can then enjoy its meal of blood, after injecting more saliva with anticoagulant and vasodilating properties. Larvae, nymphs, and unfertilized females take only small amount of blood, but fertilized females take large amounts (as much as several milliliters). While larvae, nymphs, and adult females take only a single meal, the males eat very little but eat many times. Once the tick has finished its meal, another type of saliva is used to dissolve the attachment point so the tick can drop off. A free-living stage can follow the parasitic phase, depending on outside conditions. This free-living stage of the tick's life cycle is much longer than the parasitic stage. The kennel tick usually reproduces on its host, then the female gorges on blood and drops to the ground. After a few weeks, the female lays several thousand eggs and dies. Depending on environmental conditions, the eggs incubate for several weeks and then hatch. A larva emerges from each egg, climbs a blade of grass, and waits for its future canine host to pass by. It attaches to the host and takes its first meal, lasting several days, then drops to the ground again. After a time on the ground, the larva molts and becomes a nymph. The same process occurs again: the nymph attaches to the host and eats, drops to the ground, and molts to become an adult male or female. The complete cycle is quite long, considering that the tick must attach to three hosts: under less-than-ideal conditions, it can last up to four years. Furthermore, not all eggs reach adulthood, because they may be ingested at any stage of development by various animals, particularly during the free-living stage.

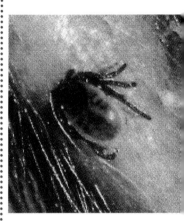

Tic on dog's skin.

Ticks are important direct pathogens, mainly because of the irritation caused by their bite and saliva. Once the tick has dropped off, the skin is weakened, and the wound left where the tick was attached can be an entry point for bacteria, causing infection. The tick's meal can represent a significant loss of blood for the dog, which can lead to severe anemia in the case of a massive tick infestation. Finally, the ticks carried by the dog—and their saliva, in particular—can have a local or generalized toxic effect. Ticks in Australia (Ixodes holocyclus) are known to have caused paralysis of the respiratory muscles that is deadly if left untreated.

The presence of ticks also affects the dog's immunity. When the dog is re-infected, it may become hypersensitive, causing violent reactions (pruritis, etc.) at the point of attachment. Such reactions make it difficult for the tick to attach, thus eventually limiting the number of ticks by a sort of acquired immunity.

Ticks can also carry various diseases, which are passed either from a female to her offspring or from one stage of development to the next. The following can be transmitted by ticks:

- *Babesia canis*, which causes babesiosis (also called piroplasmosis) and is transmitted by *Dermacentor reticulatus* and *Rhipicephalus sanguineus*.

- *Hepatozoon canis*, which causes hepatozoonosis and is transmitted by *Rhipicephalus sanguineus* when this tick is ingested.

- *Ehrlichea canis*, which causes ehrlichiosis and is transmitted by *Rhipicephalus sanguineus* in tropical and temperate latitudes.

- other *zoonoses* (diseases that can be transmitted to humans), such as boutonneuse fever in Asia, Africa, and southern Europe. This disease is caused by *Rickettsia conorii*, which is transmitted by *Rhipicephalus sanguineus*.

How to Destroy Ticks: If the dog is not heavily infested, the ticks may be removed one at a time with tweezers, preferably after dropping a bit of ether on the tick or using a felt-tipped applicator impregnated with cypermethrin. A veterinarian has also designed a small hook that can be used to easily extract a tick without breaking off the mouth parts. In fact, removing the mouth parts is essential to prevent abscess formation at the point of attachment.

If the dog is heavily infested, it will have to be washed in pyrethroids, or amitraz, which all kill ticks.

To avoid infestations in kennels or other animal populations, the floor and walls should be covered with cement, and an appropriate powdered insecticide should be used. A vaccine is also available, which is effective for six months and is designed to prevent parasite infections when a dog must frequent locations (e.g., forests) having a significant tick population.

Preventing Digestive Parasitosis

ESOPHAGUS AND STOMACH

Spirocerca lupi is the main parasite that infects the esophagus and stomach in dogs. S. lupi is a nematode usually found in the esophageal wall, more rarely in the stomach or even in the wall of the aorta. These parasites cause a serious disease that is endemic in tropical countries, northern Africa, and southern Europe. Dogs become infested by ingesting intermediate hosts, usually Coleoptera (beetles), or more commonly, small vertebrates. Diseased animals show symptoms in the esophagus (regurgitation, sometimes inability to swallow) and stomach (repeated vomiting, increased thirst). Respiratory difficulties may be observed when the parasite is located in the wall of the aorta. Treatment is very difficult, involving injectable anthelminthics such as ivermectin. Given the wide variety of intermediate hosts (vectors) of the parasite that can infect dogs, it is practically impossible to design effective prophylaxis.

STOMACH AND INTESTINE

Strongyloidosis, or hookworm infestation, is mainly due to Uncinaria stenocephala, the most common hookworm in France; to Ancylostoma caninum, particularly in torrid zones; and Ancylostoma braziliense in tropical countries. These parasites affect primarily animals living in groups, which is why in French an infestation is sometimes called "pack dog anemia," but other dogs may be infested as well. Hookworm larvae of the Ancylostoma genus penetrate through the skin or are ingested by puppies along with the bitch's milk. The infestation has several stages corresponding to larval migrations within the body. It begins with a cutaneous phase: small lesions appear on the dog's abdomen, then disappear spontaneously within about ten days. The adults develop in the small intestine, which causes digestive symptoms such as alternating diarrhea and constipation, then the appearance of persistent diarrhea with a fetid odor. Finally, the dog's general health worsens due to anemia. In its severe forms, the disease may lead to death, while in more benign forms spontaneous recovery is possible.

The parasites take blood: the adult form attaches to the intestinal mucous membrane, eats a small amount of blood, and has the same effect as bleeding the dog. The parasites probably also have a toxic effect, and affect the immune system as well: As a result, there is a stronger skin reaction on reinfestation, which hinders larval migration. In this way, dogs can become fairly resistant to these hookworms.

The primary means of prevention in areas with groups of dogs is to disinfect the area. Pregnant bitches can be given a preventive treatment of fenbendazole, which destroys the larvae. Puppies can also be treated once

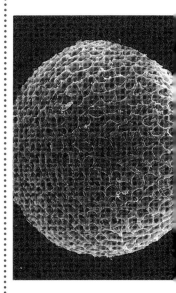

Egg of Toxacaris canis (Guitton)

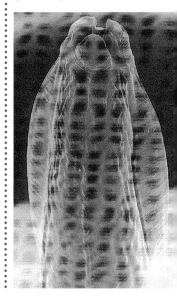

Anterior extremity of the Toxacaris canis (Guitton)

a week from the age of ten to forty-five days, then again at eight weeks and twelve weeks in areas where these parasites are prevalent.

SMALL INTESTINE

Parasites of the small intestine include nematodes (roundworms) of the Ascaris family (Toxascaris leonina) and the Toxocara family (Toxocara canis). T. canis can be transmitted to humans. These parasites infest mainly young dogs less than a year old. The puppies ingest embryonic eggs in their drinking water or food, or the eggs are transmitted from the mother to the puppies either in utero or via the milk.

Dogs that are in poor general health are more susceptible, particularly animals suffering from certain nutritional deficiencies. Massive infestation causes general symptoms such as slow growth, weight loss, and a high mortality rate in three- to seven-week-old puppies that were massively infested before birth. Of course, the puppies display mainly digestive symptoms: diarrhea interspersed with periods of constipation, vomiting (to get rid of some of the parasites), and a distinctly pot-bellied appearance. Complications may also occur in the form of intestinal blockage (by a clump of worms) or even intestinal perforation leading to hemorrhage or peritonitis. In addition to causing these symptoms, the parasites ingest blood and some of the intestinal contents, which both contain constituents that are essential to the puppy's growth.

Diagnosis is usually straightforward: the puppy's overall health is poor, its abdomen distended, and it sheds parasites in its stools or by vomiting. Analysis of a stool sample can sometimes help with the diagnosis. Many parasiticides are available, the most effective being pyrantel pamoate, nitroscanate, and ivermectin. Preventive measures include systematic treatment of young dogs and destruction of the adult worms present in the mother. It is extremely difficult to destroy eggs in the environment, as they are highly resistant.

Cestodes can also parasitize this portion of the digestive tract. These tapeworms, such as Dipylidium caninum, are transmitted when fleas are ingested. They affect dogs of all ages, leading to significant anal pruritis that causes the dog to rub its posterior on the ground. Associated digestive symptoms include the elimination of segments of the parasite (which look like grains of rice) in the stools, which may have the appearance of diarrhea. Reinfestation is common, facilitated by the fact that eggs can stick to the dog's hair and be ingested. The spoliatory effect is very slight: The parasites' main effect is to cause irritation and swelling of the anal glands.

Prophylaxis consists of first eliminating intermediate hosts, both fleas and, to a lesser extent, lice. Use of specific anti-cestode treatments such

Scolex of Dipylidium caninum (Bourdeau)

as praziquantel in the infested animals is then recommended. Multi-purpose anthelminthics such as nitroscanate can also be effective.

LARGE INTESTINE

This portion of the digestive tract, namely the cecum and colon, is parasitized mainly by nematodes of the genus Trichuris. Dogs become infested by ingesting eggs present in the environment, with adults seeming to be affected more often. A massive infestation leads to symptoms such as diarrhea (which can be bloody), anemia, and obvious weight loss. These whipworms siphon off blood and cause lesions in which bacteria can develop. Diagnosis depends on a stool analysis, which reveals the presence of parasite eggs in the dog's feces. Treatment is by administration of benzimidazoles such as flubendazole for three consecutive days, or of febantel for the same length of time. Reinfestation occurs very easily, however, so the owner must ensure that the facilities are clean and the food is sanitary.

STANDARD PROTOCOLS FOR WORMING

Puppies can be wormed after they are two weeks old, as a preventive measure. A multi-purpose wormer is used, usually consisting of a mixture of several anthelminthics providing a broad spectrum of protection. The dose should be adjusted for the puppy's weight. The dog is then treated once a month until it is six months old, then from two to four times per year depending on whether it goes out frequently or not.

Stool analysis can also reveal worm eggs, and the worms can then be more specifically targeted by choosing the best anthelminthic for the type of worm observed. The dog's characteristics should be taken into account when deciding how to administer the wormer, whether as pills, paste or liquid. Some can be given in one dose, and some require several, which will also influence the decision.

Regular worming is essential, particularly if several dogs live together and in cases where there is a risk that the worms may be transmitted to humans.

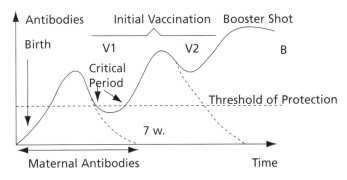

Vaccination Principle: humorale immunity

Preventing Infectious Diseases: Vaccination

Dog's Immunity

Puppies receive their first immunity from their mother via antibodies in the colostrum, which are transmitted in the first hours of the puppy's life (within a maximum of twenty-four hours) when it nurses, if the mother's immunity is good. These antibodies disappear sometime between the fourth and eighteenth week and the puppy then has no protection unless it is vaccinated. The puppy's immune system is not completely developed at birth, and is not mature until about the sixth week. During the first weeks of its life, the puppy's only weapon against infection is the antibodies received from its mother.

It is important that the puppy's first vaccinations not interfere with the maternal antibodies, which may persist until the tenth or twelfth week. Vaccination programs can be started as soon as the puppy is eight to ten weeks old.

Dogs should be vaccinated against any infectious diseases that might be fatal to them. In addition to a rabies shot, which is required by law, dogs should be inoculated against distemper, infectious hepatitis, leptospirosis, and parvovirus.

Different Types of Vaccines

When a dog is vaccinated, it is inoculated with pathogenic microorganisms, or parts of them, so that it can produce and acquire an immunity against these viruses or bacteria.

Some vaccines, called "live vaccines," contain microorganisms that can multiply within the organism, without being pathogenic. These include:

– vaccines containing attenuated agents: microorganisms (viruses or bacteria) with reduced pathogenic capability due to mutations obtained, for viruses, by successive passage through cultures of cells from other animals (chicken, guinea pig, etc.). The ability of the virus to cause a reaction in the dog is thus attenuated. For bacteria, other procedures have a similar effect.

If the strain used for the vaccination is the same as the strain responsible for the disease, the vaccine is said to be homologous. If a different microorganism is used that is closely related to the wild pathogen but less virulent, the vaccines is said to be heterologous.
– vaccines containing a pathogen that has been genetically modified to eliminate its virulence.

Vaccines containing inert agents that are incapable of multiplying in the host also exist:

– vaccines containing inactivated pathogens killed by chemical means.

– vaccines containing only the part of the microorganism responsible for the appearance of the disease.

Inactivated-virus vaccines are more innocuous than live vaccines, but not as effective. For this reason, they are often associated with an adjuvant, which prolongs their contact with the body. If an adjuvant is used with the rabies vaccine, the second injection for the first vaccination becomes unnecessary.

To avoid the necessity for multiple injections, several vaccines are often given together (the dog is vaccinated against several infectious diseases at the same time). However, care should be taken not to mix vaccines from different manufacturers.

RABIE VACCINATION

Caused by a rhabdovirus, rabies is a fatal disease that is transmitted by contact with an animal carrying the rhabdovirus.

The incubation period for this disease varies from 15 to 60 days. The virus has a marked tropism for the nervous system, which explains the nervous symptoms (locomotive and psychological). In all cases, rabies is fatal after the appearance of symptoms. Two forms are currently distinguished: furious rabies and paralytic rabies, the latter being the final phase of both forms. In furious rabies the first signs are simple modifications in the dog's behavior: it appears worried or sad or doesn't stay in place. Then

follow phases of excitation and somnolence. The least external stimulus provokes exaggerated reactions. The dog then becomes dangerous because it can transmit the virus to humans through direct contact (licking, biting). The disease continues to evolve and the dog becomes more and more agitated and has rage-related problems. It then becomes furious and dangerous. In the final stage, the dog becomes progressively paralyzed from the hind legs to the jaws. Death occurs within 4 to 5 days, with the animal prostrate.

In the second form of the disease, paralysis appears at the onset and death occurs within 2 to 3 days.

The rabies virus is primarily secreted in the saliva, which is more and more abundant during the incubation period. Transmission generally occurs through biting, while not all bites by rabid animals are contaminating. It is possible to find cases of contamination by contact with the skin or mucus membranes, where the presence of micro-lesions allow the virus to penetrate. Foxes are the primary bearers of the virus, but stray dogs also play a major role in its transmission.

The most frequently used rabies vaccine contains inactivated rhabdovirus. The first vaccination is given to puppies at least three months of age, with only one injection required if the vaccine is given with an adjuvant. Annual booster shots are required.

DISTEMPER

The vaccine is a live attenuated virus, and so is not pathogenic. The vaccination is given as two injections one month apart. The first is given at about eight weeks of age. If the puppy is older than three months, only one injection is needed. Booster shots are given one year after the first vaccination, then every two years thereafter.

INFECTIOUS HEPATITIS

Puppies can be vaccinated after they are eight weeks old. The vaccine is made from an attenuated related strain (CAV2) and is given as two injections one month apart. If the puppy is older than three months, only one injection is needed. Booster shots are given one year after the first vaccination, then every two years thereafter.

PARVOVIRUS

Vaccines for parvovirus are homologous, but the pathogen is attenuated. Three-month-old puppies are given two injections, one at the age of six to eight weeks, the other at the age of twelve weeks. If the puppy is older than three months, only one injection is needed. The first booster shot is given one year after the first vaccination, then every two years thereafter. Breeding dogs in infected kennels are vaccinated every year.

LEPTOSPIROSIS

Dogs can be vaccinated with inactivated leptospirosis antigens. They receive two injections three to five weeks apart, at seven weeks of age. Booster shots are usually given annually, except in areas where the disease is endemic, where they are given twice a year.

OTHER VACCINES

For the dog's comfort, or when it is at risk, vaccines for tetanus, babesiosis, and kennel cough can also be given.

Tetanus

Tetanus toxin, secreted by tetanus bacilli, affects the nervous system. It is secreted at the point where the bacteria enter the body, which is often a very small wound. Tetanus is characterized by involuntary muscle contractions that eventually involve the animal's entire body. Vaccinations are mainly given to working dogs or dogs often in areas where they might easily be injured (wreckage, work sites, etc.). There is no specific antitetanus vaccine for the dog. The horse vaccine, made from purified tetanus anatoxin, is used instead. The first vaccination is given as two injections four weeks apart. Booster shots are given after one year, then every three years thereafter, and whenever there is a wound.

Babesiosis

Dogs that often walk in the forest or other areas harboring large tick populations are at a high risk. The height of tick season is in the spring and fall. Dogs can be vaccinated with a vaccine containing parasitic proteins, which is effective for about six months. The first vaccination is given as two injections three to four weeks apart, with a booster every six months (preferably in summer and winter).

Kennel cough

Animals that must stay in a kennel or that are going to a dog show should be vaccinated. The disease can be kept from spreading by placing animals in quarantine before introducing them into a group.

There are various vaccines on the market, consisting of inactivated viruses or bacteria (Parainfluenza, Bordatella bronchiseptica). These vaccines are injectable, but not always effective. The first vaccination is given as two injections three weeks apart, with an annual booster shot. A more recent program seems to give better results: a live attenuated virus is administered intranasally.

Vaccines, wormers, and external parasiticides are indispensable parts of a well-designed program of prevention, which dog owners should implement if they don't want to suddenly lose the fruit of months or years of preparation of their dogs.

ANATOMY

Dogs are digitigrade animals (three phalanges rest on the ground). The different conformations of this species allow us to divide it into three categories. Long-back dogs, which are longer than they are wide or thick. Their lines are lean and sleek, like those of the Greyhound or the Bedlington Terrier. In close-coupled dogs, the proportions are just the opposite. These squat, stocky dogs are wider and thicker than they are long, like the bulldog. Mesomorph dogs have medium-sized builds, like Setters, Pointers, and French and Belgian Sheepdogs.

Animals' anatomies are studied by domains: external anatomy, osteology (study of bones), arthrology (study of joints), and myology (study of muscles).

FOREQUARTERS

1. Nose
2. Bridge of the nose
3. Eye
4. Ear (pinna, leather)
5. Neck (dorsal region)
6. Shoulder
7. Withers
8. Back
9. Loin
10. Croup
11. Tail
12. Thigh
13. Stifle (knee)
14. Leg
15. Hock (tarsus)
16. Metatarsus
17. Inguinal region (groin)
18. Prepuce
19. Coupling (flank)
20. Belly

External Anatomy

For mammals, basic anatomy is divided into three large zones: the forequarters, which go from the tip of the nose to behind the front legs, the body, and the hindquarters, which includes the hind legs and the tail.

Forequarters

The head: The different regions of the head vary according to the conformation and breed of dog. The cranio-frontal region can be rounded like in the Beagle, convex like in the Boxer, flat like in the Dalmatian, or wide like in the Rottweiler.

The nasal cavities, the primary structures of the muzzle, are spacious in Pointers and smaller in brachiocephalic breeds. Nasal cavities that are too flat can lead to jaw problems

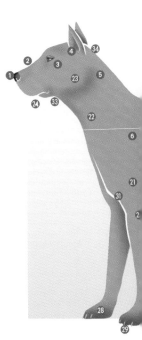

(prognathism) and respiratory ailments that will be more or less well tolerated by the dog (permanent snoring, for example).

The nose, which is made up of two nostrils separated by the septum, must remain supple, moist, and cold.

Ears can vary in shape (pointed in Belgian Sheepdogs, rounder in German Shepherds), in length, in the way they are carried (held erect or drooping), and in the place where they are attached to the head.

The neck: This region goes from the head to the start of the chest. It plays a role in the way the head is carried and serves as a balance between the head and the rest of the body. Again, its morphology mainly depends on the conformation of the dog. The neck is long and thin for long-back breeds and much more muscular and stocky in close-coupled breeds.

The forelegs: These start at the shoulder, are oblique and slightly convex, and are attached to the thoracic region by a group of muscles. Then comes the arm, the forearm, the wrist, the pastern, and finally the toes. Dogs have five phalanges or toes. The members are long and straight and only the two middle toes bear weight (toes III and IV). The two lateral toes are smaller (toes II and V). Each has a nail that corresponds to the horny plate of the 3rd phalange, which does not touch the ground when the dog walks.

The chest: This area corresponds to the underside of the body, between the shoulders and under the neck. It varies in size depending on the breed and build of the animal in question.

The body

The topline: This area refers to the entire back of the animal, from the end of the neck to the loins. It is more or less horizontal in mesomorphs, and rather saddle-shaped in young dogs. The back may also be almost horizontal, or slightly slanted. It will be arched in long-back breeds. The croup will be aligned with the loins and slightly oblique and, depending on the breed, more or less rounded.

The thoracic region: Also called the rib cage, this region represents about two-thirds of the length of the dog. It is

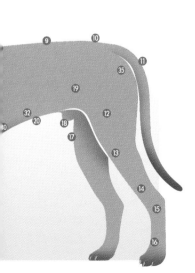

THE BODY AND THE HINDQUARTERS:

21. Upper arm
22. Neck (ventral region)
23. Cheek
24. Mouth
25. Elbow
26. Forearm
27. Carpus
28. Forefoot (toes)
29. Nail
30. Sternum
31. Point of shoulder
32. Ribs
33. Throat
34. Crest
35. Point of rump
36. Elbow.

1. Articular Cartilage
2. Epiphysis
3. Growth Cartilage
4. Metaphysis
5. Diaphysis
6. Compact Bone
7. Spongy Bone

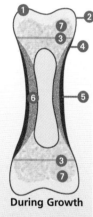

During Growth

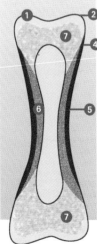

Adult

wide in close-coupled breeds and rather high in long-back breeds. The heart is located within the rib cage as is the respiratory system.

The abdomen: Located behind the diaphragm, the abdomen contains a number of vital organs (liver, spleen, stomach, intestines, and the urogenital organs). Its external projection is marked by the slightly concave flank located between the last pair of ribs and the inner side of the hindlegs.

The hindquarters

The hindlegs: These limbs start at the thigh, which is attached to the trunk by the hip-joint and extends to the stifle, the second thigh, the hock, the rear pastern, and finally the toes. The hindlegs are longer and more massive than the forelegs. In certain breeds, the first toe, or dewclaw, has two nails. Such is the case for the Pyrenean Mountain dog and the Beauceron.

The tail: The tail continues from the topline. All lengths and shapes are possible: From the Spitz's corkscrew to the Great Dane's long tail to the Terrier's little stub.

The Stance

A dog's stance refers to the direction of its limbs in relation to horizontal ground. For the stance to be correct, its axis must be vertical. Even a slight deviation can cause joint strain and early wear and tear on the animal's structure (tendons and ligaments). Stance is therefore a key element in the overall allure of a dog and in its capacity for work or sport.

Osteology

As for all vertebrates, a dog's skeleton is a rigid frame that supports the body. The skeleton also plays other roles involving protection (the rib cage, for example), movement (muscles are supported by the bone), storing chemical elements such as calcium and phosphorus, and generating red blood cells in the bone marrow.

A dog's skeleton is made up of a large number of bones that can be divided into categories based on their size: long bones (for which the diameter is less than the length), short bones such as vertebrae, carpal and tarsal bones, and flat bones such as the skull, ribs, and scapula.

Structurally, bones are made up of two different types of bone tissue: Compact bone is made up of many tightly arranged lamella with only very small amounts of space between them. Spongy bone is made up of fewer bony lamella surrounding the cavities that contain blood vessels and red bone marrow that produces other blood components.

Short bones typically have a spongy tissue center surrounded by a thin layer of compact bone. Flat bones have an internal layer and external layer of compact bone that sandwich a middle layer of spongy bone.

The structure of long bones is more complex. They are made up of a shaft (a hollow cylinder with thick walls) of compact bone surrounding a cavity of yellow adipose bone marrow, two epiphyses (extremities) covered in cartilage, and two metaphyses, where the two previous spongy bone structures are joined. The external surface of each bone, except for the joint surfaces, is covered in a conjunctive sheath called the periosteum.

During prepubescent development in dogs, bones undergo two phenomena: They grow in thickness as the periosteum adds lamella, and they grow in length as the growth plate proliferates (the connective cartilage between the epiphyses and the metaphyses) and stretches toward the diaphyses. Epiphyses grow from the deepest part of the joint cartilage. Bone growth stops when connective cartilage has become completely calcified.

Morphology of different bones

Short Bone

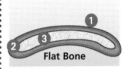

Flat Bone

1. *PERIOST*
2. *COMPACT BONE*
3. *SPONGY BONE*

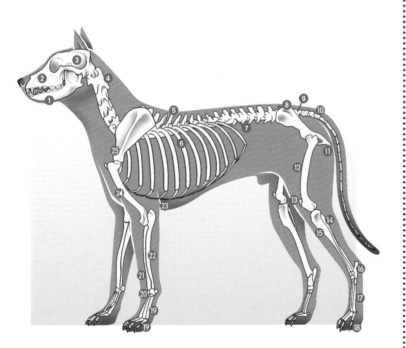

THE SKELETON

1. Mandible
2. Facial bones
3. Cranium
4. Cervical vertebrae
5. Thoracic vertebrae
6. Ribs
7. Lumbar vertebrae
8. Ilium
9. Sacrum
10. Coccygeal vertebrae
11. Ischium
12. Femur
13. Patella
14. Perone (fibula)
15. Tibia
16. Tarsal bone
17. Metatarsal bone
18. Phalanges
19. Metacarpal bones
20. Carpus
21. Radius
22. Cubitus (ulna)
23. Sternum
24. Humerus
25. Scapula.

1. Mandible
2. Premaxilla
3. Nasal bone
4. Maxillary bone
5. Zygomatic bone
6. Frontal bone
7. Os temporale
8. Parietal bone
9. Occipital bone.

SIDE VIEW OF THE SKULL

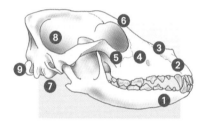

Hind Leg Knee Joint Posterior View

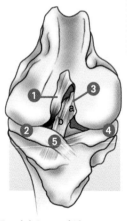

1. Caudal Crossed Ligament
2. Medial Meniscus
3. Cranial Crossed Ligament:
   a) Lateral part.
   b) Medial part
4. Lateral Meniscus
5. Transverse Knee Ligament

More Information about the Skeleton

The skull is made up of 13 flat bones that have been fused since birth. It is directly attached to the spinal column, which is made up of 7 cervical vertebrae, 13 thoracic vertebrae, 7 lumbar vertebrae, 3 sacral vertebrae, and a number of coccygeal vertebrae that varies according to the length of the tail. Each thoracic vertebrae corresponds to a pair of ribs. Ten pairs are attached to the sternum, while 3 other pairs are floating. This entire section forms the rib cage.

The presence of a 7th lumbar vertebrae, which is associated with long vertebrates and sizable intervertebral disks, lengthens the lumbar portion of the spine and therefore makes it more flexible.

In dogs, the foreleg does not have a clavicle (only a vestige), which considerably limits the animal's adduction of this limb. This explains why a dog's forelegs primarily move backward and forward, parallel to the axis of the body. Also not that the radius and the ulna are completely distinct and mobile in relation to each other, which allows for a supine movement of about 10o.

In the hindlegs, the tibia and the fibula are also separate. The femoral head is cylindrical, which allows for greater circumduction than in other species.

Arthrology

The term "joint" is generally used to describe any anatomical formation that joins two bone segments. There are different types of joints. They can be non-synovial, which is the case in synosteosis (fusing of bones in the skull), synarthrosis (attachment by fibrous tissue such as for the radius-ulna or the tibia-fibula), symphysis (attachment by fibrous cartilage tissue such as for the vertebral disks or the pubic bones), or synovial (which is also called diarthrosis).

We are particularly interested in synovial joints, which allow for greater mobility of one segment in relation to the other and which play a large role in movement. The ends of two bones don't actually touch each other. There are several other structures involved: joint cartilage, made up of collagen fibers and proteoglycans, which make up the surface on which joints slide, and synovial fluid , which works as a sort of hydraulic cushion (or shock absorber), which prevents the two bones from striking into each other. This fluid is produced by the synovial membrane surrounding the joint. The cartilage in the joint does not naturally get replenished, though the synovia does.

Joints are also categorized according to the way they are attached:
– The joint capsule which surrounds the synovial membrane.

– The collateral ligaments, and others if they exist, that hold the joint in place.

– Other means such as tendons (flexors and extensors or meniscus, for examples) that help to stabilize the joint.

Synovial joints can also be classified according to movement:

Circumduction, in which there is a bone head is inserted into a corresponding cavity (such as the scapulo-humeral joint, or the shoulder). All ranges of motion are possible and there are no collateral ligaments.

Simple condylar joints (phalanges) or double condylar joints (stifle), which are made up of a solid cylinder and a hollow cylinder and which offer a more specialized type of movement in flexing and extending with a few secondary adduction and abduction movements.

Trochlear joints (elbows), which represent perfect specialization in flexion-extension movements.

Plane joints (tarsal-metatarsal or carpal-metacarpal), which only allow for sliding or shock absorbing movements.

Myology

Any type of movement, whether it is voluntary or involuntary, brings into play a number of muscles. There are several types:

Striated muscles, which are responsible for voluntary movement of the skeleton, eyes, and the tongue;

Smooth muscles, which are responsible for involuntary movement of the organs;

Cardiac muscles, which are similar in structure to striated muscles, but which function like smooth muscles.

We are most interested in the striated skeletal muscles, which are very

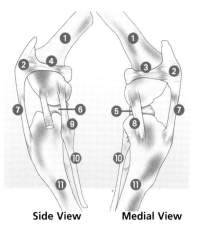

Hind Leg Knee Joint

Side and Medial Views

Side View   **Medial View**

1. femur
2. patella
3. medial femoral-patella ligament
4. lateral femoral-patella ligament
5. medial meniscus
6. lateral meniscus
7. patella ligament
8. medial collateral ligament
9. lateral collateral ligament
10. fibula
11. tibia

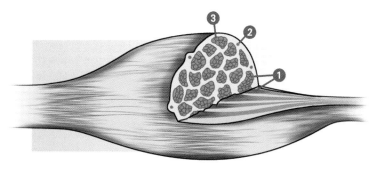

Macroscopic Diagram of a Skeletal Striated Muscle

1. Bundles
2. Blood Vessels
3. Muscle Fibers

desirable in sporting dogs and working dogs. A dog's body has about 400 muscles, which represent 40% to 60% of its total weight. Generally, they are attached to the bones by tendons.

Striated muscles are primarily made up of cells call striated muscle fibers. These fibers are grouped together in bundles that vary in diameter depending on their location (peripheral fibers are the thinnest), on their length (the longer a fiber is, the thicker it will be), and their strength (the stronger the muscle, the thicker the fiber).

Each of these cells has two special zones: a myotendinal juncture, which extends the bundle with collagen fibers, part of which makes up the tendons, and a neuromuscular juncture zone that allows information from the nervous system to be transformed into a muscle contraction.

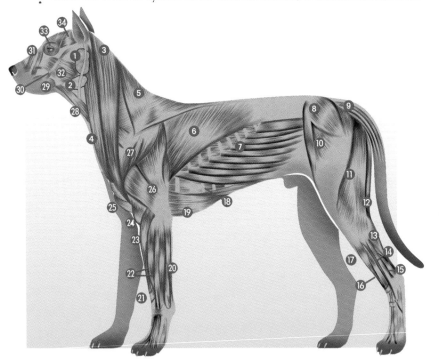

SUPERFICIAL LAYER OF MUSCLES

1. Parotid gland
2. Mandibular salivary gland
3. Brachiocephalic muscle
4. Sternocephalic muscle
5. Trapezius
6. Latissimus dorsii
7. Abdominal muscles (oblique outer muscle of the abdomen)
8. Gluteal muscle
9. Tail muscles
10. Tensor fasciae latae

11. Biceps femoris
12. Semitendinosus
13. Gastrocnemius
14. Flexor digitorum muscles
15. Common calcaneal tendon (Achilles tendon)
16. Extensor digitorum longus
17. Cranial tibial muscle
18. External intercostal muscles
19. Deep pectoral muscle
20. Flexor carpii
21. Extensor carpii radialis
22. Extensor digitorum muscles

23. Extensor carpii
24. Biceps brachii
25. Pectoral muscles
26. Triceps brachii
27. Deltoideus
28. Omohyoideus
29. Orbicularis oris
30. Zygomaticus
31. Levator muscle of upper lip and nose
32. Masseter
33. Orbicularis oculii
34. Temporalis.

During a contraction, the cell shrinks in length by 20% to 50%. To do so, it uses energy brought to it by blood vessels. The muscle is therefore tightly linked to the nervous system and to the cardio-vascular system.

Yet there are different types of muscle fibers used depending on the type of exertion required. Type I or "slow-twitch" fibers are best suited for types of exertion that require endurance. They consume less oxygen and produce fewer lactates. Their substrata are made up of lipids. Type II or "fast-twitch" fibers are used when exertion is very intense, but for a short period of time. Type IIa fiber uses energy from broken-down glucose through aerobic means and comes into play during races. Type IIb fiber refers to fibers that get their energy through anaerobic means and which therefore produce a lot of lactic acid and heat. These fibers are primarily used during short sprints.

Muscles can also be categorized according to their actions:
– Flexors (reduce the angle formed by two connected bones);
– Extensors (increase this angle);
– Abductors (bring a limb closer to the body);
– Adductors (take a limb farther away from the body).

Every muscle has an opposing muscle that "undoes" its action. Flexors are generally on the palm side or sole side of the limb, where as extensors are generally on the dorsal side.

The upper parts of the limbs are mainly made up of muscular masses, but the farther down the limb you go towards the toes, the smaller and lighter the muscles become and the more tendons there are.

Thoracic Topography

THE RESPIRATORY SYSTEM

The nasal cavities are found in the dog's muzzle and forehead and are open to the outside via nostrils. They are made up of sinus cavities and nasal concha (curled bones). A mucus membrane lines the nasal cavities and serves many purposes (warming air and saturated it with water vapor). Nasal glands inside these cavities trap particles from the air by secreting mucus. After air passes through these nasal cavities, it is routed via the posterior apertures of the nose to the rhinopharnyx, which is located in the back of the mouth. At this point, the temperature of the air is approximately the same as that of the animal.

Air then enters the pharnyx, which is made up of four pieces of cartilage (cricoid, thyroid, arytenoid, and epiglottis) and which is attached to the skull by hyoidic bones. The larynx is open as the animal breathes and closed when it swallows so that food does not enter the trachea. The larynx also contains the vocal cords, which vibrate as air passes over them and generate sounds such as growling or barking.

To reach the lungs, air circulates in the trachea, which is made up of about 40 cartilage rings held by the tracheal muscle. This muscle allows the diameter of the trachea to be varied to control the flow of air or to avoid excessive dilatation. It is possible to palpate this rings at the lower third of the neck.

Finally, inside the rib cage, the trachea separates into two bronchial tubes, which each separate into secondary bronchial tubes and then into bronchioles which carry the air to the pulmonary alveoli and collectively form the lungs. Here is where the gaseous exchange takes place thanks to the heavy vascularization of the lungs.

Dogs' lungs are separated from a flail chest by pleura that maintain a pleural cavity, ensuring a minimum amount of air after forced exhalation. They are bordered by the rib cage and the diaphragm. The left lung contains two lobes (cranial and caudal), and the right lung contains four lobes (cranial, median, accessory, and caudal). The line of projection can be traced on the thoracic region: It starts at the top of the 12th rib goes through half of the 9th rib and stops at the 7th chondro-costal joint.

THE CARDIO-VASCULAR SYSTEM

The heart is fairly round in the dog. It is located slightly to the left of the central axis and its primary axis forms an angle of about 40o with the axis of the sternum. Its weight and dimension greatly vary among breeds and may also vary within a given breed depending on the animal's physical activity. As a general rule, a dog that weighs 15 kg will have an average cardiac mass of 150 grams. In carnivores, the heart is generally surrounded in soft, yellow fat.

The heart's projection zone goes from the 3rd rib to the 6th rib. Its base, where the large vessels are attached, is located about halfway up the thoracic region at the 3rd rib, and its top is placed against the sternum at the 6th space between the ribs.

The heart is divided into four cavities. The right atrium receives oxygen-poor blood from the vena cava (cranial and caudal), sends it to the right ventricle which sends it to the lungs via the pulmonary arteries.

THE HEART

1. Third rib
2. Sixth rib
3. Aortic orifice
4. Pulmonary orifice
5. Left atrioventricular orifice (mitral valve)
6. Apex of heart
7. Elbow
8. Tricuspid valve
9. Aortic orifice
10. Third rib.

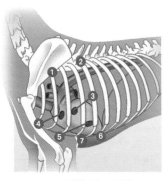

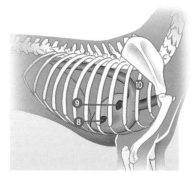

I. Side View, Right   *II. Side View, Left*

Once the gaseous exchange has taken place, the oxygen-rich blood returns to the heart via the pulmonary veins which end in the left atrium. The blood is then sent to the left ventricle and into the aorta that ultimately distributes the blood to all of the organs.

Abdominal Topography

THE DIGESTIVE SYSTEM

This system starts with the mouth, where food is ingested, then continues through the esophagus, where muscular contractions push the alimentary bolus into the stomach. The stomach is located to the left of the dog's center line, behind the flail chest. It is fairly large because of the animal's meaty diet and the fact that it can be distended affects the topography of the other organs. During a large meal, a dog's stomach can distend to the 5th lumbar vertebra. Dogs do not have a highly developed system for chewing, so the main mechanical and chemical digestive processes occur in the stomach.

The digested materials are then sent by the pylorus to the duodenum, the first part of the small intestines. The stomach empties rather slowly and the process is controlled by the sequential opening of the pylorus and by the first part of the duodenum. The materials then continue to the jejunum, which is very long in carnivores, then to the ileum, which leads to the coecum (located under the 2nd lumbar vertebra). Then begin the large intestines and the colon, where water is absorbed and fecal matter is formed. Finally, the rectum and the anal canal are located in the pelvic cavity and which serve to store fecal matter.

Other organs are involved in the digestion of food, such as the pancreas and the liver. The pancreas is a long V-shaped gland, the right side of which lies beside the part of the duodenum that is on the right in the abdomen. It produces and disperses digestive enzymes into the pancreatic canal only during meals and also has an endocrine function (insulin, glucogon). The liver, located just behind the diaphragm and a bit to the right, is a multi-lobed organ (6 lobes in all) and has many functions. This is where the gall bladder is located near the 8th intercostal space. This organ stores secretions of hepatic cells throughout the day and releases them during meals.

THE URINARY SYSTEM

The urinary system is made up of two kidneys. The left kidney is located under the first three lumbar vertebrae and is said to be floating because it is indeed suspended in the abdominal cavity (its topography changes in relation to stomach volume). The right kidney is stationary and located under the last thoracic vertebra and the first two lumbar vertebrae. Each kidney has a ureter which goes to the dorsal side of the bladder, which itself if located just in front of the pelvis. The urine stored in the bladder is then sent out through the urethra, which is longer and more narrow in males.

THE REPRODUCTIVE SYSTEM

In males, the genitals are external, except for the prostate, which is located just inside the pelvic girdle in young dogs and farther into the abdomen as the animal gets older. Female genitalia is largely intra-abdominal. The ovaries, located in the ovarian sac are located 2-3 centimeters from the kidneys, which means that the left ovary is farther back than the right ovary and also a bit more mobile. From the ovaries are the uterine horns where gestation will eventually take place, and which lead to the uterus, which is small for this species. The uterus leads to the vagina, which is located in the pelvic cavity.

GENERAL STRUCTURE OF THE DIGESTIVE TRACT

1. Anus
2. Rectum
3. Descending colon
4. Stomach
5. Liver
6. Cardia
7. Esophagus
8. Mandibular salivary gland
9. Parotid gland
10. Molars
11. Canine teeth
12. Tongue
13. Trachea
14. Diaphragm
15. Pylorus
16. Small intestine
17. Duodenum.

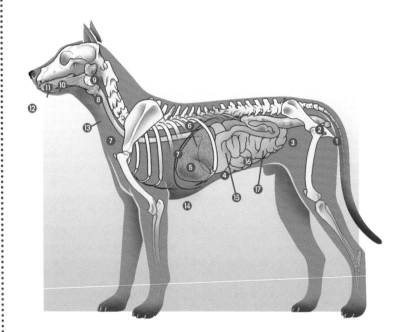

THE SPLEEN

The spleen is part of the dog's defense system. It is located to the left and behind the stomach under the last two intercostal spaces. It is "sock-shaped" and fairly vertical in position. When an animal has eaten a lot, the spleen moves toward the back to accommodate the distended stomach, enters the flank cavity, and is virtually horizontal.

These basic anatomical elements will help the reader to understand the chapters devoted to physiological and pathological information.

BIOMECHANICS

If you are interested in Sporting dogs or Working dogs, you are interested in the way dogs move. The following information on biomechanics will help readers better understand the forces at work and therefore better prepare their dogs to avoid certain pathological affections.

Definitions

Biomechanics deals with the forces and accelerations acting on living organisms in much the same way as physical mechanics deals with the forces to which inanimate bodies are subjected. The field of biomechanics is divided into:

– **Biostatics**, which deals with forces and their equilibrium as they act on an animal at rest or moving in a uniform fashion, in a straight line.
– **Biodynamics**, which studies the changes in movement that are caused by an unstable system of forces and the forces that are necessary for all changes in movement.
The study of biomechanics allows us to understand the basis of numerous ailments of the motor system as well as their treatments.

A **force**, defined by its intensity (expressed in Newtons, "N"), its point of application, and its direction, refers to any cause that produces a change in the state of rest or in the uniform movement of a body. It is represented by a vector.

A body is in **equilibrium** if the forces applied to it are in equilibrium. For this to happen, each force must have a corresponding force of the same intensity, but in the opposite direction. The term "reaction" is often used to refer to this resistance, for example, the reaction of the ground to the dog's feet.
When several forces are applied to a single body, it is possible to add them to find the resulting force R. We often use the components F1 and F2 of a force R, rather than the force itself. In this case, we have chosen the two perpendicular forces. The same principle may be applied to a system of n forces.

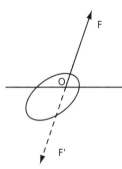

A force acting on a point O of a body, balanced by F', of the same intensity, but in the opposite direction

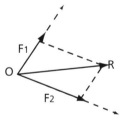

R is the result of F1 and F2
R = F1 + F2

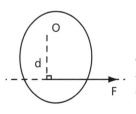

The moment of force F on the point O is equal to F x d

The **momentum** of a force F is its tendency to cause the body to which it is applied to turn around an axis. The momentum (express in kg) is the product of the intensity of the force multiplied by the length of a perpendicular line to the line of action of the force, extending to the axis of rotation.

The direction of rotation is expressed as clockwise or counterclockwise. The resulting momentum is the sum of the momenta around the body's axis, which is in equilibrium if the resulting momentum is zero.

Notes: properties of the result R of two parallel forces F1 and F2.

- R is equal to F1 + F2 if they have the same direction and R is equal to F1 – F2 if they are in opposite directions.

- R is parallel to the two forces and acts closer to the stronger force, between F1 and F2 if they are in the same direction and outside of them if they are in opposite directions.

- The perpendicular distances from the resulting forces given are inversely proportional to the intensity of these forces: F1 = b

$\qquad\qquad$ F2 $\quad$ a

- The parallel forces in opposite directions cannot be replaced by a single result. This is a couple system.

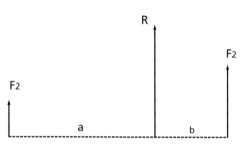

R, resulting from two parallel forces, F1 and F2, is equal to F1 + F2 and F1 x a = F2 x b

Application to Muscles

These basic principles may be applied to the action of muscles in the body. Let us first analyze the force exerted by a single muscle with parallel fibers on a hinge-shaped joint. To obtain equilibrium, the result R of the muscular force F and of the weight W passes through the joint's center of rotation.

The intensity of the muscular force F is a function of the area D of the transverse section of the muscle at rest, perpendicularly to the fibers, and of the contractility f. Therefore, F = f x d.

Muscles also develop pressure and tension forces on bones. If a muscle develops, through a tendon, a force F on a bone with an angle _, we can break down F into a normal force N, acting the length of the bone's surface, and a shearing force H, perpendicular to the bone shaft.

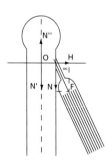

A muscle exerts a force F on the shaft of a long bone, through the intermediary of a tendon.

The bone is therefore submitted to the action of tension from the forces and reacts with a force called pressure. The bone also supports a tendency to rotation Mb, which results in the NN couple, at the N u momentum.

This situation is relatively common in the construction of the motor system since permanent tensions of various intensities exist. The construction of the motor system is such that the forces of tension are as close to the central axes of the bones as possible and the tensions are spread out over areas that are as large as possible.

The action of the muscles on the reduction of loads to which a joint is submitted can be shown through mechanical calculations. Let us take the model of a pelvic limb, constructed like a column without a joint and supporting a given load. We can then calculate the maximal pressure and momentum of rotation exerted on the model.

We add hip and knee joints to the model, as well as two muscles: a hip flexor (and knee extensor) and a hip extensor. For the knee to be in equilibrium, the sum of the momenta of force around its rotation center must be zero. The calculation of the forces shows that the muscles, besides controlling movements, reduce the intensity of the pressures.

The momenta of rotation and pressure in the bone are influenced by the number of muscles going through a given joint. Let us examine a model of an elbow joint, balanced by the action N of a single muscle, the weight W of the forearm, and the reaction S to the elbow joint. The forearm is divided into 10 equal sections and we note a peak in the momenta of rotation for section 3. When a second muscle acts on the forearm, the momenta of rotation for the 10 above-mentioned segments are reduced and we note two peaks in sections 3 and 6, less sharp, however, than in the previous case. The incidence of two muscles acting on a single joint reduces the tendency toward rotation of the bones to which they are attached.

The insertion of a fan-shaped muscle greatly tempers these momenta of rotation. Moreover, biostatical analysis of the skeleton reveals that most of the long bones are only slightly submitted to rotation thanks to their hollow structure, which allows the pressures to be spread out more homogeneously.

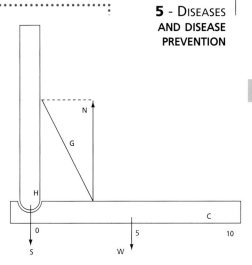

Balance of the joint H of the elbow. The force N is exerted by the muscle T1 and is balanced by S (reaction of the elbow) and W(weight of the forearm).

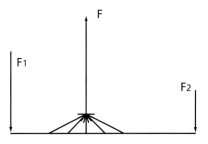

Fan insertion of a muscle, exerting a force F on a long bone, balanced by F1 and F2

Application to the Joints

The forces exerted by the weight and force of a muscle are transmitted from one bone to another through the intermediary of contact surfaces in the joints. These are covered in joint cartilage and are lubricated with synovial fluid.

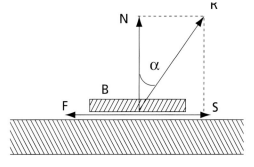

The body B exerts a force F on the body C, countered by the force of friction S. N is the normal reaction of B on C. R is the result of S and N.

Stabilization of the joint between the bone elements B and C:

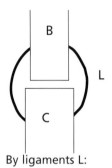

By ligaments L:

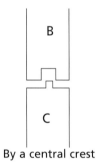

By a central crest

When a force F is applied perpendicularly to a surface, only a vertical reaction N is brought into play by the material. When this force is applied with an angle _, it translates into two components: a vertical component and a horizontal component H, called the shearing component. The reaction of the material to H is the force S, a frictional force. The intensity of S depends on the coefficient of friction, F, which is very small in the joints. The angle _ limit is 1 degree. If _ is greater, the sliding of the joint surfaces in relation to one another is such that certain surrounding tissues may be broken. We therefore note the importance of peri-articular structures such as the joint capsule, collateral ligaments, or bony joint reliefs.

A knowledge of the distribution of pressure on joint structures helps in understanding functional disorders of the joint cartilage.

Application to the Body and to the Limbs

The body's axis for vertebrates is made up of various kinds of tissue (bone, cartilage, conjunctive tissue). It must not only support the weight of the body, but also transmit the locomotive power of its hindlegs. This axis can be represented by an arc and a string. The body's axis is made up of a series of rigid elements—the vertebrae—that are linked to the intervertebral disks and form an arc that can be curved in various ways. This curve may be momentarily stabilized by three muscular "strings" whose tension can vary. We distinguish the "dorsal string," which is made of muscles covering the sides and back of the arc and which serve to straighten it, from the "ventral string," which is made up of two levels: the interrupted string," which joins the skull and the front side of the cervical and thoracic vertebrae, as well as the lumbar vertebrae to the pelvis. The "interrupted string" joins the thoracic skeleton to the pelvis. This ventral string generally serves to bend the arc.

The action of these muscle groups is important during locomotion, especially in running (alternately flexing and extending the back).

The body

The trunk is balanced on a static plane. When a quadruped is at rest, its spinal column is maintained in an unstable equilibrium by the intrinsic elasticity of he intervertebral disks and ligaments. Only zero or very

Structure of the arc and cord:
The arc is formed by the spinal column,
its ligaments and muscles (1).
The cord is made up of an interrupted level
(2 and 3) and a non-interrupted level (4).
The forces of gravity (W, w) and propulsion (F)
are transmitted to the support points.

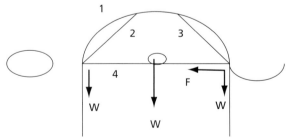

slight muscular activity can maintain this posture. A minimal muscular contraction can produce a force that exceeds the elasticity and breaks the equilibrium to produce a flexion or extension of the arc. The muscular forces can produce several types of distortion. Flexing or extending the back, bending it to the left or to the right, a torsion the length of the longitudinal horizontal axis, a vertical or horizontal shearing, a longitudinal tension or compression. These forces of distortion are countered by ligaments and controlled by muscles.

Legs act like slanted pillars. The tension of the abdominal muscles is increased when the legs extend toward the back of the body. Moreover, there is a relationship between the reaction R to the legs, made up of the normal reaction N and the friction S, and the tension imposed upon the dorsal musculature.

We call F the result of R and weight W. Depending on the amplitude of S, F may pass above, through, or under the spinal column. If there is a lot of friction, F, will pass above the spinal column and tends to extend it. If S is very high, F will pass under the spinal column and tend to flex the back. If F passes through the spinal column, its momentum is zero and there is no effect on the curve of the back.

The distribution of the load (the way the weight is spread out) on the forelegs and hindlegs is relative to the location of the dog's center of gravity, which is easily determined.

The animal is represented by a rectangle ABCD, the four angles of which correspond to the points of contact between the limbs and the ground, and E is the point of intersection of the diagonals in the rectangle. If the center of gravity w is in the triangle ABE, the animal can only lift a hindleg, since w will always be in the triangle ABC or ABD. If w is located in the triangle CDE, the dog can only raise one of its two forelegs.

Two situations exist in regard to the static function of the limbs:
– The limbs act as vertical columns, such that the point of support of the leg is vertical to the point of application of the weight on the shoulder or hip;
– The members act like slanted pillars, the two previous points cited forming a straight line that leans in relation to the vertical line.

In both cases, the limb joints are a certain distance from the line of action W, such that the weight has a momentum in relation to these

Relationship between the friction S of the foot and the balance of the intervertebral joint L. W is the weight, R1, R2, and R3 are the results of F1, F2, F3, and W. R1 tends to extend the spinal column. R3 tends to flex the back. R2 has no momentum and does not act on the spinal column.

Position of the center of gravity W.
The dog can only lift C or D.
The dog can only life A or B.

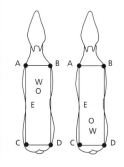

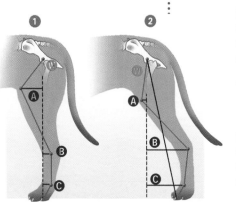

Fig. 1: the member acts like a vertical pillar.
Fig. 2: the member acts like a slanted pillar. The momenta W on the joints of the member depend on A, B, and C.

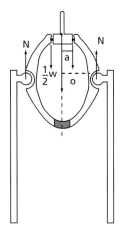

Pressures exerted on the pelvic symphysis, cross cut.
In this case, the distance separating the hips is greater than the distance between the sacro-iliac joints. The symphysis is therefore submitted to a force of tension.

joints, and the farther they are from the line of action of the weight, the greater they will be. The stabilization of the joints therefore implies the action of the limb's muscles, which must exert an equal but opposite momentum.

The shoulder

The shoulder is inserted into the chest with muscles, since the clavicle is absent or only rudimentary. This structure is only capable of supporting the forces of tension exerted by the muscles between the thorax and the scapula and serves to counter the rotation of the scapula.

The reaction of the weight is produced by the serratus anterior muscle of the chest.

The pelvis

The connection between the pelvis and the axis of the body is established by the sacroiliac joint. Nonetheless, it is difficult to determine the proportions of which the stability of the joint is affected by the action of the surrounding ligaments and muscles. In quadruped mammals, the hip joint is caudal-ventral to the sacroiliac joint. The reaction N to the hip joint has a momentum in relation to the sacroiliac joint that serves to turn it clockwise. This rotation can be prevented by contracting the abdominal muscles. Another rotation can occur: The sacrum can turn around the sacroiliac joint. This is prevented by the tension of the ligaments linking the sacrum to the caudal vertebrae and to the edge of the ischium. The stabilizing effect of the muscles and ligaments surrounding the sacroiliac joint decreases or even eliminates the joint's force of torsion.

The pelvis shows interesting static implications in the transversal plane. The bones of the pelvis form two half that are more or less curved, attached dorsally to the sacrum and ventrally joining on the pelvic symphysis. The positions of the sacroiliac and hip joints determine the direction and intensity of the pressure in the symphysis, all depending on the width of the sacrum. If the distance between the hips is greater than that between the sacroiliac joints, the symphysis is submitted to a force of tension. When these two joints are vertical in relation to one another, no force is exerted on the symphysis.

The most favorable position of the ilium in relation to the spinal column depends on the animal's position. In an animal standing at rest, the most favorable position is the one such that the sacroiliac angle equals 90o. That way, the momentum of the force of the rotation of the femur in relation to the sacroiliac joint is zero. When the dog is walking, the momentum of the force of propulsion in relation to the sacroiliac joint is zero when the spinal column and the ilium are aligned. The biostatic and biomechanical requirements are apparently opposite. Nonetheless, the obstetrical requirements must be taken into account: the sacroiliac angle is a measure of the real diameter of the pelvis, through which the young pass during birth. Therefore, in the dog, we find a sacroiliac angle that is between 15o and 40o, constituting a compromise between these various requirements.

Other joints

The biomechanics of the carpals and tarsals are interesting in the adaptation of postures and specific progression. The respective positions of the different bone parts in the hand and foot are maintained by a dorsal extensor system and a plantar flexor, which is aided by a deep layer of muscles and ligaments (plantar aponeurosis). The problem that arises is that of balancing several joints consecutively, the interphalangian joints and the metatarsal or metacarpal joints. In a static state, or while walking, the plantar side supports a greater load than the dorsal side. The presence of plantar calluses—pads—further establishes that this side is more apt to support heavier weights than the dorsal side. The momenta of the forces of flexion are therefore greater than those of extension and, as a result, the group of flexors is better developed than the group of extensors.

Nevertheless, in a medio-lateral direction, the degree of curving is very slight. This is why a slight deviation of the direction of the load, translated by the appearance of a shearing force, will be countered by a medial bony crest, or by strong peri-articular structures.

The dog is moving

In the standing dog, the horizontal motor force is zero. If a horizontal force exists, for whatever reason, a resulting horizontal force toward the head, the animal begins to move. The leg muscles contribute to the forward propulsion. The retraction and protraction (backward and forward movements) of the limbs are principally cause by muscles outside of the limb, but also by the action of the limb's intrinsic muscles, which by the changes in angles in the different joints, contribute to the double capacity of the limbs to act as support and lever.

An animal that is not moving cannot accelerate without disturbing the equilibrium of the vertical forces. To start, part of the body weight is transferred from the forelegs to the hindlegs, implying that the decrease in weight supported by the thoracic members in turn decreases their propulsive power. Therefore, a dog that is trying to rapidly accelerate using its forelegs runs the risk of slipping on the ground.

The dynamic principles governing the propulsive forces exerted by the limbs are primarily the same and static principles. One limb can act as a pillar or a lever. If the axis of the limb is retracted (under the body), the limb can act as a propulsive pillar. If the axis of the limb is stretched toward the front, the limb then acts as a brake. During a cycle of motion, the limb is alternatively protracted and retracted.

For the dog to conserve energy while moving, the coordination of the effort of these limbs must be such that the result of all of the propulsive forces acts on the body's center of gravity. That way, the momentum of the propulsive forces in relation to the center of gravity is zero and the body is not submitted to any tendency toward rotation.

The total propulsive power of a limb is the sum of its actions as pillar and lever. It is made up of a vertical component, exerted by the limb onto the body, and a horizontal component that exerts propulsive force. When the limb acts as a propulsive lever, the push of the retractors serves to flex the back, especially in the lumbar-sacral region. A similar flexion occurs in the thoracic region, if the thoracic limbs act as brakes.

In a complete motion cycle, the thoracic limb acts as a brake, while the pelvic limb pushes the body forward.

Despite the great diversity in the contour of movements, there are relatively few basic principles. They are based on Newton's three laws of motion:

– The first law says that a body at rest or in uniform motion in a straight line stays at rest or in uniform motion in a straight line unless

acted upon by forces (gravity, air resistance, etc.)

– The second law states that the change in momentum by units of time is proportional to the force applied and takes place in the direction of this force. When a dog exerts a propulsive force F, its speed is proportional to the amplitude of the force and to the time T during which it acts and inversely proportional to the mass M of the body:

$$V = \frac{F \times T}{M}$$

The acceleration (at each second) is $\frac{F}{M}$

– The third law says that the forces always act in pairs and that each pair is made up of two equal but opposite forces. For every action there is a reaction. When a dog submits its body to a forward propulsive force, the ground exerts an equal but opposite force, in the opposite direction. In other words, the animal advances because the ground resists the movement of the limbs in relation to the body.

The study of biomechanics, which can be done through cinematographic analysis of the movements of bone segments in relation to one another, allows us to better understand the appearance of ailments in the motor system and to better prevent them and treat them.

Gastro-enterological Ailments Related to Physical Exertion

Digestive tract ailments are generally not extremely serious in nature, but do nonetheless account for the second most frequent type of malady in the area of pathological problems specific to sporting and working dogs, after traumatic injuries. These specific digestive problems, though indeed quite frequent, are only partially understood. Some are directly related to physiological stress caused by exertion, whereas others result from a combination of poor nutrition and the development of pathogenic agents that would ordinarily be harmless.

Physiopathology of Digestive Ailments Related to Physical Exercise

Since we are only dealing with those ailments that have been specifically brought on by physical exertion, it is important to pinpoint the different factors that precede their appearance in order to better understand the ailments themselves.

Impact from the Stress of Exertion

Regardless of whether a physical exertion is correctly performed or not, it is a stress on the organism that can affect the functioning of the digestive tract in a number of ways, be it secretory (changes in digestive secretions) or motor (changes in the passage of food through the digestive tract). The dog's digestive capabilities and its ability to fight off disease will be changed. Physiological digestive changes linked to the stress of exertion will also affect the stomach and the intestines. Overall, the following changes may occur:

– Emptying the stomach more quickly or more slowly after a meal (it varies according to the individual dog);
  – Loss of motivity in the pyloric antrum
  – Narrowing of the passage of food into the small intestine;
  – Enlarging of the passage of residue in the large intestine;
  – Decreased absorption of electrolytes;
  – Increased permeability of the mucus membrane in the intestines, which "opens the door" to large molecules that can cause an inflammation of this membrane;

– Drop in splanchnic blood flow;

– Finally, we can observe an increase of digestive secretions that brings about a change in the protective physical properties of intestinal mucus.

ROLE OF FOOD

The overall acceleration of the digestive tract caused by the stress of exertion must be taken into account in a dog's diet so that the nature of foods in the diet as well as the way in which those foods are distributed maximize the energy consumed and more importantly do not cause further digestive problems.

It is most important to try to use the diet to maximize the amount of gastric time for the alimentary bolus. If the bolus is too short, the physiological pre-digestion of the proteins in the food is incomplete, which will become a source of diarrhea. The undigested proteins will "ferment" in the large intestine and generate a large intake of water. On the other hand, food that remains in the stomach for too long will provoke vomiting or perhaps even dilatation-torsion of the stomach upon resumption of exertion.

Though little information is available on the subject, experience has shown that the type of food and the way in which it is distributed play a major role in this area. The best results seem to come from using complete dry foods that are rehydrated by simply covering the dry pellets with lukewarm water for thirty minutes before serving. We look for some pellets sticking up from the liquid to maintain their consistency without getting soggy in the "soup" because a meal that is too liquid may "flush" the stomach and release undigested proteins into the intestine which would in turn cause osmotic diarrhea.

It is also important to choose foods that are easily digested. Since the passage through the digestive tract has been accelerated by exertion, this decreases the amount of time the digestive enzymes have to perform their jobs. It is therefore essential to choose dry foods that are very easily digested ("premium" or "super-premium" lines, though these terms do not generally refer to the nutritional value). Do not hesitate to ask the manufacturer of the dog food for the results of digestibility tests carried out in its research center.

So far as the nutritional content of the diet goes, starches can only cause problems for sled dogs or certain breeds of working dogs with upright ears. These animals are frequently deficient in pancreatic amylase (the enzyme in pancreatic juices that ensures the breakdown of starches), which therefore makes it extremely important that the starches come from plants and that the food has been cooked for the appropriate length of time. Food should be as easily digested as possible or the animal will develop diarrhea.

In general, dogs are physiologically capable of consuming large amounts of protein, especially animal proteins. Gastro-intestinal problems linked to dietary protein are therefore rare for "ordinary" dogs.

Nonetheless, sporting dogs and working dogs cannot tolerate poor quality proteins that can sometimes be found in cheap dog food (scleroprotein from feathers, collagen from tendons, proteins from poorly cooked eggs, etc.). Such foods will result in diarrhea and their use should be immediately discontinued. Lipids (fats) are the best energy source for working dogs. They are very filling, easily digested, and well tolerated, provided that they are not rancid, which would irritate the digestive tract and cause oxydating membrane stress phenomenon.

Therefore, the energy consumed by the dog must be easily and rapidly assimilated by its organism during exercise. It is essential to use complete dry foods that are easily digested and concentrated (so a smaller amount of food is necessary), and which generate small amounts of excrement. Simply put, the amount of excrement generated by a high-quality food should vary between 40 and 50 grams for every 100 grams of dry food ingested.

IMPACT OF ENTERIC ISCHEMIA

During long and intense exercise, the blood is sent to the muscles that are working and that need a continuous heavy oxygen supply carried in red blood cells, which causes blood circulation for digestive purposes to drop by almost 80%. The lesser supply of oxygen and nutrients results in damage to the mucus membrane of the digestive tract, a slighter renewal of the protective mucus in the intestinal lumen, and a decrease in the re-absorption of water in the end of the large intestine, which causes osmotic diarrhea. This change in the defense systems of the intestinal wall weakens the whole intestines and makes them much more vulnerable. Prolonged mesenteric ischemia can cause the intestinal cells to become necrotic and blood vessels to erode, which can lead to blood in post-exertion stress diarrhea.

OTHER FACTORS INVOLVED

Hormonal factors play a major role in the mobilization and use of different energetic substrata by muscle cells. They can also be a factor in causing diarrhea. Levels of endorphines, catecholamines, gastrin, and motilin increase during exercise and contribute to changes in the motivity of the stomach and the intestines.

The "cecal slap syndrome," caused by repeated micro-trauma to the mucus membrane in the intestines when excrements strike it during their passage, is responsible for numerous micro-hemorrhages in the large intestine and in turn for bloody diarrhea. An excess of iron-rich mineral salts in the diet aggravates this process (the tiny particles are very sharp), which leads us to prefer foods with nutritional trace elements in the form of chelates (the iron is bound to an organic molecule).

– Runner's trot is linked to a series of involuntary muscle spasms of the colon wall. In humans, these spasms cause abdominal cramps and pains as

Any form of stress can cause diarrhea in dogs.

well as diarrhea that is heavy in mucus and blood. The same symptoms apply to dogs.

– The drop in intestinal blood flow can also provoke ischemic colitis (inflammation of the colon).

– Finally, the stress of exertion is responsible for dehydrating extracellular areas, which slightly weakens the affected cells.

These partial physiopathological explanations can help us better understand gastroenterological ailments linked to physical exercise in dogs and therefore help us better prevent and treat such ailments.

Gastric Ulcers

A gastric ulcer is a lesion on the mucus membrane of the stomach that is visible to the naked eye. Such ulcers rarely occur in dogs, but when they do, there may be several ulcers at once, appearing as a loss of surface tissue on the membrane or as large "holes" that reach the gastric muscles. There are several possible etiologies (causes) for such conditions, but the most common source of ulcers in sporting dogs is too much stress (overtraining) or too great a use of certain drugs (non-steroid anti-inflammatories such as aspirin, flunixin, phenylbutazone, indomethacin, or naproxen). The most frequent symptom is bloody vomit, but certain cases may be quite severe and lead to a rupture of the stomach and sudden death for the animal. Owners or competitors should immediately take a dog with bloody vomit to the veterinarian so he may begin appropriate treatment (antacids, anticholinergics, and gastric dressings). Clearly, prevention is the best medicine for gastric ulcers. The best way to prevent the problem is to avoid using anti-inflammatory drugs on a daily basis, carefully devise all elements of the dog's life that could be a source of cumulative stress (housing, environment, transportation, heat, training).

Stomach Torsion

Owners of working dogs are haunted by the risk of stomach torsion for their animals because it is an all-too-frequent problem for such breeds. It a real emergency and requires immediate attention. Stomach dilatation torsion syndrome tends primarily to affect large breeds, though there is little statistical evidence on the subject. The affection is characterized by a swelling of the abdomen, vomiting, or rather "attempts" at vomiting that are more or less unproductive, and a rapid drop in the animal's overall health. The dog will then go into shock and die if serious surgical intervention is not undertaken immediately. We have not deemed it useful to go into further detail on this subject at this time since it is a well-known problem for dog owners and there is already a great deal of literature for them to consult. Let us simply stress that there are a few basic rules to follow in order to prevent stomach torsion from occurring or from recurring:

– Feed voraciously hungry dogs separately in a calm setting.
– Break up a dog's daily food intake into at least two meals.
– Choose concentrated food that is extremely easily digested so that the amount ingested is as small as possible.
– Re-hydrate the food before distributing.
– Allow the dog to rest for one or two hours after eating.

Stress-related Diarrhea

Stress-related dehydration and diarrhea are particularly common problems for sled dogs, but can affect all sporting dogs and working dogs. For the same reasons given earlier, stress from exertion can cause diarrhea, which can rapidly cause the dog to become dehydrated. The problem will then only get worse as a vicious cycle takes hold of the animal's health. It will likely experience a loss of appetite and stop eating and drinking, which will of course exacerbate the dehydration). The animal will vomit and lose more and more blood in its diarrhea…

This is a well-known problem for long-distance sled dogs, but the number of occurrences has dropped over the years thanks to nutritional progress and to a better understanding of the physiological changes brought about by exertion.

When faced with this type of acute diarrhea in training or competition, treatment is a combination of a commonly-used anti-spasmodic drug (loperamide or diphenoxylate) and a remarkably effective substance called smectite which is used to protect the mucus membranes in the intestines. Antibiotics should be avoided and only considered if the initial treatment is ineffective after 48 hours.

Acute stress-related diarrhea may be prevented through a balanced diet, sensible distribution of meals, and an awareness and concern for the dog's overall environment.

NUTRITIONAL PREVENTION

Generally, if the owner of a working dog or sporting dog bases the animal's diet on the previous texts, he will opt for a complete dry food that is adapted to the type of exertion required of the animal. The food will be concentrated, offering maximum energy for minimum quantity, and will be easily digested.

We also know that another consequence of stress from exertion must be taken into account: membrane oxidative stress. The peroxides and free radicals generated by this type of stress destroy digestive cells and must be combated with a diet that is rich in antioxidants (of which vitamin E is probably the best known).

Certain lipids are also important. Essential polyunsaturated fatty acids from the "Omega 3" series are mainly found in fish oils, and have a direct

Stress-related
diarrhea
in sled dog.

anti-inflammatory effect on the mucus membrane in the intestines, which helps prevent diarrhea.

Finally, recent studies have shown that it is possible to prevent pathogenic bacteria from developing in the digestive tract with:

Fructo-oligosaccharides (FOS), natural glucides found in the pulp of beets, psyllium, etc… are particularly rich in fermentable fibers. This fermentation takes place in the colon, freeing up fatty acids in short chains (acetate, proprionate, butyrate) that slightly acidify the area and create unfavorable conditions for pathogenic bacteria to multiply and survive. At the same time, they have numerous beneficial effects on the mucus membrane of the intestines. These glucides are also referred to as "prebiotics."

Probiotics, a purified group of micro-organisms primarily made up of lactic bacteria that attach to food and prevent the development of pathogenic micro-organisms while stimulating the dog's local immune system. The bacilla cannot colonize the digestive tract and must be added to the dog's daily food rations.

Prevention through Environmental Conditions

As soon as a dog suffers from episodes of acute stress-related diarrhea from physical exercise, everything must be done to reduce the sources of psychological and physical stress in its environment as much as possible. Since there is a chapter devoted to this subject in this book, we shall only mention the possible influence of practical ways to ration the animal's food at this point. Other than the choice of food, which is indeed essential, the amounts distributed must be carefully adapted to maintain the weight and shape of the dog. They must therefore evolve to accommodate times of rest, training, competition, and untraining.

The time meals are distributed is important to consider: Dry "high-end" foods now take less time to pass through the digestive tract (about 12-14 hours will pass between the meal and the fecal elimination of the meal). For example, a dog that starts working at 8:00 in the morning will still have its large intestine full of feces if it was fed at 8:00 the evening before. This will undoubtedly cause stress-related diarrhea for the animal, which is why it is always preferable for dogs with regular working hours to be fed their primary meal as soon after the exertion as possible so that they can "empty their intestines" before beginning work again the following morning. So, forget the old wives' tale that dogs shouldn't be fed for hours after exercise!

Clearly there is a close connection between gastro-enterological ailments and exercise and work for dogs. It is quite similar to the one for human athletes—just ask a marathon runner or tri-athlete!

SPECIFIC DENTAL AILMENTS

Defense dogs sometimes have dental problems, most often in the form of fractures of one or more teeth, caused specifically by this type of activity.

Basic Dental Anatomy

Dogs have different types of teeth, which are specialized for different functions:
- Twelve incisors for cutting, gnawing, and performing delicate work
- Four canines for grabbing, holding, and tearing
- Sixteen premolars for holding, cutting, and tearing
- Ten molars for cutting and grinding

The number of teeth varies from breed to breed, but shepherd dogs, which make up the majority of defense dogs, have 42 teeth as adults.

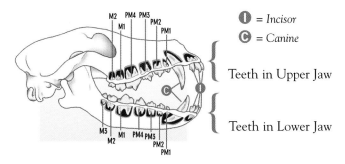

Ⓘ = *Incisor*

Ⓒ = *Canine*

Teeth in Upper Jaw

Teeth in Lower Jaw

Canine Dentition, Side View
(with the roots of the teeth exposed)

The canines are very big and special teeth:

– Given their length and their position very near the front of the mouth, they are predisposed to trauma

– The great length of the crown (the visible part of the tooth) acts like a long lever on canine teeth and can weaken them over time.

A tooth is made up of three parts (from the inside to the outside):

– The pulp cavity which contains the pulp,
– Dentinum continuously produced by the pulp
– Enamel (which stops being produced once the tooth erupts)

Length-wise cut of a tooth

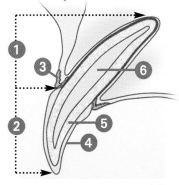

1. Root	4. Enamel
2. Crown	5. Dentin
3. Gum	6. Pulp cavity

The formation of canine teeth is evolving toward a smaller pulp cavity and an increase in dentinum. Canine teeth are therefore getting stronger and stronger.

Biomechanics of Biting

The constraints undergone by a Working dog's jaws have been studied during traction exerted by the dog onto a constraint gauge. The traction forces exerted on the four canine teeth vary from 1,000 to 1,120 newtons, depending on the direction of the traction. These studies were carried out on a dog holding a rubber stick in his mouth that was attached to a constraint gauge.

Under real conditions, when a dog bites it does not necessary catch the jacket or sleeve with its whole mouth. The entirety of these forces is therefore spread out over three teeth, two teeth—or perhaps just a single tooth. In this case, the teeth can no longer support the traction and break.

Symptoms

A tooth fracture can be one of several types:
– A fracture of the enamel and dentinum of the crown
– A fracture of the enamel, dentinum, and pulp cavity of the crown
– A fracture that reaches the root

When a tooth fracture reaches the pulp cavity, it always causes intense pain and bleeding, due to the rupture of the pulp. Even if the symptoms are sometimes unclear, septic complications linked to the pulp's contact with ambient air can cause an abscess, which cannot go unnoticed.

What To Do:

There is no home treatment for such problems in the mouth because it is such a highly septic area of the body. Consult a veterinarian as soon as you notice a fractured tooth. In most cases, surgery is necessary. There are two types: Implanting a prosthesis to replace the missing tooth or simply "deadening" the tooth to prevent future infection.

For a prosthesis to resist traction forces, it is often constructed around the following principles:

– Shorten the "lever action" of a long canine, by shortening the crown of the prosthesis (2/3 the length of a normal canine tooth)

– Increase the contact surface between the tooth and the prosthesis with the help of a radicular pivot and by placing the base of the prosthesis under the gum.

Prevention

Since fractures occur most frequently to young canine teeth, it is possible to decrease this risk by guiding frisky pups to tug with their whole mouth, which is safer than a weaker hold with fewer teeth.

Repeated trauma will weaken teeth. It is therefore necessary to correct bad biting habits as early as possible in a dog to help avoid fractures.

Surgery is almost always necessary to repair fractured teeth and a prosthesis is never as strong as a real tooth. It is entirely that the prosthesis will also break.

PATHOLOGY OF MUSCLES AND TENDONS

Traumatic Muscle Pathology

Traumatic muscle disorders are common in Sporting dogs. They are incapacitating and painful and leave serious muscular scarring that can put a dog's sporting career at risk.

CLASSIFICATIONS AND DEFINITIONS

We can use a classification system inspired by that used in human medicine to specify the diagnosis and prognosis.

A **cramp** is an involuntary permanent contraction of the muscle, which gradually regresses through stretching.

An **ache** is a type of myalgia that appears after inhabitual exertion and entails localized inflammation. It regresses when the muscle is warmed up and disappears when physical activity is resumed.

A **contracture** is an involuntary permanent contraction of muscle fibers that cannot be relieved by simply stretching the muscle.

A **sprain** is a simple lesion of certain muscle fibers that is caused by stretching the muscle too far or too quickly.

A **pulled muscle** is one in which the muscle fibers have torn, associated with desinsertion from the aponeurosis.

A **rupture** is a significant break in the entire muscle.

Specialists in racing Greyhounds prefer to use a different classification system, which is more arbitrary and divides the muscular disorders into three groups:

Stage 1: Development of myositis from a simple contusion with localized inflammation.

Stage 2: The localized myositis is associated with a sprain and/or tear in the corresponding fascia.

Stage 3: Rupture of the muscle fibers with development of a hematoma.

LOCATION

Dogs can damage any of their muscles during sports or work, but the muscles of the forelegs are most often the ones affected. These limbs are indeed greatly solicited. During exertion, they support two-thirds of the animal's body weight and participate in the acceleration process (20% of muscular power). They also serve as shock absorbers (80% of power).

Stages 1 and 2 are generally encountered in powerful muscle groups like the triceps, femoral biceps, quadriceps, fascia lata, semi-tendon and semi-membrane groups. Dorsolumbar muscles may also be affected.

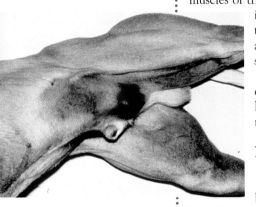

Muscle rupture on Racing Greyhound

ETIOPATHOLOGY

We make a distinction between muscular accidents caused by direct or exogenous trauma and muscular accidents caused by indirect or endogenous trauma.

Direct Trauma

The cause varies. It may be bumping into other dogs (during Greyhound races for example), from bumping into a hard object (ring, sled), or from falling. The seriousness of the lesions depends on how violent the trauma was and on the functional state of the muscle during impact (contraction or relaxation).

Indirect Trauma

Indirect traumas are specific to the sporting activity in question. The physiopathogenic mechanisms of these disorders is not completed understood, but we do know that they are caused by sudden neural-vascular-muscular dysfunction. This type of accident is always linked to activity that solicits a muscle for performance that is beyond its capacities for contraction, extension, and elasticity. The collection of intramuscular hematomas is encouraged by the elevated capillary density inside the muscle from training.

CONTRIBUTING FACTORS

Factors that contribute to direct trauma are generally human in origin, such as poor preparation of the terrain or equipment or improper use of the lure in Greyhound racing. These factors are easily controllable.

On the other hand, the factors contributing to or predisposing an animal indirect trauma vary greatly and are quite numerous:

– the dog: The extremely muscular close-couple body type is the most often affected, especially if the animal suffers from articular asynchronism;

– the preparation of the muscle: poorly managed training (either excessive or lacking), insufficient or nonexistent warm-up of muscles, and general fatigue considerably increase the risk of accidents;

– the stress from the environment, insufficient rest and/or sleep, unbalanced diet, and neglected water supply are also contributing factors to accident;

– finally, use of anabolic drugs is an aggravating factor.

SYMPTOMS AND DIAGNOSIS

When a muscular accident happens, a simple and precise clinical exam is enough to establish a diagnosis. From least to most serious, we distinguish between: sprains and aches, tears and ruptures, ruptures from endogenous trauma, and contusions from exogenous trauma.

A muscular injury is diagnosed through a visual examination, careful palpation, and witnesses accounts of the accident. Indeed, Sporting dogs don't show pain very much and may not limp despite serious injury. For these reasons, it is extremely important to study accounts of the accident since the animal may not really begin to limp until 24 hours after the trauma, but may simply show a slight drop in performance a subtle change in its gait (stiffness in the first three or four minutes of walking).

The easiest time to pinpoint a muscular injury is, in fact, the day after it happens, once the dog has resumed training.

Jumps may often cause muscular traumas.

During Stage I of an injury, if the animal is examined before inflammation and swelling have developed, there will be localized pain and firm palpation of the muscle is painful. Nevertheless, we do not note a hot zone and there is virtually no loss of function.

During Stage II, clinical symptoms become more severe. There is noticeable loss of function and limping, and we note a weakness in resistance to force and an asymmetry. The injured area is swollen and hot. The pain is localized and sometimes we can palpate the rupture in the tissue.

In Stage III limping is extreme and there is complete asymmetry in the animal's limbs. There are clear localized signs: hematoma, swelling, subcutaneous hemorrhaging. The pain is severe and we can easily palpate the rupture in the tissue.

EXPLORING FUNCTIONS

Several other examinations may be done to determine the diagnosis and prognosis for the muscular trauma.

Biological amounts (CPK, LDH, blood and urinary creatinine) are only useful in obtaining an overview of the lesion and determining the prognosis.

Echography is not used enough yet in the field of canine muscular-tendinous pathology, despite the fact that it allows us to quickly determine the extent of the muscular lesions (dissociation of fibers, ruptures, amount and location of hematomas) and sometimes to intervene by puncturing the hematomas. Echography does not, however, allow us to track fiber scarring that may prove incapacitating for the animal.

Infrared thermography allows us to objectively visualize the vascular reactions to the trauma (hyperthermia of hematomas), and/or reflex vascular reactions (hypothermia due to vasomotor problems). It also allows us to monitor the evolution of the lesions and helps the veterinarian make decisions regarding therapy. The high price of infrared thermography limits is use in current practice.

Finally, scanning can also be quite helpful by providing very precise diagnoses. Its use is generally reserved for extremely valuable dogs because it is a very expensive exam, unusable in current canine sports medicine.

THERAPEUTICS

Before determining local and general treatments, certain basic principles must be specified. First of all, rest is imperative and no weight whatsoever must be put on the limb in the case of serious ruptures or tears. Nevertheless, the limb must not be immobilized in a cast because it may cause serious vascular complications. Massages are contraindicated for serious injuries because they actually slow and hinder healing and can cause severe or recurring complications (extensive fiber scarring). Finally, to guard against infection, avoid puncturing or injecting into hematomas.

Classic Treatment

During a traumatic muscular accident, treatment depends on how serious and how old the injuries are.

Medicinal treatments must take into account the pharmacokinetic information of the molecules listed on the drug products for Sporting dogs, sled dogs, ski-pulka dogs, and racing Greyhounds.

If the injury is recent, we apply ice to the damaged muscle for a few hours at a time for two to three days. A compressive bandage should hold the limb at the place of injury. We apply anti-inflammatory and antalgic liniments. At first they should be applied without massage and held in place by the bandage. Then, once the injury has begun to heal, (after four to six days), the liniments should be applied during massage.

For injuries in Stage II (7% to 8% of cases) or Stage II (2% to 3% of cases), we administer non-steroid anti-inflammatories orally for one to two weeks, with a low posology. For serious Stage II lesions, reparative surgery is often necessary. Surgical intervention generally takes place 72 hours after the accident, after the application of ice and compressive bandages have reduced the hematomas. In the event of a large, palpable hematoma, we perform an aseptic puncture to reduce pain and the risk of neurological complications from compression.

Convalescence takes about two weeks. The rehabilitation period is evaluated based on the severity of the muscular lesions. For example, for four centimeters of damaged muscle, rehabilitation will last four weeks. During a Stage I injury, rest is prescribed in addition to the local treatments. Only walking is allowed for four to six weeks. Training can then be resumed with progressively longer work loads.

Non-Traumatic Muscular Pathology

These are primarily muscular lesions that appear after metabolic disorders or for which the exact cause remains undetermined or poorly understood.

A "STITCH IN YOUR SIDE"

Even if the terminology is based on the phenomenon experienced by humans, dogs also frequently get shooting pains that appear to be abdominal during and after exertion. When this happens, the dog will examine its flank. The pain decreases and ultimately goes away on its own.

A stitch in your side can be defined as a pain caused by physical exercise that is located in the anterior part of the abdomen at the edge of the ribs. It will mostly disappear if the dog's hindquarters are lifted fairly high, which allows us to differentiate it from other painful ailments.

Certain conditions seem to favor the appearance of "stitches":

– Eating or drinking too close to the start of exercise
– Running on very uneven terrain
– Poor physical condition of the animal
– Lack of warm-up before maximum exertion
– Nervous excitement
– Cold weather

The exact cause of the phenomenon remains unknown. Whatever its cause may be, the affliction itself is harmless, but may sometimes be mistaken for an acute abdominal syndrome. "Stitches" are only temporarily debilitating in terms of performance.

The only possible prevention for dogs is to refrain from feeding them the last three hours before exertion, or for animals with a recurring problem, injecting them with an anti-spasmodic two hours before competition.

RHABDOMYOLOSIS FROM EXERTION

Also called paroxysmal myoglobinuria, rhabomyolosis from exertion is a frequent pathological muscular disorder that can be associated with acute renal failure, the progression of which can prove fatal for the animal.

Symptoms

Hyperacute form
The hyperacute form occurs during exertion—especially during short, intense periods of exertion and is a classic problem for racing Greyhounds. The animal stops suddenly, instantly manifesting motor problems. Its muscle groups (especially the croup) are swollen and painful, and certain neurological problems may appear (propioceptive deficiency). Urinary symptoms appear rapidly. The dog's urine first appears brownish, then there is a complete lack of urine as acute renal failure begins and leads to the animal's death.

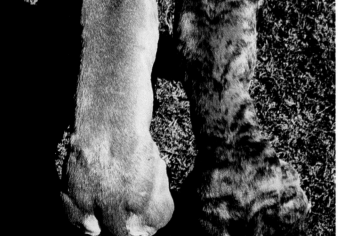

Clinical scarring of rhabdomyolysis : fibrosis of the back muscles on the right-hand Greyhound.

Acute Form

Appearing immediately after exertion, the acute form is expressed in the same muscular symptoms as described above. The onset of acute renal failure is slower and occurs less frequently with macroscopic myoglobinuria. Though death is rare, muscle scarring is a frequent and debilitating problem.

Subacute Form

Finally, the subacute form occurs 24-48 hours after exertion. There is more or less overall muscle pain, which generally subsides after 3 or 4 days. Urinary symptoms are more discreet, with the appearance of macroscopic myoglobinuria that rarely evolves to effect the kidneys. In terms of biochemical effects, we note a marked rise in all enzymes involved (CPK, LDH, ASAT, ALT), the levels for which make take two to three weeks to return to normal. Sometimes an extracellular dehydration associated with passing hyperkalemia may be observed.

Diagnosis

Diagnosis includes clinical and perhaps biochemical symptoms for each of the forms described and is based on a state of shock, muscle pain, and discolored urine.

The veterinarian should carefully check for possible neurological or cardiac (myocarditis) complications.

Etiology

The hyperacute form always appears during sudden extreme exertion in an animal that hasn't been properly trained. Among the different etiological and contributing factors are:

– Psychologically stressful environment
– Excitation or nervousness in the dog
– Transportation conditions
– High temperature with high humidity
– Demanding too much of the animal
– Lack of warm-up

Pathogeny

During all muscular exertion, 80% of the chemical energy used by the muscle when it works is transformed into heat, which accumulates in the muscle. Moreover, the degree of thermal accumulation in dogs doubles for every $10°$ C above the animal's neutral thermal zone (approximately $20°$ C). The changes in the animal's thermal conditions associated with the potentially high production of lactic acid lead to a drop in intramuscular blood flow and to progressive cellular necrosis.

Predisposing Factors

The most predisposed breed to exertion-related rhabdomyolysis is without question the Greyhound. This predisposition is also related to the presence of muscle mass, which makes up about 60% of the total body weight, as well as to a genetically higher red blood count than for other breeds.

In all cases, the following are predisposing factors:

– Using anabolic steroids
– All changes in muscular blood flow
– Unbalanced diet

Treatments

Depending on the form and how serious the case, some or all of the following therapeutic elements may be used:

– Extreme rehydration
– Cooling down of muscle groups
– Injection of non-steroid anti-inflammatories, analgesics)
– Rest in stress-free environment
– Potassic nutritional supplement

Prevention

The prevention of exertion-related rhabdomyolysis primarily involves appropriate physical training, psychological preparation of the animal (stress linked to the competitive environment), and establishing a systematic process for warming up.

In racing locations, environmental and transportation conditions should be completely free of stressful elements for the dog. The dog should be given an appropriate amount to drink before and after exertion. Finally, care should be taken to provide a nutritional balance in the diet with an effective L. Carnitine supplement... but also keep in mind the following factor: chance.

Tendinous Pathology

Tendinous disorders are often associated with articular disorders in Sporting dogs. They are discussed below according to anatomical location.

TENDINITIS

Tendinitis refers to an acute or chronic inflammation of the functional and anatomical parts of the tendon. Any of these parts may become inflamed. Depending on the terrain and the type of activity in question, however, certain tendons contribute more and are therefore more likely to become inflamed.

Diagnosis

Dogs suffering from tendinitis will demonstrate a drop in performance, which may be associated with limping or some degree of pain. During palpation or pressure, the dog will react to localized sharp pain in the injured tendon. Moreover, a hot area may be felt where the lesion is located by touching with the back of your hand.

Treatment

In the case of acute tendinitis occurring in sled dogs, for example, snow can be immediately applied to the injured area and held in place with a slightly loose bandage. In the absence of snow, there are several very effective cool packs on the market.

A somewhat slower treatment is the application of an anti-inflammatory cream, which is then covered with a bandage. For severe pain, this treatment can be accompanied by non-steroid anti-inflammatories given orally.

For chronic tendinitis, local anti-inflammatories can prove effective, associated with certain non-medicinal treatments or physical therapy.

In all cases, the dog must immediately be allowed to rest in order to relieve the inflammation. Often three to six weeks are necessary to regain normal locomotion. A gradual return to work is recommended.

BURSITIS AND TENOSYNOVITIS

Bursitis is an inflammation of the protective synovial sacs between ligaments or tendons and bony protuberances. We make a distinction between these and tenosynovitis, which is an inflammation of the tendinous sheaths. These inflammations cause increased pressure in the synovial fluid as the capsule of the bursa or sheath thickens or as the liquid fails to be eliminated. This pressure in turn presses against adjacent structures (tendons or ligaments). If the inflammation is not relieved quickly, the damage caused on the other anatomical structures may be permanent.

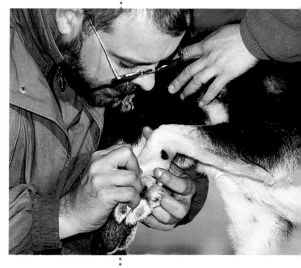

Veterinary examination of the carpal flexor tendons.

Diagnosis

There is generally a more or less noticeable amount of swelling in the tendinous sheath or bursa, particularly around the wrist (especially in Working dogs). The swelling is soft and liquid-like in consistency. The animal does not necessarily limp if the distension is due to a slight inflammation, though the dog may bothered by the way it feels.

Treatment

The goal of treatment is to stop the inflammation before it causes damage in other structures and to return a normal pressure to the synovial fluid.

The medical treatment is the same for tendinitis and certain anti-inflammatory creams with hyper-oxygenated fatty acid bases are particularly effective. On the other hand, for more serious cases, we recommend punctures of the synovial fluid to relieve the pressure and local injections of anti-inflammatories to reduce inflammation. Extreme care should be taken with these injections, using a completely aseptic technique to avoid infectious contamination.

TENDONS IN THE TOES

Slipping of the superficial flexor tendon in the toes

From time to time, many breeds of Sporting dogs may develop a limp accompanied by fluctuating swelling of the dorso-caudal portion of the tarsus. This is generally due to a lateral or medial slipping of the superficial flexor tendon in the digits and is related to a tear in its lateral or medial attachment.

The prognostic for athletic recuperation is excellent following surgery to suture the collateral attachments of the tendon.

Toe Flexors

Problems with the flexor tendon in the toes are most frequent in racing Greyhounds. According to certain authors, these problems make up 40% of all pathological problems for racing dogs. They affect the upper part of the toes in the left front leg (dogs turn to the left when racing) or the second toe of the right front leg past the metacarpal. Upon clinical examination, the toes appear raised or bent, depending on where the problem with the tendon is located.

– a drooping toe corresponds to an injury near the second phalange.

– a raised toe is caused by a problem with the tendon at the base of the third phalange (the extensor tendon that lifts the toe and prevents the nail from touching the ground).

– A toe that is twisted to the side corresponds to a problem with the collateral ligament.

Rapid surgical repair of the ligament support is recommended in all of the above cases. Nevertheless, injecting sclerosing agents or amputating the phalange or toe can be a palliative treatment.

CARPAL LIGAMENTS

Sprained carpal ligaments can be accompanied by pulls, but rarely by a tear in the tendon. These are frequent injuries during long periods of exertion (long distance sled dogs) or if the terrain is uneven, downhill, a hard surface, or rubble.

Sprains are often benign: support is conserved or slightly relieved. We note a slight pain with hyperflexion.

If the sprain is recent and no swelling has yet developed, it is useful to apply a cold pack to the area. But, in general, the best treatment is still the application of local anti-inflammatory creams covered with a slightly tight bandage.

For serious sprains, anti-inflammatories may also be administered orally. In all cases, the dog is allowed to rest for two to four weeks, except for benign sprains in sled dogs.

CARPAL ULNAR FLEXOR

The carpal ulnar flexor is made up of two heads: the humeral and the cubital. The cubital head is attached to the secondary carpal bone like a cord. The humeral head attaches to the posterior side of the secondary carpal bone and can therefore be subjected to transversal tears.

Injuries to the carpal ulnar flexor's insertion are often related to tendinous sprains. In general, the first warning sign is a simple drop in performance. Then, local symptoms of the injury appear: the affected area develops contusions and swelling. The insertion of the ulnar head can become detached and cause avulsive fractures of varying degrees. Whatever the case, many injuries are chronic and appear gradually. Early diagnosis is the best treatment. Nevertheless, if the injury has progressed, surgical intervention will be necessary with two to three months of rest associated with physiotherapy.

INFRASPINOUS TENDON

This is a frequent injury in canine sports. Its cause remains unknown, though in most cases appears to be related to trauma.

In the beginning, the dog will tend to avoid putting pressure on the injured leg. Limping becomes increasing marked over a period of one to two weeks and ultimately results in a characteristic gait: the dog presents with a persistent abduction and external rotation of the humerus with extension of the shoulder (helicopod walk) with no sign of pain.

Recommended treatment consists of infraspinous tenotomy (division of the injured tendon) with a lateral approach to the shoulder joint. Relief is immediate and the prognostic for recuperation of function is excellent.

TENDONS OF THE BICEPS BRACHII

The biceps brachii begins on the glenoidal tubercle of the scapula, enters the bicipital splint of the humerus and attaches to the radius and cubitus on the medial side of the elbow.

The two primary injuries to this muscle are: tenosynovitis of the tendon as it passes through the intertuberal groove and its slipping out of this groove after a rupture in the transhumeral ligament connecting the two tuberosities.

In both cases, the injury results in a diminished flexion of the shoulder joint and intense pain.

The best treatment of tenosynovitis is prolonged rest, with local application of anti-inflammatory creams. Should the tendon slip out of the shoulder casing, surgical intervention will be necessary. These two injuries have a very bad prognostic for functional recuperation of the shoulder.

ACHILLES TENDON

A rupture of the Achilles tendon occurs when the dog suddenly accelerates. It may occur at the insertion point of the tendon or within the actual tendon.

A marked limp appears and the dog presents with a characteristic plantigrade gait of the hind legs. Sometimes, the superficial flexor of the toes is intact. In this case, the animal holds his toes like a crab's claws.

A rupture in the Achilles tendon requires surgical intervention. There is a somber prognostic for Sporting dogs with this injury, which is not the case for companion dogs. In sporting canine traumatology, it is one of the injuries with the longest convalescence.

It is difficult to prevent muscular tendinous injuries in Sporting and Working dogs, but certain principles can play an important preventive role:

– good physical condition of the dog during work and racing
– systematic warm-up prior to exertion
– early detection of injuries
– regular biological and clinical check-ups

Rupture of the Achilles tendon on Alaskan Husky

Osteo-articular trauma

In training or working, dogs can be subjected to osteo-articular injuries. Articular traumas can be violent and often cause articular swelling. We make the distinction of closed traumas, without rupture to the articular capsule or cutaneous effraction, which upon direct action, cause articular contusions that may or may not be associated with articular fractures, and upon indirect action cause sprains or luxations.
Open traumas present a continuous solution between the outside and the articular cavity.

Dogs with intense activity are frequently subjected to microtraumas, which take a gradual and dangerous toll on the body. These microtraumas occur during movement. In Sporting dogs, exertion is intense and frequent, which could cause progressive degeneration in the articular cartilage and result in the appearance of arthrosis. Articular pain is often the only clinical sign of articular trauma.

Sprains

These are closed traumas related to the execution of a movement that goes beyond the physiological limits of the joint. They are characterized by an alteration of the joints contention structures (especially the ligaments and the capsule). They occur during exaggerated twisting movements or during violent muscle contractions. Fatigue, lack of balance, or uneven terrain can encourage their appearance.

A benign sprain consists of an elongation of a ligament. More serious cases may involve a complete rupture of ligamentary elements or injuries to bones and cartilage.

The dog then avoids applying pressure to the limb, due to pain, which is accentuated by the involuntary contracture of the surrounding muscles. Moreover, the injured joint is warmer, painful, and swollen.

While benign sprains have a good prognosis and can heal spontaneously or through simple immobilization, serious sprains leave scars without surgical treatment. The prognosis is also more reserved and depends on the nature of the associated injuries.

Different Types of Sprains

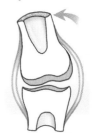

Sprain from elongation

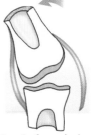

Sprain from desinsertion

Rupture of Crossed Ligaments

This is a particular form of serious sprain to the knee. The cranial crossed ligament stabilizes the knee joint in internal rotation as well as in the antero-posterior direction. When it is broken, either following sudden hyperextension, or during a fall in rotation, we observe an anterior pull of the tibia (the tibia can advance in relation to the femur).

Rupture of the cranial crossed ligament means that the dog is suddenly incapable of putting any pressure at all on the affected limb. Arthrosis appears very quickly from the first week following the rupture and even before radiological signs.

Conservative medical treatment is only indicated in small dogs. Surgical treatment is therefore the solution of choice in treating the rupture of the anterior crossed ligament.

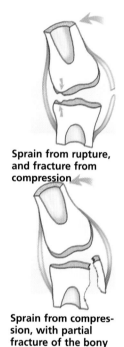

Sprain from rupture, and fracture from compression

Sprain from compression, with partial fracture of the bony insertion

Meniscal lesions

Lesions to menisci (lamina of cartilage located in the knee joint) rarely occur as isolated incidents. They are generally associated with articular instability due to the rupture of a cruciate ligament. The medial meniscus is more susceptible to damage than the lateral meniscus because its ligamentary connections make it relatively immobile. When an anterior cruciate ligament ruptures, the internal rotation of the tibia increases in relation to the femur and crushes the internal meniscus. This abnormal wear can strain the meniscus. Moreover, the elements connected to the caudal "horn" can also be pulled, causing the meniscus to collapse. Meniscal lesions are also associated with multi-ligamentary injuries.

Diagnosing a meniscal lesion can be done through witness accounts as well as clinical examination. The appearance of meniscal lesions are often observed with a chronic limp that suddenly worsens as the dog's crossed ligaments degenerate. During manipulation, a "click" can be heard when the injured portion of the meniscus is in front or behind. On the other hand, the absence of a click does not exclude the presence of a lesion. Definitive diagnosis can be done either through x-ray, exploratory arthrotomy, or with an arthroscope.

Open Septic Arthritis

This is the most serious complication of an articular wound. The action of pathogens following a trauma determines an acute inflammation of the articular tissues and leads to more or less long-term suppuration. We distinguish between four stages of evolution in open septic arthritis.

The latent stage, during which the dog presents no clinical symptoms, precedes the acute inflammatory stage, which is comparable to the evolution of an abscess. The membrane and the synovial liquid change. The synovial liquid's volume increases, as does its viscosity and its reabsorption is abnormal. Suppuration occurs during the acute inflammatory stage. The synovial pus becomes inappropriate for cartilage nutrition and parts of the cartilage detach, forming arthroliths or "jointmice." The synovial membrane proliferates (the proliferations are called "fungosities"), and ultimately close off the joint, thereby encouraging the collection of pus. Hypersecretion of pus leads to added pressure on the surrounding tissues. The pus is evacuated through fistula and through the initial wound. It also gradually reaches the bone, first detaching the periost, then worsening into osteomyelitis (bone lysis).

Finally, the chronic inflammatory stage leads to secondary repercussions such as ossification of the fungosities, and we ultimately observe the disappearance of the joint.

A drop in overall health accompanies these localized symptoms: The dog is exhausted, refuses to eat, and its body temperature rises 2 or 3 degrees from normal. The injury also causes the animal to limp and completely avoid putting pressure on the limb.

Recovery is rare without treatment and the situation may worsen and ultimately lead to death. Treatment is primarily local and varies depending on the evolutionary stage.

Arthrosis

This non-inflammatory articular disorder is characterized by pain and its evolution is chronic. Arthrosis is often caused by abnormalities of intensity, frequency, and/or the distribution of mechanical constraints (during the rupture of a crossed ligament, for example). These are abnormal constraints acting on cartilage that is initially healthy. Arthrosis is incapacitating because of the pain and limping it causes. It is often incurable (only palliative treatments exist).

Cartilage injuries are the first to appear. They are characterized by a loss of substance, followed by a rapid wear and tear revealing the subchondral bone. Areas of exposed bone become more dense in reaction to the loss of cartilage. Around the apparently intact cartilage zone osteophytes appear (ossification from newly-formed cartilage). These repercussions mean a wearing of the cartilage until its disappearance, as well as a closening of the two epiphyses. The synovial membrane also reacts and the articular capsule ultimately thickens and hardens.

The evolution of arthrostic phenomena occurs in spurts and is therefore irregular. The dog presents with an intermittent limp that subsides after warm-up and reappears with fatigue. The dog uses the affected limb less, which results in amyotrophy since the muscles are not being used, and also perhaps muscular contracture.

The prognosis for work or sport is extremely reserved because of the incapacitating aspect of the disorder and its irreversible evolution as it worsens. Two types of treatment may be used depending on the location and the stage of evolution. The basic treatment may in some cases be surgical correction and medical treatment in others. Medical treatment consists of using chondro-protectors, possibly in conjunction with antioxidants and fatty acids. Symptomatic treatment consists in administering anti-inflammatories, preferably non-steroids, that are well-tolerated during prolonged use. Moderate activity, such as walking, should be maintained.

Luxation

Luxations are characterized by an abnormal displacement of articular surfaces and are most often permanent. Depending on the displacement, we distinguish complete luxations (complete loss of articular contact) from sub-luxations; depending on the evolution, recent luxations from old luxations; depending on etiology, traumatic luxations from non-traumatic luxations.

Recent luxations are caused by a violent trauma or a forced movement that causes an articular displacement beyond the physiological limitations. They may be encouraged by a malformation in the joint. The trauma causes a displacement by the involuntary muscle contraction and is maintained by the contracture. Various injuries are associated. The articular capsule, ligaments, and synovial membrane are systematically broken or distended. Muscles always present contractures accompanied with contusions, which sometimes reach distension or rupture.

Bones are not always injured, but we can sometimes observe complete or incomplete intra-articular fractures (fissures).

The dog presents with functional impotence, and a deformation of the limb (shortening, lengthening, or angulation), pain upon palpation, and abnormal mobility. Without treatment, we observe a gradual reshaping of the joint, as cavities are overcome and cartilage is worn, which leads to definitive functional impotence. A luxation is never benign and complications are fairly frequent. Nevertheless, the prognosis should be made based on the location of the problem.

Luxations of narrow joints (elbows, ankles) are rare, but serious and stable. Reducing them is difficult, but very effective and must be done within 24 to 48 hours before the opposing muscle contractures begin.

Luxations of flat joints (shoulder, carpus) can be easily reduced, but reoccur frequently. They always require surgical treatment.

Luxations of the shoulders are in intermediate case in that they must be reduced within 4 to 7 days.

Application of a setting bandage or implants can set the joint. Ankylosis caused by immobilization can be avoided with passive mobilization of the joints.

Old luxations are characterized by cruder symptoms. Pain has almost completely disappeared, as have any signs of inflammation, but the deformation persists and functional impotence is more or less marked. The articular cavities are overcome with fibrous tissue and changes in the bone. Surrounding muscles are retracted. The prognosis is much worse than for recent luxations and reduction must be surgical.

Luxations of the Rotula

Luxations of the rotula may be caused by trauma. In large breeds, they may be medial as well as lateral.

We classify them according to seriousness:
- Stage I: Occasional luxation
- Stage II: More frequent luxation, which reduces itself
- Stage III: Same as Stage II, but the reduction must be manual
- Stage IV: Permanent uncontrollable luxation

The dog maintains the leg supported during luxation. Diagnosis is performed through palpation and x-rays will help to determine skeletal abnormalities.

A dog presenting with a Stage I luxation will especially benefit from physical therapy, as well as from controlled activity, whereas, as the severity of the luxation increases, surgical treatment is recommended.

The prognosis for functional recuperation is good for luxations of the three first stages, in the absence of arthrosis, but more reserved for Stage IV because of the greater bone deformations it causes.

Bone Contusions

These are traumatic disorders of bone tissue without invaded the skin and without continuous bone solution. Three types of phenomena may occur depending on how violent the trauma is: a simple hemorrhagic infiltration of the periost (equivalent of an ecchymosis), a sub-periost hematoma or a cortical change.

An acute inflammatory phenomenon develops locally, accompanied by heat, swelling, and redness (which is generally difficult to detect). Pain subsides after a few hours, but is revealed upon palpation of the injured area.

If the trauma is moderate, the bone may scarcely react and the limp may go unnoticed. If the trauma is severe or repeated, we move toward a simple traumatic osteitis. Osteitis consists of an initial localized demineralization of the bone, which becomes fragile, followed by the reconstruction of bone tissue as inflammation diminishes.

The prognosis is good. Treatment consists of simple monitoring of the injury and may be associated with anti-inflammatories and the application of cold, for the animal's comfort.

Fractures

A fracture is the rupture of a part of the bone or cartilage in the skeleton. It is accompanied by soft tissue damage (muscles, nerves, etc.) in the surrounding areas. Fractures have external causes (trauma) or internal causes (solicitation of bone tissue by a muscle contraction that is too great: landing after too great a jump). There is a predisposition related to age. Young, growing dogs have growing cartilage, a zone of less resistance, which leads to "Salter" type fractures. Older dogs are slower and therefore less able to avoid trauma.

Fractures can be caused by direct trauma, in which case the bone breaks in relation to the point of impact. Most often, the fracture is simple, transverse, or oblique. If the trauma is violent, several splinters form and we then speak of "comminuted" fractures.

An indirect trauma fracture is a fracture located in a different area from the point of impact. We divide fractures into the following categories:

– flexion: This type of fracture generally affects a long bone subjected to compression forces acting on its main axis.

– shear: the impact is carried to an area far away from the trauma. For example, in landing from a long fall, impact received on the carpus, the dog typically presents with a fracture of the humeral condyle. The trauma is transmitted by the radius.

– Torsion: The fracture line is a spiral (it wraps around the bone). This fracture occurs mainly after a limb is trapped in an obstacle.

Types of fractures

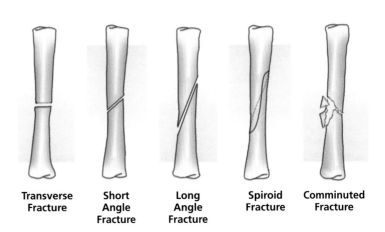

| Transverse Fracture | Short Angle Fracture | Long Angle Fracture | Spiroid Fracture | Comminuted Fracture |

– Wrenching: During extremely intense traction on the point of insertion of a ligament or tendon. The wrenching of a bone is more or less serious.

– Compression: This is a type of fracture specific to short bones (carpus, tarsus, vertebrae, etc.). The spongy bone is crushed; there is shortening and interpenetration, but no fracture line.

SIMPLE FRACTURES

When a fracture is complete, the two fragments can be moved in relation to one another because of involuntary muscle contractures or very violent trauma (displacement of splinters is random).

If we take the example of a simple medio-diaphysary fracture, we observe the following types of displacement:

– angulation: the two fragments no longer have the same longitudinal axis

– translation: one of the two fragments moves laterally in relation to the other

Fractures from indirect trauma

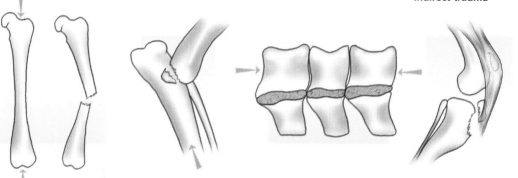

Fracture caused by flexion   Fracture caused by shearing   Fracture caused by compression   Fracture caused by tearing

– overlapping: sliding of one fragment in relation to the other along the large axis of the bone

– gapping: the two fragments move apart from each other

– telescoping: impact of one fragment into the other

– axial rotation: one of the two fragments turns around its longitudinal axis

The soft tissues are subjected to lesions after trauma, but also caused by extremely sharp bone fragments. The periost can be loosened or torn and muscles and nerves may be cut or crushed. Vascular lesions, symptomatic, cause the appearance of a fractuary hematoma. Also, if the cutaneous covering is broken, the fracture is said to be "open" and the prognosis is worse.

The symptoms are related to the rupture of the bone part, which no longer plays its intended role, as well as to the local action of the fracture.

Bone movements during fractures:

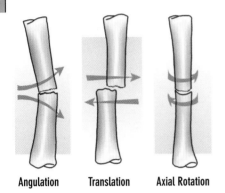

| Angulation | Translation | Axial Rotation |

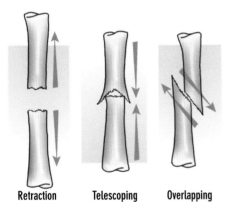

| Retraction | Telescoping | Overlapping |

The general symptoms depend on the severity of the trauma. They may simply be absent. The dog may present with transitory hyperthermia (for about 48 hours) or be in a state of shock during multiple trauma. If the fracture is isolated, the general symptoms are often not very pronounced. With regard to function, the injured limb is held up and the dog moves about on the other three limbs. We can then note the presence of an extra "joint" (except if the fracture is incomplete or involves the joint). Locally, the fracture zone is deformed because of hemorrhaging, which leads to the appearance of a hematoma that collects in the area of the fracture. The blood infiltrates to the subcutaneous tissue and leads to ecchymosis. The deformation may also be caused by a displacement of the bone fragments.

The pain, quite sharp at the moment when the bone breaks, diminishes if the bone fragments are immobilized in the following hours.

The treatment may not be surgical (orthopedic treatment) or may require surgical intervention (osteosynthesis). Orthopedic treatment consists of external maneuvers aimed at reducing and immobilizing the fracture. When the reduction is stable, we set the area appropriately, using a specially adapted bandage.

If the displacement is too severe, we must turn to osteosynthesis: plates, pins, screws, or even external means of holding the segments in place depending on the nature of the fracture.

The prognosis is always serious, but it depends on the type of fracture, where it is located (in relation to the passage of nerves, for example), the animal's age, and also on the treatment.

Complications may develop during healing, such as fractuary diseases, thereby hindering functional recuperation. Certain scars are related to the healing of peripheral soft tissues, leading to muscle retractions, fibrosis, and various adhesions. As a result, the joints develop ankylosis and sometimes the skeleton is deformed. Treatment is complex and generally disappointing since the ideal is prevention through early mobilization of the limbs.

OPEN FRACTURES

In this case, the location of the fracture is exposed to the outside through an opening, however small it may be. The primary cause of open fractures is trauma. Two mechanisms of formation exist: from the inside to the outside (bone fragments puncture the skin), or from the outside to the inside (the fracture results from the action of an provocative agent).

Theses fractures are divided into three categories:

All of these fractures can lead to local complications (abscess, osteomyelitis, etc.) or general complications (septicemia, tetanus, etc.).

Treatment depends on how old the fracture is. If it is recent (less than 12 hours), it can be immediately reduced, of course after having correctly disinfected and dressed the wound. The presence of splinters poses some problems. If they have muscular insertions, they must be saved. Otherwise, we can keep them provided the area is sterilized. In the opposite case, they can be the site of an infectious process and must be removed.

If the fracture is more than 12 hours old, treatment is more random. The first steps are the same as those for a recent fracture: disinfecting and dressing the wound, irrigating the fractured area and removing all of the devascularized splinters. The difference is that the fracture is gradually stabilized and that the would is left open to granulation. We can then further intervene with the bone if the stability is insufficient.

ARTICULAR FRACTURES

These are fractures in which the fracture line ends in a joint. They are complex and functional recuperation can only be obtained if the (very difficult) treatment is perfect. The symptoms are identical to those of another fracture, but more difficult to pinpoint. An x-ray is necessary.

The spontaneous evolution toward ankylosis occurs for two reasons:
– the change in articular profiles and calluses pose additional problems
– arthrosis appears because the joint has changed.

X-ray: fracture of 4 metatarsals, frontal view

Reduction of the fracture must be perfect and in order to do it perfectly, we must intervene very quickly (within 4 days of the fracture). Immobilization of the joint should not last more than 2 or 3 weeks in order to avoid ankylosis. Again, early immobilization of the joint will aid in recuperation. If the damage is too great, the joint is definitively arthrosed (immobilized).

STRESS FRACTURES

Sporting dogs may be subjected to stress fractures just like human athletes. These often affect the metacarpus and the metatarsus. The structure of the bones, exposed to high degrees of activity deteriorates. Limping is noticeable after training or working and manifests through a decreased amount of pressure applied to the affected limb. This limp lasts for about 3 days instead of the usual 24 to 36 hours and even longer if the bone is even more fatigued.

The bone breaks after transitory periods of limping, each time being more marked than the last. A radiological examination reveals bone damage and possibly the presence of a fracture callus (bone fatigue having developed over several weeks).

X-ray: fracture of 4 metatarsals, side view

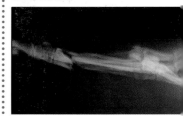

These fractures can be medically treated or surgically treated. When the dog is subjected to acute stress microtrauma, with no obvious radiological signs, a medical treatment based on anti-inflammatories, application of cold, and strict rest for approximately 10 days (until the limp has disappeared) is used. Exercise is then limited for 6 to 8 weeks and the dog is checked through x-ray to monitor the evolution of the fracture.

A stress fracture accompanied with severe bone calluses can be treated medically or surgically. Conservative treatment will give less satisfactory results than surgical treatment. The dog will need 2 to 3 months rest without activity, which allows for better repair of the bones.

The list of this disorders is not intended to be exhaustive, but to give you an idea of the types of osteo-articular trauma that Sporting and Working dogs can undergo in training and in working conditions.

Depending on the intensity and location of impact, osteo-articular traumas of varying degrees of severity can be caused. The prognosis for functional recuperation depends of course on the injury in question, its treatment, and post-traumatic and/or post-operative rehabilitation.

TRAUMA PREVENTION

High-intensity sports such as ring competition, Greyhound racing, and dogsled racing have a big impact on the dog's body. The result is that pathological disorders may emerge due to:
- specific traumas
- repeated sustained exertion in conditions that may sometimes be difficult, causing microtraumas,
- possible over-training of the animal
- great stress on the animal's body during training, but especially during competition

We have deemed it useful to group together the elements that would best prevent the trauma in question.

Influence of selection on angles: Alaskan Husky selected for speed races

Prevention by Genetic Selection

Genetic selection is without doubt the most effective means of preventing a certain number of specific traumas in the long term work of breeding Sporting dogs.

– Morphostatic angulations between different bone segments must allow the animal to have good overall balance. These directly affect the development of muscle masses and therefore their yield. The opening of the sacro-femoral angle, for example affects the efficiency of impulsion:

an acute angle provides a big push and a very large step (the angle must of course be able to open up, hence the importance of morphodynamic examinations); an angle that is too large (as is the case with the German Shepherd) proves ineffective because the angle does not open and therefore results in a marked weakness of the extremities (suspension effect—shock absorption diminishing the work of the distal parts).

– The conformation of distal extremities of the limbs may also be important. In a very long race, therefore, we look for narrow feet with interdigital spaces with as little webbing as possible in order to limit the occurrence of interdigital problems (friction, inflammation, accumulation of snow, etc.).

– One last important factor is the psychic behavior of the dog. The animal with the best build may prove to be a terrible athlete for purely psychological reasons: lines of dogs that are very "stressed" or that refuse certain racing rhythms in sports or dogsledding (the dog tries to brake its race, which causes tendinous inflammation in the extensors and/or flexors of the toes).

Influence of selection on angles: Siberian Husky selected for beauty

Influence of the sacro-femoral angle on the development of muscle mass

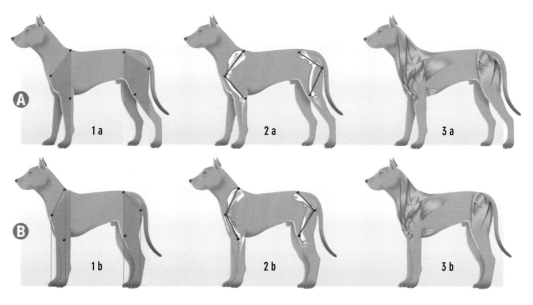

Prevention through Training

– The prevention of muscular accidents is especially linked to rigorous and gradual training, which allows sufficient vascularization for the effort required. In the beginning, a progressive warm-up is absolutely necessary, as is systematic stretching after training.

– Quantitative balance of opposing muscles remains an extremely important element of prevention. Certain general pathological conditions (following infectious diseases, infectious environment, etc.) seem to encourage muscular and tendinous accidents. Owners should be particularly attentive in these circumstances.

– The development of neuromuscular acuity contributes to the prevention of trauma-related problems: free-run races on uneven terrain, gradual adaptation to the movements involved in racing or working. This way, it seems important for a racing Greyhound (going counterclockwise) to negotiate each turn with the front right leg. Indeed, if the turns are to the left, a left handed Greyhound will have to modify its gait each time it enters or leaves a turn, which makes its balance very unstable (and two-thirds of its body weight are carried on the front legs), hence, an increased risk of fall and trauma to the toes. During training it is possible to transform a left handed dog into a right handed dog by wrapping medical tape two or three times around its right metacarpal. This extra weight on the right front leg reverses the gait in three to five training races and is generally definitive.

– From the point of view of the physiology of effort, training is generally speaking a permanent process for adapting to the demands of work. Training stimuli altering the homeostasis (maintaining the internal biochemical balance of the organism) cause the transformation and adaptation of the systems involved. As performance capacity improves, specific and non-specific adaptation phenomena play an essential role.

– The specific adaptations particularly affect immediately operational systems such as the neuro-muscular system (coordination) and the energy system. Non-specific adaptations affect auxiliary systems involved in the particular sport. Moreover, the determining factors for performance have different potentials for developing. While speed can only be modestly increased (an untrained adult dog can only improve its speed by 15-20%), just the opposite is true for strength and endurance, which can be improved by more than 100%. As the animal improves through training, the effort demanded by the training no longer has the same impact on the homeostasis and its effect on the dog's system's equilibrium is less and less marked. For this reason, adaptation phenomena are less and less noticeable and the disorders caused (hypoglycemia, rhabdomyolysis-myglobinurea, extracellular dehydration, exertion-related hyperthermia, etc.) occur less frequently.

– Finally, after sessions that are too long or too repetitive, with insufficient or improper recuperation, signs of biological or psychological overload may appear in Sporting dogs. This is part of what we refer to as "over-training." Overtraining in canine sports can be caused by:

- Too rapidly increasing the amount and level of training
- Using training methods and means that are too exclusive (training must remain a game for the dog)
- Accumulation of competitions with insufficient recuperation intervals.

Other than the classic problems of anemia and stress fractures in Sporting dogs, overtraining can have more insidious consequences, which are broken down into two types in humans: Basedowian types (sympa-thicotonic) and Addisonian (parasympathicotonic) as mentioned earlier.

Basedowian overtraining effects disappear within one or two weeks if specific training sessions are discontinued (associated with the taking of tonics); Addisonian overtraining requires months to disappear after ceasing virtually all forms of training.

Nutritional Prevention

A perfectly balanced diet that is adapted to:

– The type of effort required of the animal
– The level of training or competition, greatly contributes to the emergence of disorders related to metabolism, bones, muscles, and tendons.

Physical activity causes increased wear and tear on the animal's body. The rate at which the cellular components are renewed increases (increase in blood level of urea, uric acid, creatinine, and methylhistidine urinary excretion). Moreover, overtraining and excessive participation in competitions can cause anemic phases. In these conditions, the dog needs a constant supply of protein, which remains the food best adapted to dogs where overall nutritional balance is concerned. The accelerated renewal of contractile structures accompanies an increase in membrane exchanges and their indispensable permeability. This permeability is largely determined by its degree of polyunsaturation, which is ensured by its supply in essential fatty acids, which will authorize the intensification of the energetic metabolism and optimize athletic abilities. A supply of series n-3 (C20:5 and C22:6) polyunsaturated fatty acids, in the form of salmon oil for example, improves the membrane's permeability to oxygen and the flexibility of the red blood cells. An increased supply of anti-oxidants may also prove useful (vitamin E, vitamin C, etc.). Contributing to the protection of cellular structures from oxidizing agents, their presence is even more indispensable as oxidizing processes associated with intense exercise develop.

Finally, the anchoring of the functional part onto the bony skeleton (which also has accelerated changes, hence the increased phosphocalcic requirement) generates considerable traction effort. Resistance to ligament and tendinous tearing requires perfect cohesion between tendinous fibrils and the bony protein matrix. Again the protein supply is important, but the presence of copper and manganese is just as essential, given their role in building and maintaining the matrix network. Magnesium also plays a favorable role, especially in limiting tendinous laxity, while at the same time preventing the appearance of spasmodic muscular problems related to hypomagnesemia after exertion. Chondroitine sulfate or glycosaminoglycanes will greatly contribute to the quality of articular cartilage.

As for the breakdown of foods to give the dog, the principle of the dissociated diet (initial deprivation of dietary fats for one week prior to the test, then an overload of fats 2 to 3 days before competition) should be proscribed for Sporting dogs because of the increased risk of rhabdomyolysis. During long periods of exertion, Sporting dogs have a clear need for fats, particularly those with a short chain. Faced with the rapid exhaustion of glycogenic muscle reserves, which can cause the muscle to harden and cramps to develop, which favor muscular and tendinous injury, it is best to stimulate the metabolic use of fatty acids as much as possible (addition of L. carnitine), which goes through a gustative and digestive adaptation in animals, but which is short in dogs and the introductory rate is very high if we judge by the rations currently used by Nordic dogs during periods of work.

Dehydration phenomena are fairly frequent in Sporting dogs, with varying degrees of seriousness. They may be linked to the race itself (water loss due to panting to regulate body temperature), to excessive heat (heat stroke), or stress-related diarrhea (stress diarrhea dehydration syndrome). Other than the typical steps taken, the prevention of this type of dehydration is based on a water supply with a rehydrating element 60 to 30 minutes before competition. Preventing an episode of heat stroke is based on some obvious points:

– protect the dogs from sun and heat
– avoid all long training sessions between 10:00 a.m. and 6:00 p.m. when it's hot
– always have cool water available, if possible with a rehydrating element mixed in.

Prevention through Warm-Up before Exertion

The warm-up is made up of exercises that prepare the dog psychologically and physically for optimum performance. It serves to prevent numerous injuries by:
– increasing heart rate (transition to exertion is less sudden);
– increasing blood pressure (peripheral vasoconstriction providing more blood to the muscles in exertion);

– increasing circulating blood volume (limiting metabolic and muscular acidosis);

– decreasing muscular viscosity (increasing elasticity, lowering risk of tears);

– improving body temperature, which provides quicker dissociation of the oxygen fixed by the hemoglobin in the blood and better use of the oxygen;

– improved neuromuscular processes (better motor coordination, decreased sense of fatigue).

Warm-ups are performed in dogs by having them use different muscle groups and segments in a specific way in the form of low-intensity races and games.

Prevention through Recuperation after Exertion

After training or competition, fatigue or even exhaustion manifests as a function of the work demanded.

Physiologically, the current systematic approach and explanation of the fatigue phenomena is based on the following elements:

– exhaustion of energy reserves

– decrease in enzyme activity by metabolic acidosis

– disturbances in the hydric and electrolytic metabolism

Poor recuperation after exertion will therefore bring together all of the factors predisposing the animal to rhabdomyolysis.

Among the different types of recuperation, a distinction should be made between the active means (cool down) and the passive means (massage, baths, etc.) because the effectiveness of these methods varies. An active recuperation (fast walk, trot) increases muscular blood irrigation by about 6 times, which is particularly important for eliminating metabolic waste. The different forms of massage practiced by dog owners are far from attaining theses numbers. Moreover, the lactacidemia drops much quicker after 30 minutes of active rest than after passive rest (compensation for the oxygen debt during exertion is brief and intense). Methods of passive recuperation are only necessary when the recuperation is slow in coming, after truly exhausting exertion by the animal.

Prevention through the Quality of the Racing Environment

The quality of the track plays a large role in preventing trauma in Greyhounds and sled dogs.

In Greyhound races, the controversy continues between grass and sand surfaces and probably will continue to be debated until the perfect surface has been discovered. While the best tracks are without question made of grass, hard sand remains the only material that can be regularly maintained without too much difficulty. With sand, maintenance is kept to a minimum, which allows for a reliably good track. With regard to incidents of injury, it has been shown that grass tracks are responsible for more luxations and phalangian fractures than sand tracks. On the other hand, sand tracks have been proven to cause more or less chronic articular disorders. Finally, the appearance of plastic-coated surfaces must be mentioned. These require a lot of work, but have proven extremely effective in all respects. At the very least, they have allowed for a better surface as the dogs come out of the box, which is itself a source of fractured nails and interphalangian luxations.

In pulka and dog sled races, it is impossible to predict the quality of the snow because the trails must be blocked off and sheltered from use since footprints will leave actual holes in the surface, which are dangerous for the dogs' legs and joints.

"Mechanical" Prevention

By "mechanical" prevention, we mean any means of prevention that uses an external physical element with the animal.

With regard to the different types of contentions dog owners have toward the use of adhesive bands around a joint, we must first note the slight (or non-existent) effectiveness of these methods. With little relation to "strappings" used in humans (which are often ineffective as well), these contentions basically serve to reassure the owner more than the dog.

What is more useful is the prevention of problems for pads and interdigital spaces in Sporting dogs such as sled dogs, which are subjected to difficult tests in training as well as in competition. This inflammatory process is even more serious in longer races and even more acute in dogs with interdigital spaces that are very furry, which causes the snow to turn to very sharp bits of ice. The result is wounds in the interdigital spaces and cuts or cracks in the pads, which are quite painful and slow to heal. Prevention and care for the feet must therefore become systematic and involve all of the dogs in a given team:

– Trim the hair between the pads (unless the race is very long, in which case the hair will for a protective padding despite the risk of snow and ice accumulating)

– Systematically lubricate the dog's feet with creams that are antiseptic and promote healing if necessary (horse tail lubricant, lanolin, equal parts of Norwegian tar; vitamin A creams or creams with approximately 5% Diethylsulfoxide; aloe vera creams, etc.)

– Do not hesitate to put protective boots on the dogs as soon as necessary.

In addition to the physical stress of effort, psychological stress is frequent in Sporting dogs, demonstrating a difficulty in adapting that ends up as a drop in performance and in certain specific pathological disorders.

Overall prevention of these last elements entails respecting all of the rules listed above even in difficult terrain.

PODALIC PATHOLOGY

The entire locomotive apparatus is clearly essential in all Sporting and Working dogs. If there is a body part that is particularly put to the test in Working dogs, it is without a doubt the lower ends of their legs (toes, interdigital spaces, pads), especially for sled dogs, hunting dogs, and search and rescue dogs working in avalanches or rubble.

Interdigital Dermititis

Interdigital Dermititis refers to an inflammatory process that develops between a dog's toes and pads, making this area both painful and more vulnerable. This type of inflammation is common in hunting dogs, but sled dogs clearly represent the category of Sporting dogs that is most often affected with the problem. This is why, quite naturally, we shall refer to the sled dog in this section, while the information provided can easily be applied to any other type of dogs.

Symptoms

Because this is an area of intense perspiration and repeated friction, cutaneous inflammations of varying degrees can develop in the spaces between the toes. Moreover, in the case of sled dogs, the accumulation of tiny balls of snow or ice (following repeated freezing and thawing of snow and ice) between the toes and the pads causes swelling and inflammation of the soft tissues, and loss of the protective interdigital fur, which leaves the area vulnerable to infection. The result, without effective prevention or immediate treatment, is problematic interdigital wounds that are quite painful and very slow to heal.

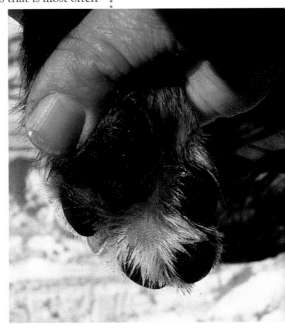

Stage 1 interdigital lesion

This malady typically progresses as follows:

Stage I: The cutaneous spaces between the pads redden, are slightly swollen (looking like "strawberries"), and painful to the touch.

Stage II: The skin begins to crack between and around the toes, gradually becoming crevasses.

Stage III: The crevasses ultimately join together and form clear cuts.

Stage IV: With the local exacerbation of perspiration, maceration follows with infection and abscess of the wounds.

Stage V: The infection spreads through the entire foot, affecting the tendon sheaths and can lead to septicemic problems or serious endotoxinic shock.

Steps to Follow

Generally speaking, Sporting dogs are only affected by Stages I or II, which are benign, but nevertheless justify removing the dog from competition or work. Up to Stage III, treatment consists of applying healing and antiseptic creams. Hyperoxygenated fatty acids (Algyval TM) provide excellent results for Stage I afflictions. Aloe Vera creams prove to have very helpful healing and antiseptic qualities in Stage II.

For instances of local superinfection, a mixture of (lanolin-based) creams containing zinc oxide, which promotes healing and dries the area, will prove successful. In Stage IV, oral antibiotic treatment will be necessary.

Prevention

Prevention is essential is podalic pathology, because if done correctly, it allows you to avoid most of these problems altogether. Prevention should play a role in all levels of animal preparation:

– genetic selection of lines in which the dogs have narrow interdigital spaces

Stage 2 interdigital lesion

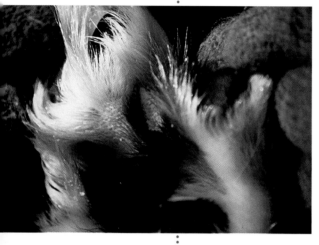

Stage 3 interdigital lesion

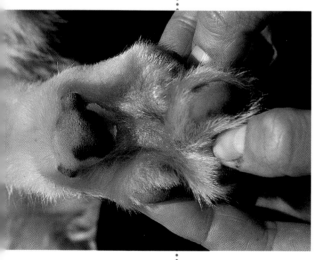

– hardening of the skin in the interdigital spaces during training (avoid pavement, sprays that will toughen the skin, picric acid, pure or hydrolysized nutritional gelatin supplements – 1g per kg of body weight daily).

– mechanical prevention: owners should pay more attention to lubricating the interdigital spaces and pads and use protective booties for Working dogs on difficult terrain (pavement, very rocky ground, rubble).

As silly as booties may look, they are sometimes necessary to protect the animal. In medium- or long-distance races, they are even part of the mandatory equipment to be carried in the sled.

Among the different types of materials used are:

– thick nylon, polypropylene, cordura or new synthetic fibers, waterproof materials that provide good protection;

— polar fleece, which wears quickly and is not waterproof, but which provides a protective cushion and better stability for dogs on slippery surfaces.

The booties are held in place by Velcro, but in some cases we prefer to add a piece of tape. It is important not to apply the tape around the dewclaw. The size of booties used is important to consider because if they are:

– too big, the foot will slide up and down and the heat generated by this friction can cause problems, especially since the toes will strike against the bottom of the boot during the race;

– too small, they squeeze the feet (which impairs circulation and is painful for the dog) and compress the nails against the bottom of the boot, which causes extreme inflammation in the ends of the toes and the sub-ingueal space.

— closed too tightly with the Velcro, they squeeze the dewclaw and can cause it to cut the skin and lead to painful problems from hypovascularization.

– closed too loosely, they allow foreign objects (pebbles, snow, ice, etc.) to get into the booties and cause intense pain and injury.

Sub-Ingueal Disorders

There are two types of sub-ingueal disorders (affecting the nails) in Sporting or Working dogs:

– bacterial infections at the base of the nail, frequently secondary to a traumatic subcutaneous hematoma or break. To maintain the Working dog, it is then necessary to remove the nail, disinfect the area (draining the hematoma, if there is one), and protecting the area with a moleskin sleeve that can safely be glued to the base of the claw.

Different types of booties used: nylon, cordura, polar fleece

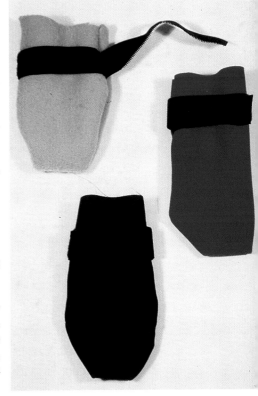

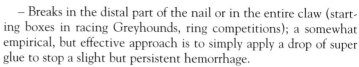

– Breaks in the distal part of the nail or in the entire claw (starting boxes in racing Greyhounds, ring competitions); a somewhat empirical, but effective approach is to simply apply a drop of super glue to stop a slight but persistent hemorrhage.

Problems Affecting Plantar Pads

Ruptures or cuts in the pads require immediate rest and classic treatment for the dog. Sometimes, however, more or less serious nummular abrasions develop on the dog's pads (for sled dogs, tracking dogs, dogs working in rubble, etc.). In such a case, it is perfectly possible to maintain the dog in competition without any complications or pain for the animal by applying moleskin "patches" (or several layers of nylon hose) with super glue (without allowing the glue to touch the wound), after having completely cleaned and dried the wound.

Application of moleskin patch to injured pad

Surprising though it may be, this simple process is very effective and allows the wound to heal within 72 hours. The dog may continue its work during this time without consequence.

Interphalangian Luxations

This is a classic problem for racing Greyhounds, consisting of a partial or complete tear of an interphalangian ligament and the articular capsule, often associated with tendinous lesions. This injury to the toe, which at first seems minor compared to the other orthopedic accidents that can befall racing breeds, is nevertheless a serious problem for the Greyhound. It is one of the main causes of early retirement for the breed.

Pad abrasion

When you realize that a Greyhound that weighs 30 kg (65 pounds) running at 60 km/h (37 mph) will take his first turn with practically all his weight on two toes, you can easily see that the force exerted on these toes (nearly a ton) could cause the interphalangian joints to give way. This phenomenon alone explains why so much money has been invested in the United States and Australia to develop the safest track design for the dogs (slope in the turns, particle size of the material used to make the track, etc.).

Whatever the case, other than the

Metatarso-phalangial luxation on racing Greyhound

dog's limp at the finish line, the injury can be confirmed by the lateral rocking of the distal phalange in relation to the proximal phalange when put into position, there may be only a partial rupture to the structures in question. A radiography will determine or eliminate the existence of another fracture. Since the ruptured ligament does not spontaneously repair itself, the ends being permanently distanced from each other by the articular gap while walking, surgery is the only solution. Several surgical techniques exist, from blocking the joint to using prosthetic ligaments, which may not completely resolve the problem.

"No feet, no dog," as the Eskimos have been saying since the dawn of time. This simple, common-sense expression certainly applies to Working and Sporting dogs today, too.

Droped toe—avulsion of the superficial digital flexor tendon—on racing Greyhound

Necessary materials for pad abrasion

CARDIOLOGY

Heart problems are fairly rare in Sporting dogs, except for the few cases we note here.

Cardiology and Training

Based on how intensely a dog is trained, the animal's cardio-vascular system adapts to the level of exertion required.

PHYSIOLOGICAL ADAPTATION

In the same way as for human athletes, training brings about changes in dogs' hearts. A dog's heart considerably increases in size with exercise. An average heart represents about 0.8% of the dog's total body weight, whereas an actively trained Alaskan Husky has a heart that measures about 1% of its total body weight—and Greyhounds' hearts can weigh as much as 1.2% of their body weights!

Short, intense exercise causes a rise in blood pressure against the heart walls. In dogs trained as sprinters, the heart's size is therefore due to the thickening of these myocardial walls while the volume of the cavity remains normal.

Endurance exercise changes the volume of blood in the heart. In dogs trained for endurance, the size of the heart is therefore due to the thickening of the myocardial walls and to the increase in size of the heart cavities.

CLINICAL MODIFICATIONS

Upon clinical examination, the following can be observed in a Sporting dog:

– Bradycardia (decrease in cardiac frequency) at rest. Cardiac frequency can reach 35 beats per minute in a sleeping Sporting dog, whereas the heart rate for dogs without physical training is approximately 40-60 beats per minute under the same conditions.

– A slight heart murmur, which is never superimposed onto the two characteristic heart sounds during auscultation. This is due to an increase in blood volume while the ejection time remains the same.

– An increase in heart size revealed upon x-ray examination;

– Changes characteristic of heart expansion revealed during electrocardiogram (longer QRS complex duration, increase in the amplitude of the R wave and the QT interval).

– Increase in heart dimensions revealed during echocardiograph.

It is extremely important to be familiar with these changes so as not to confuse an athletic heart with an infirm heart that may present with the same symptoms.

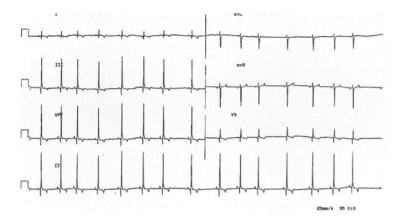

Modifications of readout of electrocardiogram, linked to training, showing ventricular hypertrophy

Cardiac Syncope

Cardiac failure is not linked to any specific sport, but can occur in dogs that are insufficiently trained or during particular environmental situations (heat stroke…). Cardiac syncope occurs when the heart stops beating, which can be checked by taking the dog's pulse at the femoral artery (on the inner side of the thigh) or by placing a hand behind the dog's left elbow to feel for the precordial rhythm.

The animal remains in a real unconscious state, and his organs are almost completely not functioning.

The consequences of heart failure are very serious (often death) and it is very important to act quickly.

Cardiac massage on a large dog

Heart Massage Technique

– Two methods can be used, depending on the size of the dog:
Large dog with round chest or obese dog:
Lay the animal on its right side.
Massage behind the point of the elbow (4th-6th intercostal space).
Press the heel of your hand behind the dog's elbow.
Put your other hand on top of that hand.

– Small dog or dog with flat chest:

Place one hand on each side of the chest, just behind the elbows.
Keep your hands flat and press with the heels of your hands.

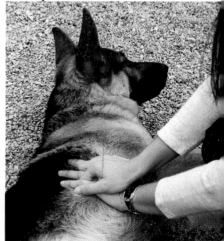

Regardless of the dog's size, you must maintain a rhythm of one compression about every 10 seconds.

Massage the dog for 1 minute and check for a femoral pulse:

– If there is a strong pulse, stop the cardiac massage and see if the animal is breathing.

– If there is no pulse, continue the cardiac massage for 2 minutes and check for a pulse again.

Heart failure is often accompanied by respiratory failure (the dog is not breathing). It is therefore often to combine cardiac massage with a technique for blowing air from your mouth into the dog's nose. To do so, hold the animal's muzzle shut with your hands and slowly breath air into the dog's nostrils. The animal will exhale on its own. Breathe into the dog's nose 12-16 times per minute for a large dog and 15-20 times per minute for a small dog.

If the two techniques are performed together, breathe into the dog's nose 1 time for every 5 heart compressions.

Sometimes during heat stroke, the dog can show the beginnings of syncope without exactly being at the stage of heart failure. In such a case, a spray of nitroglycerine under the dog's tongue can be very effective.

Cardiac massage on a small dog

Mouth-to-nose technique

SPECIFIC RESPIRATORY AILMENTS

Despite the importance of the respiratory apparatus in sporting dogs and working dogs, there are few ailments that affect it and that are directly linked to physical exercise.

Cases of acquired tracheal collapse have been described in young greyhounds during competition, apparently due to an unbalanced diet primarily comprised of meat. Deficiencies in calcium and in chondroitin sulfate develop and lead to the gradual replacement of tracheal cartilage with fibrous tissue that has lost all elasticity. The animal begins to breathe noisily after exertion, then gradually can no long exert itself and experiences extreme difficulty in breathing. The problem can only be treated through surgery in conjunction with a return to a balanced diet, but the animal's athletic career is finished.

Search and rescue dogs who search through rubble after a fiery explosion may have their respiratory systems affected by the residual smoke and fumes, which can trigger tracheo-bronchitis requiring classical medical treatment. Such teams working with dogs should always have an oxygen tank and masks specially adapted for the dogs because of the toxicity of certain emanations.

Dogs may also suffer from bronchiospasms brought on by physical exercise. These spasms generally occur when there is a low hygrometry in the air (very dry) or if the air is very cold. Symptoms include a dry unproductive cough that starts during or immediately after great exertion. It seems that very dry or very cold air can cause certain protective cells (mast cells) in the dog's airways to release chemical mediators such as histamine, leucotriens, prostaglandins, and thromboxans. Thromboxans cause the bronchial tubes to constrict and become inflamed, preventing air from passing through. Emergency treatment consists of inhaling medicines such as B2 adrenergics (albuterol, clenbuterol, salbutamol…), which may be combined with inhaled corticoids.

Prevention entails long and slow warm-up periods and, for dogs with recurring brochiospasms, abstinence from exercise under very dry or very cold conditions.

Intrabronchial hemorrhage from exertion is well-known for race horses, and can also occur in dogs after very intense exertion. In the case of the greyhound, the frequency with which blood appears in the respiratory canals varies between 10 and 15% for dogs in competition. Though this phenomenon is not yet entirely understood, the hemorrhages seem to be due to an increase in vascular pressure in the lungs during exertion, which is directly related to a "stress effect" that is too great for the animal in question. Diuretics such as furosemide are commonly used for horses with this problem, but no treatment has yet been proven effective for dogs. Owners of dogs with such an ailment must therefore pay careful attention to remove all potential stress factors from his dog's environment.

Visible consequences of bronchial hemorrhage from exertion

In conclusion, given that sporting dogs are generally more vulnerable to all sorts of infectious diseases, those that effect the respiratory system will be even more prevalent in such a population. The therapeutic approach remains traditional and preventive efforts must be reinforced.

PATHOLOGICAL CONSEQUENCES OF STRESS

In Sporting dogs, types of stress caused by environmental conditions or by physical exertion can produce changes in behavior (barking, problems with motivation, etc.), neurovegetative problems (salivation, tachycardia, mydriasis, etc.), digestive problems (vomiting, diarrhea, stomach ulcers, etc.), endocrine problems, and possible anemia. A good number of these ailments reported by veterinarians and dog handlers in sporting competitions can be attributed to this type of physiopathological processes.

Stress: A Few Reminders

Since the introduction of the concept of stress by Selye, there has been a general consensus that very diverse aggressive factors mostly from the individual's environment can cause harmful reactions, especially when they exceed the degree necessary to return the animal to a healthy state.

This concept is generally described as follows:

Stress is the process by which environmental factors overload an individual's regulatory systems and disturb the way the individual adapts to situations.

This implies that multiple stimuli, or stress factors, are all acting upon the central nervous system, causing it to respond through actions that can be harmful for the individual.

In the case of the Sporting dog, the stimuli in question may be:

– Before competition: transportation, immobilization, concentration of many dogs, interaction with other dogs, fights, etc.

– During competition: possible pain, variations in temperature, exhaustion, manifestation of an intercurrent, but undiagnosed illness…

Purely psychological factors, such as the animal's anxiety at being in from of a large audience under competitive conditions may—over time, as the situations are repeated—cause the animal to become accustomed to the situation, or may exacerbate the clinical problems caused.

As the animal receives stressful stimuli, three categories of reactions may develop:

Purely nervous reactions that modify the dog's behavior
Nervous and hormonal changes that produce catecholamines (adrenaline, etc.) and other physical symptoms (increased heart rate, for example)

Predominately endocrine reactions with a greater concentration of plasma in corticoids (cortisol, etc.), which ultimately cause the biochemical, cellular, or symptomatic changes noted.

Behavioral Manifestations of Stress

Stress-causing situations often create anxiety for animals that externalize behavior characteristic of their species. In dogs, anxious or frightened behavior is expressed in some very well-known ways (repeated defecation and urination, barking and howling, chewing on objects, carry cages, digging, etc.).

The fecal and urinary elimination behavior is common to all types of animals.

When like animals are placed together, the reactions are produced primarily through social interaction. But in the presence of stimuli from imposed constraints or environmental conditions, the dog's reaction may be stimulating, invigorating, indicative of healthy adaptation, or harmful—the source of potentially serious pathological problems. These last two possibilities of "good stress" and "bad stress" reinforce the idea that stress mechanisms and consequences must always be considered on an individual basis. A clinical description of the behavioral modifications

Physical and behavioral manifestations of stress in Sporting Dogs

No Stress	Slight Distress	Severe Distress
Barking	Growling	Silent
Alert Inattentive	Does not respond	
Good behavior	Behavioral mistakes	Apathetic
Stimulated	Irritable	Depressed
Seeks companionship	Avoids companionship	Ignores entourage
Runs well	Runs poorly	Avoids effort
Recuperates rapidly	Recuperates slowly	Does not run
Well-hydrated	Slightly dehydrated	Dehydrated
Drinks well	Drinks little	Refuses to drink
Eats well	Eats little	Refuses food

caused by stress in Sporting dogs and in Working dogs is provided in the attached table. Let us remember that the primary symptoms or precursors are vocalization, interest in the group and in competition or indifference and changes in eating habits.

Dogs also react and behave very differently from one breed to another and from one individual to another. A description of physical and behavioral characteristics by breed was published by Hart in 1985 and includes 13 criteria such as excitability, level of spontaneous activity, aggression, or natural tendency to defend territory. In regard to stress, even if the concept of "excitability" remains somewhat poorly defined (ability to go from a calm state to an excited state), excitability is nevertheless a good criterion for judging differences between breeds and a predisposition toward stress-related neuroendocrine reactions and behavior. Breeds generally used for working or sporting ends are not among the most sensitive in terms of hyperexcitability.

Neurovegetative Consequences of Stress

Apart from specific stress-related illnesses (syndromes) covered elsewhere (digestive problems) or later in this chapter, dogs, like most animals placed in unfamiliar or upsetting situations, can react with a variety of clinical manifestations such as tachycardia, polypnea, mydriasis, ptyalism, or increased blood pressure. Emotional tachycardia was not fully understood for a long time, though it is a frequent problem. Using an electrocardiogram and telemetry methods has allowed us to record and measure the heart rate in situations of complete rest and observing the extremely low rates (45-70 beats per minute during the day, 35-60 at night, depending on the dog).

Still generally speaking, marked cumulative stress can also manifest itself in the form of persistent kennel cough, which upon analysis seems to be due to a drop in immuno-defense mechanisms, predisposing the animal to infection. The same goes for hair loss or a decrease in coat quality, especially for dogs under prolonged exertion.

Endocrine or Metabolic Imbalances

Stress-Related Diabetes Insipidus

Diabetes insipidus refers to an abnormal anti-diuretic secretion (ADH) by the neurohypophysis (central diabetes insipidus or "CDI"). The title "stress-related diabetes insipidus" is given to a large number of conditions that lead to polyuro-polydipsia in racing Greyhounds and sometimes in certain hunting breeds. Unlike the dog suffering from central diabetes insipidus, which necessarily entails polyuria followed by polydipsia to compensate for it, the dog in this case, may present with polydipsia followed by polyuria to compensate for it and vice versa.

Clinical Symptom

The hyperacute form is directly related to the stress of exertion. Within five minutes of racing or training, the dog demonstrates extreme thirst, to the point of drinking its own urine or vomit. It may continue to drink while it urinates, significantly dehydrating itself and losing a significant amount of weight in a very short period. Dogs affected with this ailment may survive, but will likely develop severe handicaps.

The acute form is also linked to stress and manifests itself in a polyuropolydipsic syndrome within 24 hours of racing or being in a stressful situation. Often the dog has just had its best performance ever or participated in a competition that is longer than usual. In this case, it may hold its urine and only urinate in the kennel, and maintain a normal appetite, but become dehydrated and lose weight.

The chronic form is related to a different kind of stress. It affects dogs who chronically drink far too much water in the kennel and who are generally poorly maintained.
A dog may experience stress-related diabetes insipidus only once in its life or the problem may recur several times.

Diagnosis

Other than clinical observation, typical results of exploring certain functions include a urinary pH between 6.1 and 7.2 and a specific urine density lower than 1,015. A hematological exam reveals a stressed differential leukocyte count linking hyperleukocytosis and a drop in or absence of eosinophils.

One confirmation is the hydro-restriction test or the change in the animal's response to an ADH injection (an oily solution of vasopressin tannate), which allows the differential diagnosis to be refined.

Etiology

We will not go into detail on the complex etiopathogenic backgrounds here, but will simply note that:
Hypokalemia and hyperadrenocorticism are often linked to stress and may be sources of acquired nephrogenic diabetes insipidus in racing Greyhounds.
A psychogenic form of the polyuro-polydipsic syndrome may be a precursor if there have been changes in the environment, traumatic experiences, or stress from transportation.

Treatment

When a hyperacute or acute form of the illness develops, the first step to take is to remove drinking water, which will sometimes solve the problem, but which will unfortunately cause severe dehydration and weight loss. In any case, do not allow more than eight liters of water (for a dog weighing 35 kg [78 pounds]) on the first day, distributed in at least six servings with at least one hour between each dose. This amount of water is then gradually decreased to two liters per day until a normal consumption (1.7 liters) has been reestablished. The antidiuretic hormone should be administered as soon as possible (IM injection of 3-5 units of the oily vasopressin tannate solution every 24-72 hours). All types of stress should be avoided for the animal with rest in the kennel, minimal activity, small frequent meals, comfortable environment. A potassium supplement may also be effective.

Prevention

Dog owners should be educated to recognized symptoms early on and to minimize stress in Greyhounds.

HYPOTHYROIDISM

Hypothyroidism is one of the most common endocrine disorders in dogs. That being the case, studies conducted on racing Greyhounds and sled dogs have shown that these Sporting dogs are affected more often than other breeds and is associated with the following specific symptoms:

– Reproductive problems
– Change in cellular metabolism with intolerance to exertion
– Neuromuscular depression that contrasts with the clinical chart typically observed in dogs with hypothyroidism

Diagnostic methods are the same as those for the classic disorder. The results from 218 Greyhounds confirm others observed by other authors by pinpointing serum concentrations of thyroxin that are lower than those observed in sedentary breeds. Treatment is also traditional, with a good prognostic for recovering performance (levothyroxin with a posology of 0.1 mg/5 kg every 12 hours).

STRESS-RELATED HYPOGLYCEMIA

Characterized by excessive fatigue, despondency, and even convulsions (primarily in hunting dogs), though we have never encountered this or detected it in blood analyses performed during post-exertion tetaniform crises. On the other hand, without the least presence of hypoglycemia, recent work has demonstrated that administering a small amount of glucides (2g/kg of weight in the form of glucose polymers) to the dog immediately after exertion increases the rate of intramuscular glycogen reconstitution.

STRESS-RELATED HYPOMAGNESEMIA

Changes in magnesemia during physical activity primarily depend on the length of the period of exertion. Brief physical exercise (Greyhound racing) leads to a significant increase in magnesemia, whereas longer periods of exertion (hunting, sledding) are accompanied by a potentially large drop in magnesemia. Given that there are no labile organic reserves of magnesium, this post-exertion hypomagnesemia can sometimes cause tetaniform muscle spasms in poorly trained animals that have suffered intense tissue lipolysis. Prevention and treatment simply entail providing appropriate food and possibly administering magnesium-glycocol orally.

STRESS-RELATED HYPERTHERMIA

Energy dissipates through the muscle in the form of heat during exertion and, depending on the current environmental conditions, will:

– Help regulate the animal's temperature
– Provoke potentially severe hyperthermia

All Sporting dogs experience heat stroke. The consequences can be serious if the ambient temperature is too high, if the dog's coat is dark, of if the effort they exert exceeds their physical capabilities. Without going into further detail on an issue that is so well known, let us stress the importance of prevention a veterinarian should play on site in competitions. In some cases, he should not hesitate to postpone or cancel a competition. This is the case for sled dog races where the ambient temperature exceeds 10o or 15o C (50 to 60°F), depending on sunshine.

Exertion-related hyperthermia. Heat stroke on sled dog

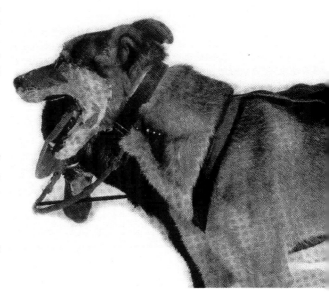

Pathology of Over-Training

After poorly recuperating from a series of illnesses, the dog may demonstrate various physical and psychological signs of being overworked. These are considered signs of "overtraining" and their causes are numerous:

– Increasing the amount and intensity of training too quickly for the animal

Pathological consequences of overtraining

OVERTRAINING

BASEDOWIAN	ADDISONIAN
Easily fatigued	Easily fatigued
Hyper-excitable	Inhibited
Difficulty sleeping	Normal sleep
Anorexia	Normal appetite
Weight loss	Constant weight
Tachycardia	Brachycardia
Slight hyperthermia	Normal temperature
Delayed recuperation	Normal recuperation
Effort-related hypernea	Normal respiration
Trembling	Lack of coordination

– Psychological pressure that is too great for the dog (the owner is too stressed)

– Using training methods that are too exclusive

– Too many competitions with not enough time in between to recuperate

The rhythm of the training sessions must capitalize on the phenomenon of overcompensation. Training cycles must therefore only be scheduled after the animal has completely recuperated from previous exertion.

In humans, there are two types of syndromes related to over-training: Basedowian (sympathicotonic) and Addisonian (parasympathicotonic). Basedowian over-training is characterized by the preponderance of excitation processes and sometimes with a marked overexcitation. Addisonian over-training causes a preponderance of inhibiting functions, physical weakness and lack of motivation. Given our current information, such a dichotomy is difficult to establish in dogs. In this species, signs of over-training as we understand them today tend to be Basedowian:

– Easy dependability

– Constant excitation

– Disturbed sleep

– Drop in appetite

– Loss of weight, normal temperature regulation, but slight chronic hyperthermia

– Tendency toward tachycardia

– Abnormal hyperpnea under treatment

– Delayed recuperation (time to return to a heart rate at rest)

– Hypersensitive to sounds.

As soon as a dog demonstrates any of these symptoms, certain therapeutic measures can prove effective after one or two weeks:

– Decrease specific training, keeping daily sessions to less than an hour of slow trot
  – Stress-free environment
  – Regular light massage
  – Stress-type diet (high in energy, high in protein)
  – Possible medicinal treatment

In the absence of pharmacological possibilities for prevention or treatment, safeguarding Sporting or Working dogs from the effects of stress includes drawing up an appropriate and intelligent training plan, providing a calm and normal psychological environment, and especially carefully choosing the dog's diet. These are all key elements in preventing problems related to the stress of exertion or over-training in dogs.

Clinical estimation of the degree of dehydration in dogs

Percentage of Dehydration	Clinical Exam	Attitude to Adopt
≤ 5	No clinical change	Drinking
6	Slight persistence of skin fold (a)	Oral rehydration
8	Significant persistence of skin fold 2-3 seconds refilling time for capillaries (b) slight endophthalmia Dry mouth tissues	Perfusion
10-12	Extreme persistence of skin fold More than 3 seconds refilling time for capillaries Pronounced endophthalmia—cold extremities Muscle spasms-occasional tachycardia	Perfusion Perfusion
12-15	State of shock Imminent death	Emergency

FUNCTIONAL REHABILITATION

In the beginning, functional rehabilitation, or physical therapy, was considered to be treatment for disorders or traumas by using heat or cold, massage, and exercise. Fortunately, physical therapy has evolved dynamically. Currently, all of the techniques used in human chiropractic medicine have been adapted to veterinary medicine, whether they be manual methods, thermodynamics, or instrumental methods.

Before any protocol is chosen, the therapist must examine the locomotive apparatus of the dog in order to know which structures need to be worked (muscles, tendons, ligaments, or joints). Gathering this data is important to objectively monitor progress: measuring the circumference of the limb, measuring the range of motion and observing the animal's walk. Objectively monitoring the progression allows us to evaluate the animal's progress and to best adapt the rehabilitation program.

Normal measurements must be known. First we measure the affected area, then the zone to be treated. The circumference of the limb must be measured while the dog is applying pressure to it on the floor, with specific anatomical references. For goniometric measurements, allowing the evaluation of the maximum degree of extension or flexion of a limb, which must be relaxed, and the joint must be brought to its maximum range of motion.

Observation is one of the best ways of detecting changes in a dog's walk. It is also a way to evaluate the moment at which the dog is fatigued.

Massage

Massage was mentioned as long ago as 1000 BC in Chinese literature. We may, certainly, wonder what are the physiological and psychological effects of massage. Massage can serve to eliminate an exsudate, to increase circulation, and to stretch the matrix of collagen fibers of a scar. Massage can also increase muscular relaxation, thereby allowing other exercises to be begun more calmly.

There are different forms of massage. It can be a large movement of effleurage, the length of the muscle, toward the heart. Indeed, this direction must always be used: massages in which the movements go away from the heart can break the integrity of the veins and cause damage to the valves, facilitating the return of blood into the veins.

This type of massage is effective for reducing swelling. It reduces the excitability of the nerve endings and therefore has a sedative and relaxing effect. It also allows for correct muscular relaxation.

Petrissage uses smaller movements that are concentrated on one muscle in particular. The muscular body is gradually pinpointed and relaxed. This massage is deeper than effleurage and improves circulation in deeper zones.

Friction massage is another type of deep massage, performed along scar tissue or across muscle fibers. It is indicated to eliminate abnormal scar tissue, to promote healing, and reestablish full mobility to a joint. It must always be followed with effleurage to improve circulation in and around the affected zone.

In addition to its physiological results, massage can also be very useful for calming down a nervous animal after injury or surgery. It is also a way to make contact with the animal before undertaking a more painful exercise.

Massage can begin on the day of intervention, or of the injury, and continue throughout the rehabilitation period. It is generally used in the following situations: during neurological injuries, after a period of immobilization, in the presence of muscular and peri-articular contractures, as a warm-up prior to mobilization and exercise, and after intense work, to reduce muscle stiffness.

Conversely, because of the increase it causes in blood circulation, massage is contraindicated whenever there is infection (as it would promote a quicker spreading of the infectious agents), when the dog has a fracture, when it has phlebitis or weakened veins, or a dermatological condition.

Massage is therefore primarily used to limit and reduce adhesion under a scar, which allows us to maintain a maximum degree of articular mobility.

Mobilization

Such manipulation has been described as a "skilled passive movement of the joint." All joints have a classic range of motion, which is the real movement allowed by the muscles. They also have accessory movements which are referred to as the "play" of the joint. This is the internal movement of the joint, allowing it to slide, role, or turn. When a joint is injured, we note that often the play in the joint as well as the classic movement is affected. The range of motion is therefore lost. If all of the movements—classic and accessory—do not return, it is easy to predict that the joint may be subject to further injury.

When a joint is stretched and its range of motion is improved, it is also necessary to reinforce the muscles in the new range of motion.

PASSIVE RANGE OF MOTION

This is similar to manipulation in that it consists of mobilizing a joint in its normal range of motion, but more so. The muscles must be relaxed in order to avoid muscle contractures, and the movement must be performed slowly. Movements taking the joint from one end of its range of motion to the other are useful in preventing contractures. Ideally, it should begin the day of surgery and be practiced for 2 to 3 weeks. Its goal is clearly to maintain or increase the range of motion in one or more injured joints.

Research shows that it is possible to increase the length of a muscle by slowly stretching it. The joint is slowly brought to the limit of it range of motion, and held in place there for a few minutes, then brought to a new range of motion. Sets of 10 to 15 movements should be practiced 3 times per day on average. This way the owner can actively be involved in his companion's rehabilitation.

The range of motion of an injured joint must always be compared to that of the healthy joint. There are in fact average ranges of motion, but we note individual variations, not where age is concerned, but rather according to solicitation of the various joints.

Dogs demonstrating a loss in their range of motion must be gradually introduced to a program to re-establish their range of motion.

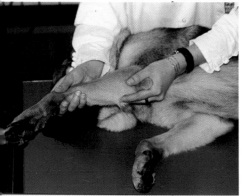

Mobilization of the elbow joint

This type of exercise is contraindicated in the site of an unstable fracture, non-reduced or non-reducible luxation, and in hyperlax joints. Special precautions are indispensable when working around bone tumors or in an area where a skin graft has been performed.

ACTIVE RANGE OF MOTION

Active exercise is not easy to perform on animals. Indeed, in humans, we ask the patient to mobilize his joint by reaching his maximum range of motion, which cannot be done with a dog. Active exercises are therefore performed by using obedience exercises, such as "sit" or "lie down." The active range of motion can be improved with hydrotherapy.

To return a dog to its sport, exercises involving muscular resistance are encouraged. These aim to gradually increase the weight supported by the affected limb. Such activities include walking, trotting, using the starting position for races, and swimming against the current.

The program starts by placing the dog in standing position, then applying pressure to the front or hind legs depending on the location of the muscular deficiency. Then walking. The animal first walks in a straight line, alternating slow and fast. Then he turns left and right circles, then figure 8s to modify the distribution of his body weight on his left and right legs. When the dog turns in circles, the inside leg will support more weight than the outside leg. The dog should therefore turn circles toward his injured side. It is also possible to have the dog run while attached by a harness to improve resistance. The next stage is running in a straight line, then zigzag.

Concurrently with the running exercises, the dog can be made to climb slopes, which will increase muscle strength.

Stairs should be only used with caution and at the end of a gradual program. The dog should not rest on the man accompanying it and should climb stairs very slowly.

It is then time to start returning the dog to its normal activity, by progressing slowly. If the dog limps or shows any sign of functional problem, its activity must be decreased.

Cryotherapy

Cold has been used to treat humans since the beginning of time. Ice was used to stop bleeding and cold drinks used to combat fever. In the 19th century, ice cubes or cold compresses were used to treat inflamed injuries. During the last 40 years, cold has become important in the treatment of burns, muscular spasms, preventing and reducing inflammation, relieving muscular-skeletal pain, and in neurological situations.

The most widely used technique is the application of cold through conduction, which means directly applying the cold to the skin.

The **bowl of cold water** is certainly the oldest form of cold treatment used. Ice is another old form of applying cold. Artificial ice, which is easier to use than natural ice was not available before the end of the 19th century. Applied directly to the skin, ice can be dangerous because it anesthetizes the skin and causes burns after a short period of time (5 minutes). This is why the skin must be protected from ice by a layer of material, so the patient only feels the cold and not the other sensations that are associated with it, such as pain or burning. No anesthetic effects should be produced.

Ice packs are a healthy way of using cold. They are also very easy to use. The heat is transferred from the body to the pack and the process continues until the temperatures of the body and the pack are the same or until the pack is removed.

Reusable cold packs are advantageous since they can be used more than once. These are plastic bags containing hydrated silica gel. When they are recooled in the freezer, the low thermal conductivity of the gel makes the pack flexible, which retains the cold longer than the standard 20 or 30 minutes of treatment.

Instant cold packs provide a low temperature when they are activated through pressure. They create cold through a chemical reaction. Each pack contains a small sack filled with liquid, usually water. The outer case contains a powdered chemical product that, when mixed with water after the sack has been broken, creates instant cold. These packs can only be used once. Moreover, they produce a change in temperature, not a specific temperature. The temperature provided depends on the temperature at which the sack was stored.

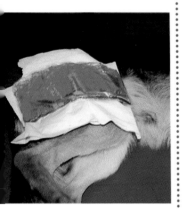

Cryotherapy:
Application
of a cold pack

Cryotherapy units have been produced for several years. The refridgerant circulates in flexible cushions, which can be attached to the animals legs. The surface of the cushion may or may not be insulated with a dry or moist towel.

The effectiveness of cold depends on a certain number of characteristics linked to the technique used and to the patient. Dogs respond to the application of cold by local and general circulation as well as by metabolic reactions. The initial reaction is to lower the superficial temperature by constricting superficial vessels. This phenomenon allows for the internal body heat to be transferred to the periphery. Applied to a joint, cold produces an involuntary reaction of lowering the temperature of the affected joint, but also other joints.

Cold reduces temperature to a noticeable depth. Muscular spasms, and therefore pain, are reduced by cold. Tissue metabolism drops in the zone where cold is applied, the demand for oxygen is therefore restrained, and the capillaries contract. Therefore, the cold allows us to prevent hematomas and reduce swelling.

The application technique of choice consists of wrapping the cold pack in a towel that has been soaked in lukewarm water, then wrung out. The smoother side is placed against the dog's skin, which can gradually become accustomed to the cold. For a longer accommodation period, simply place the pack in a dry towel. The pack is then held in place with bandages. The dog is kept in a warm room during treatment.

Treatment may be daily for acute problems and every two or three days for chronic problems. It should last 15 to 20 minutes. Less than 15 minutes and the analgesic effect has not yet occurred and over 20 minutes cutaneous burning will appear.

There are few contraindications. Only extensive injuries should not be treated with cold—vasoconstriction will slow healing—freezing, and hypersensitivity to cold.

Heat Therapy

Heat is another treatment that is as old as the hills, which has always been used, first instinctively to relieve pain. Some of these methods are still used, such as conduction: heat is transferred from the warmer object to the cooler object. The effectiveness of this technique depends on the difference in temperature between the two bodies and the thermal conductivity of the body (low when the skin is covered with fur).

An animal has elaborate mechanisms for regulating its body temperature, balancing heat loss and heat gained through the intermediary of ambient temperature as well as through its activities. In normal conditions, these mechanisms balance out, so well that body temperature remains in a relatively small range.

Heat packs are reusable packs, filled with silica gel—some may even be cooled, then reheated—that are placed in water that is nearly boiling. Other packs must be kept moist and are reheated in water. Finally, there are packs that instantly produce heat by breaking the internal sack in the same way as for instant cold packs.

During application of a heat pack, the dog's thermo-regulation mechanism responds to cool down the zone. The intensity of this response depends on the temperature of the pack, the size of the zone being treated, the difference in temperature between the pack and the skin, the length of treatment, and the dog's ability to distribute heat. To avoid all risk of cutaneous burning, it is a good idea to wrap the pack in towels before placing it on the dog's skin. Exposing the area to heat for 20 minutes should be sufficient.

Increasing the temperature of the tissues causes a sedative and analgesic effect, increasing blood flow and blood pressure in the capillaries. This increase may cause or exaggerate swelling. Increased circulation allows the heat to be dissipated quicker and increases the supply of oxygen, nutrients, and antibodies.

Heat packs are therefore used to relieve pain, relax muscles, and increase blood flow in a given area. Their use is beneficial for subacute or chronic pathologies, such as contusions, sprains, or myositis. They relieve the pain associated with arthritis and neuralgia (pain along a nerve).

If the method of transporting heat and blood circulation are intact in an area, the application of heat will promote healing. If the heat cannot be removed from the treated site, heat packs may be applied to another area that will trigger involuntary vasodilatation in the site to be treated.

For areas of suppuration or abscess, the application of heat accelerates the suppuration process and brings antibodies to the site. Nevertheless, it is best to use lukewarm packs since too much heat can cause painful reactions.

The application of heat packs is best combined with other therapeutic methods. They may be applied prior to massage, exercise, or electrostimulation.

They should not be used during the first 48 to 72 hours following injuries such as contusions or sprains. We recommend in these cases using moderate cold. After a luxation or a fracture, it is indispensable that specific treatment has been established before undergoing physical therapy. Acute inflammations, such as tendinitis or bursitis must not be treated with heat. In fact, animals are less tolerate to heat. The presence of swelling is another contraindication for the application of heat.

The patient's age must be taken into account for this type of treatment. Thermoregulation mechanisms are less effective in young dogs and may be lacking in older animals. Sensitivity to pain may be deficient and diminished cardiovascular and respiratory reserves may be responsible for a lesser tolerance to heat.

Hydrotherapy

Water is a very useful element as a therapeutic agent. It has only been used since the beginning of the twentieth century to treat patients with locomotive problems. Thanks to its physical properties, the effects of exercises performed in the water will be considerably more effective than exercises performed in another setting.

The buoyant effect of water, as opposed to gravity, is beneficial in treating muscle weakness. Moreover, animals seem to weight less in water. The support offered by the water can play an important role when the limb is moved parallel to the surface of the water. If the movement descends vertically, the force of the water works in opposition to the movement.

Water exerts a pressure on the body that is equal at all points if the body is immobile and increases with depth. This pressure is felt by the dog as soon as it is in the water. Respiration is more difficult and, as a result, care should be taken when immersing dogs with respiratory or cardiac problems.

Turbulence created by the dog or by a machine is useful in that it creates greater resistance than a continuous uni-directional flow. Also, the faster the movement, the greater the water's resistance.

The temperature of the water depends on the desired effect. To perform active exercises, such as swimming, a temperature of 18 to 20° C (64 to 68°F) is sufficient. On the other hand, to obtain a relaxing effect or to perform calmer exercises, temperatures of 35 to 40° C (95 to 105°F) are appropriate. Keep in mind that exercising in warm water causes rapid muscle fatigue. The physiological effects of the temperature combine with those of the exercises. They vary with turbulence, length of treatment, type of exercise, speed, the energy with which the movements are performed, and the physical condition of the animal.

During the period of immersion, the effects of the water are the same as those caused by a general application of heat or cold. If the temperature of the water is higher than that of the animal's body, the dog's temperature will increase, heart rate increases, muscle spasms subside, and the pain is relieved.

One of the most important points to take into account is the fear of water that dogs may experience, especially if the water is deep and if it is the first time the dog has swum. Small animals may be held by the therapist, at least during the first sessions and until their fears have dissipated. It is also possible to put the dog's feet in the water the first time, then gradually increase the depth of water in the pool throughout the sessions. If at all possible, the bottom should not be slippery so the dog can stand easily.

Exercises in warm or cold water have few disadvantages. They relieve pain, relax the animal and relieve muscle spasms. When the pain is no longer as severe, the dog can then move about more easily with minimal effort. Thanks to a decrease in the effects of gravity, the normal or paralyzed muscles easily increase the range of motion for the joints on which they act.

Almost all locomotive system problems can be improved through hydrotherapy. Neurological disorders often cause a great amount of muscular atrophy, which can be avoided or treated through swimming. If the paralysis is complete, the passive exercises performed in water will prevent contractures. Also, water allows us to avoid burns caused by urine in neurological patients. Indications for hydrotherapy include subacute or chronic inflammatory states, such as myositis, arthritis, fractures, luxations, and articular ankylosis.

Hydrotherapy is nevertheless prohibited in dogs with advanced peripheral vascular diseases, presenting a tendency for hemorrhages, either from injury or acute inflammation in the joints. Warm water may, in both cases, cause or prolong swelling. Warm water baths are contraindicated in patients with hyperthermia, until the dog's body temperature has returned to normal for 72 consecutive hours. This treatment is not appropriate for dogs with cardiac or respiratory insufficiency, nor is it intended for dogs with eye problems.

Finally, it is indispensable to note that swimming abilities vary from one animal to another and also can depend on previous training. Patients should be examined every day before entering the water. The length of treatments and the amount of exercises should be varied depending on the animal's condition. The first treatment may only last 5 minutes; regular treatments lasting 15 to 20 minutes, but the beneficial effects may occur in less time, especially for smaller animals.

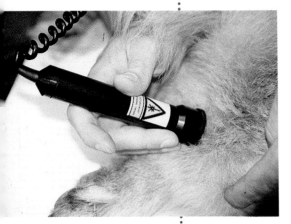

Laser Treatment

This is generally performed with a cold laser or a low-energy laser. It is used to increase collagen synthesis, to treat muscle injuries, and to relieve pain. The laser is applied directly to the skin for 30 seconds, with care taken to avoid having hair between the laser and the skin. The operation should be repeated daily. Nevertheless, no scientific studies have been carried out to show the effectiveness of this technique. The use of lasers has therefore remain empirical and somewhat marginal.

The faradic

Widely used in certain countries such as Australia, lasers are far less used in other places. The faradic current is induced by a coil. Two electrodes are put into place and the current passes through the tissues at a frequency of 6 to 8 waves per minute. The therapeutic effect comes not from the heat produced, but from the rhythmical contractions of the muscle, which reduces inflammation, releases adhesions, increases circulation, and generally tones the muscles. The current should be such that the contractions do not cause pain or discomfort. The contractions obtained through this method allow us to work the muscles in question independently of other muscles, unlike with active exercises.

Faradism also helps to localize painful muscles, since they are more sensitive to the current than normal muscles, but it takes a lot of skill to distinguish the reaction of an injured muscle from superficial nervous stimulation.

The treated muscle must be completely relaxed. The dog will preferably be lying on its side. The power is gradually increased until a complete contraction of the muscle is obtained. The frequency is such that the muscle is completely relaxed between two contractions. Producing 15 to 30 contractions of each injured muscle is sufficient. These treatments may, in urgent cases, be separated by only 4 hours, but 1 to 2 per day is generally sufficient.

Electrostimulation

This is stimulation of a muscle by the use of a current, either indirectly through exciting the motor neurons (motor nerve cells) or directly by stimulating muscle cells when the nerve can no longer ensure its function. This current is produced in pulses, not as a continuous flow, which prevents the appearance of cutaneous burning. The frequency, the length of the pulses and their intensity can be varied.

We can therefore work in monopolar mode—a small active positive electrode placed on the motor point (the place where the stimulation of the nerve causes the greatest muscle response), and a large negative or neutral electrode placed along the muscle—or in bipolar mode—two electrodes of the same size, both are active.

The first indication is the prevention or treatment of amyotrophy. The extent of the prevention of amyotrophy is related to how quickly treatment is undertaken. In fact, during prolonged immobilization, half of the muscle mass lost occurs before the tenth day of immobilization. Thanks to the use of electrostimulation immediately after surgery, post-operative functional recuperation is faster, which is essential for a Working or Sporting dog.

We must then work in monophasic mode, using a sufficient intensity to recruit the greatest amount of muscle fibers possible. The treatment consists of three sequences: warm-up for 2 minutes at a low frequency; 10 minutes of work, alternating high-frequency tetanic contractions and lower-frequency relaxation phases; 3 minutes of recuperation and relaxation at a low frequency.

In the case of muscle contracture, there are two ways of using electrotherapy: either by stimulating the opposing muscles to the contractured muscles (treating amyotrophy), or by using the decontracture and tonolysis treatment.

We work in monopolar mode, the active electrode being placed directly on the contractured fibers if there are not many or on the motor point of the muscle if the tension of the whole muscle is too great. The frequencies used are very low. Once the muscle tension has been reduced, manipulation of the limb is facilitated.

When muscles are not longer innerved (traumatic avulsion of the brachial plexus, lesion of the sciatic nerve following a fracture of the pelvis), the use of electrostimulation aims at avoiding muscular fibrosis by waiting for the nerve structures to recuperate. In this case, we directly stimulate muscle fibers by working in bipolar mode. The two electrodes are positioned along the muscle.

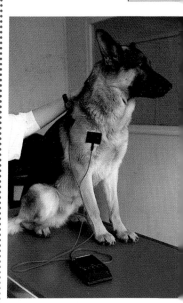

Electrotherapy: Working the shoulder muscles

Electrotherapy is contraindicated in the cervical region. We risk stimulating the carotid sinus and causing cardiac syncope.

Finally, we must take into account the dog's training and how quickly his muscles may become fatigued in order to best adapt the parameters of intensity and the length of treatment.

Ultrasound Therapy

Ultrasounds are material vibrations, like sound vibrations, but whose vibration frequency is much higher (higher than 20,000 periods or Hertz per second). These elastic vibrations are characterized by their frequency and their amplitude. The speed at which they propagate depends on the characteristics of the matter through which they travel. For a given frequency, it is much faster in water than in air.

The farther from the emitting source, the lesser the amplitude of the sound wave. The speed at which this decreases depends on the location of the wave's propagation. In the air, the propagation of ultrasounds is practically zero.

Ultrasound session

When a beam of waves arrives at the surface separating two different areas, part of the energy is transmitted to the second area, whereas another part is reflected on the interface. The various tissues absorb the ultrasounds to an unequal degree according to their elasticity, mass, and percentage of water. It therefore appears that the propagation is very good in bones, good in muscle and tendinous tissue, less good in fat and nervous tissue, and very bad in the lungs and intestines because of the presence of gas.

In living organisms, ultrasounds cause heat to be released because of the violent mechanical agitation of the molecules as well as a mechanical effect, qualified as micromassage. Another effect exists, but not in therapeutic doses: cavitation. This is manifested in the form of small gas bubbles that are created inside the liquids crossed by the ultrasound beams and which come to the surface and burst. They therefore produce analgesic effects, vasodilatation, and effects on the nervous system while triggering distant phenomena.

The frequencies used in veterinary medicine are 1 to 3 MHz, involving treatment heads of different sizes. The depth of penetration of the ultrasounds in tissues depends on the frequency used. At 3 MHz, the ultrasounds only penetrate superficial tissues. The treatment head of 1 MHz penetrates up to 3 or even 5 cm (1 _ - 2 inches). This is the one most often used.

The application of ultrasounds may done in continuous mode or in pulses. The ultrasounds produced continuously induce unstable cavitations, which are destructive to tissue. During pulsating mode, the heat created by the application of ultrasound may be dissipated between two pulses.

The biological effects of ultrasounds may be considered as a physiological reaction to mechanical and thermal effects. We first note an activation of blood circulation due to warming. The increased circulation triggers phenomena of muscle relaxation. The ultrasounds also have a beneficial effect on healing. The antalgic action is more difficult to explain. The contributing factors are improved blood circulation in the tissues, decreased muscle tone, and stimulation of nerve fibers (very sensitive to ultrasounds).

The transfer can be done in two different ways, either by direct application of the contact head to the skin (by using conductive gel), or by immersion, when the treated surface is too irregular or contact is painful.
The length of sessions depends on the surface to be treated: It is set at 1 minute per cm^2 with a maximum of 15 minutes.

In the case of acute trauma, treatment only begins 24 to 36 hours later, so as not to inhibit the repair of vascular lesions. Acute problems should be treated daily and chronic problems only 2 to 3 times per week.
The range of indications for ultrasounds is quite vast, the limiting factors being time and depth of penetration. They are therefore indicated for inflammation-related problems such as periostitis, arthritis, bursitis, capsulitis, and tendinitis. We can also use ultrasounds to promote muscle or cutaneous healing and to reduce adhesions developing under scar tissue. Ultrasounds may also be used on a fracture zone because of their capacity to reduce inflammation and pain and to speed up the formation and maturation of bone callus.

Nevertheless, certain organs cannot be treated with ultrasound. This is the case for the eyes, heart, and testicles, which may be subject to cavitation. The presence of metallic implants also prohibits the use of ultrasounds, as do localized bacterial infections (multiplication and dissemination of pathogens), rapid growth tissues, such as tumors and fetuses. Finally, the treatment must be avoided in animals with sensation problems because it is therefore impossible to get an indication of pain.

Pulsating Short-Wave Therapy

Pulsating short-wave therapy, or electromagnetotherapy is similar to ultrasonography in the extent of its indications. It is based on the use of pulsating electromagnetic fields, created by the interaction of the electric

Pulsating
short-wave therapy
on hip joint

field and a magnetic field. This field is created by a magnetode—or treatment head—placed at the treatment zone. This has two types of effects on the organism: so-called athermal effects, which are therapeutic due to localized metabolism, and thermal effects, related to an increase in local temperature. We talk about thermal effects when the increase in temperature can be measured.

The organism can react to heat in several ways: either by general reactions, an increase in blood temperature or the stimulation of receptors sensitive to the heat causes a dilatation of blood vessels as well as a decreased production of heat. These mechanisms allow the temperature of the organism to be maintained stable.

It may also cause local reactions: the local metabolism intensifies, then local irrigation is modified, allowing temperature variations to be regulated locally.

In the event of overdose, which means that the tissue temperature has exceed 42o C, the tissues may be deteriorated by the heat. To avoid such phenomena, the treatment should not reach the point of pain.

Pulsating short-wave therapy has a favorable effect on all stages of healing, except during the bleeding stage (which lasts 20 to 30 minutes).
During the inflammatory stage (24 to 48 hours), it encourages local metabolism through heat and the athermal application of electromagnetic energy.

During the stages of proliferation (2 to 4 days) and production (4 days to 3 weeks), a slight increase of the amount of electromagnetic energy produces a slight sensation of heat, stimulating the growth of blood vessels.

In the remodeling stage (3 weeks to 3 months), it warms the conjunctive and scar tissue, giving it back its elasticity.

Pulsating short-wave therapy can therefore be used to encourage the healing process, especially when circulatory problems slow healing.

It is therefore indicated in many cases of inflammation: periostitis, tendinitis, bursitis, synovitis, as well as ligamentary lesions. In the case of ligamentary lesions, electromagnetic stimulation, when applied the trauma the following day, increases blood flow and triggers a greater production of collagen. By doing so, the return to function is much quicker.
We also not a beneficial effect in the treatment of muscular-tendinous lesions, hematomas and muscle contractures.

In general, pulsating short waves are proscribed in all cases where blood flow is unable to evacuate the heat produced, which might worsen the inflammation. More specifically, this therapy is contraindicated when metallic implants (pins, plates, etc.) may alter the characteristics of the field, in the presence of bacterial infection (which causes the multiplication and dissemination of germs), during gestation, on rapid growth tissues (growth cartilage, tumors), in the case of sensation problems (absence of sensation of heat or burning).

The treatment lasts 20 to 30 minutes depending on the average power chosen.

In the case of acute trauma, treatment should be daily. Outside of the inflammatory stage, treatment shall take place only 2 to 3 times per week.

If there is no improvement after 5 sessions, pursuing the treatment will be in vain. In the case of improvement, the number of sessions will depend on the clinical results (10 to 20 sessions).

PHYSICAL EXERTION IN HIGH ALTITUDES

Just like people, dogs can be involved in physical exertion in high altitudes. Some sled dog races therefore take place above 3,000 meters (9,850 feet), as is the case at the International Rocky Mountain Stage Stop Sled Dog Race held each year in Wyoming. More often, however, in the event of a natural disaster (avalanche, earthquake, etc.) or a plane crash, specially-trained dog teams (rescue dogs that search through avalanches and rubble) are called upon to search for survivors and victims in the mountains. How well they do their jobs depends primarily on their health and motivation and on their handler's health and motivation. The effects of high altitudes on humans have been relatively well studied, but what are they for dogs?

BIOLOGICAL CONSEQUENCES OF HYPOXIA AND MOUNTAIN SICKNESS

Respiratory Function and Oxygenation

In very general terms, capacities for physical exertion at altitudes greater than 1,500 meters (5,000 feet) are diminished and this seems to be directly proportional to the altitude. The harmful effects of high altitudes on living organisms have been known since the late 1800s and certainly our understanding of these phenomena has only grown since that time. In physical principles, the value of the concentration of oxygen in dry air being constant (20,93 %), we refer to the pressure of oxygen in tracheal air saturated with water vapor, to note that this pressure goes from 149 mm of mercury at sea level to 107 mm of mercury at 2,000 meters (6,560 feet) in altitude, 87 mm at 4,000 meters (13,120 feet), and only 75 mm of mercury at 5,000 meters (16,400 feet).

The respiratory mechanism is also affected by the decrease in air density, so the respiratory muscles' ability to function is diminished, while the drop in resistance to the flow of air entails a drop in respiration to mobilize a given volume of air. Finally, the higher the altitude, the drier the air and water loss through airways is therefore much higher than at sea level. This phenomenon is particularly marked in dogs, since they do not sweat (except through the pads on their feet) and are much more easily dehydrated than humans in high altitudes.

Therefore, exercise or work done in acutely hypoxic conditions will provoke a much greater hyperpnea than that caused by an equal amount of exercise or work at sea level. We have also noted an increase in cardiac output for a given amount of oxygen consumed, which compensates for the decreased oxygen saturation in the blood, but this compensatory mechanism does not counter the effects of the drop in oxygen pressure. The result is an overall drop of 15% in the body's ability to transport oxygen above 4,000 meters (13,120 feet).

INDUCED CELLULAR STRESS

Acute exposure to high altitudes causes overall physiological stress that greatly affects cells. Our goal is not to go into great detail on the numerous experiments already carried out on humans in regard to this subject, but let us simply note that to date, these experiments have focused on one aspect or another and have not taken an overall synthetic approach.

In very broad terms, the un-acclimated body in high altitudes experiences stress, with organic, endocrine, and cellular ramifications.
Therefore, a decrease in the oxygen supply to a cell will cause serious problems in the cell's functioning, such as:

– Blocking the Krebs cycle and the respiratory chain at the mitochondrial level
– Lack of ATP, causing problems in membranal exchange
– Overall change in cell structure and therefore in membranes, which can no longer adequately regulate calcium exchanges.

The following has been confirmed by examining muscular biopsies on humans in high altitudes:

Drop in the oxidating potential of the muscle through disappearance of mitochondrial structures

Gradual destruction of muscle fibers

Significant change in enzyme activities that guarantee the functioning of the Krebs cycle, the respiratory chain, and the oxidation and energy valuation of ketone bodies.

Therefore during an acute hypoxic phase in high altitude, everything leads to a change in the energy functions of the cell and to the breakdown of its structure, which makes the cell membrane very fragile and very easily broken down.

OTHER INDUCED CHANGES

Among other biological changes caused by high-altitude hypoxia are:

Falling asleep with bouts of apnea

Panic attacks in humans, which is a sign of acute mountain sickness

Increase in cerebral brain flow, which partially explains the cephalic symptoms of acute mountain sickness

Increases risk of blood clots and transient ischemic attacks

Accentuated fatigue phenomena linked to smaller availability of glycogen supply and to a drop in glutamin synthesis.

ACUTE MOUNTAIN SICKNESS

One of the first effects of high altitudes is commonly called "mountain sickness," which entails:

– Headache
– Nausea
– Vomiting
– Physical and mental fatigue
– Insomnia
– Digestive problems

The symptoms that appear in the hours following exposure to an altitude above 3,500 meters (11,500 feet) disappear in most cases in 2-3 days. In more serious cases, acute pulmonary edema may develop or even cerebral edema. These disorders, still poorly understood in dogs, are the direct consequence of the physiological and cellular changes caused by hypoxia-mountain sickness.

Scientific Expedition: Licancabur Rescue Dogs "Chiens des Cimes"

To better prepare rescue dogs for the hostile environmental conditions involved in a high-altitude operation that does not allow for pre-acclimation, in 1996, we led a scientific expedition with the collaboration of the Parisian Firemen's Brigade, the Chilean Police Corp, the National Veterinary School in Alfort, the Animal Biosociology Lab of the Sorbonne, and the Royal Center for Canine Research. The expedition had the following objectives:

– To note and quantify the physiological incidences of exertion during acute exposure to
– high-altitude environmental conditions of hypoxic and mountain sickness
– To better understand the phenomena caused in cellular membranes, a site of oxidation stress
– To compare certain affects or changes in dietary nutritional balance with the goal of controlling the harmful consequences of this hostile environment

Organizing and Carrying Out the Expedition

CHOICE OF SITE

To reproduce conditions of catastrophe intervention, the site chosen had to meet the following criteria:

– Allow arrival from sea level to an altitude above 4,000 meters (13,120 feet) in less than 24 hours
– Allow men and dogs to work at plateaus of altitude spread out between 2,500 (8,200 feet) and 5,500 meters (16,400 feet)
– Have no snow
– Have ruins or rocky places that can serve as rubble

For these reasons, we chose the Licancabur volcano, which is 5,980 meters (19,620 feet) high and borders the Atacama Desert in the region north of the Cordilleras in the Chilean Andes.

Conducting experiments in high altitude

Carrying Out the Expedition

The French members of the expedition gathered in Santiago, Chile (after a 14-hour flight with a layover in Buenos Aires). Air France graciously allowed the five French dogs to remain in the plane's main cabin with their handlers. Joined upon their arrival by the Chilean Police Corps' five canine teams, the people and dogs were immediately flown to the port at Antofagasta, 1,700 kilometers (1,050 miles) to the north of Santiago. This time the dogs flew in a pressurized baggage hold area.

From Antofagasta, the expedition was joined by the local logistical team and took the road to San Pedro de Atacama (2,500 meters (8,200 feet) in altitude, in the Atacama Desert), then the path to spend the first night in a higher elevation (4,300 meters) (14,100 feet) in the military camp at El Tatio. The altitude of 4,500 meters (14,760 feet) was then reached, still by the path, and base camp was set up at the foot of the volcano. With the goal of reproducing real emergency intervention conditions, the different transfers were made as quickly as possible, without

The Licancabur volcano in northern Chili, reaches 5,980 meters (19,620 feet).

stopping to acclimate at gradual increases in altitude, except for a three-day period at the base of the volcano before beginning its ascent.

After nine hours of hiking, which was very difficult because of the steep grade (45o) and the crumbly volcanic rock, the first team (11 people and 8 dogs) reached 5,750 meters (18,860 feet) or 230 meters (760 feet) below the summit. Due to the common desire of all the participants to preserve the dogs' health (dehydration and problems with the pads of their paws), the ascension was stopped after the last tests and samples were completed.

Protocol for the Experiment

OBJECTIVES

Given that this was the first experiment of its kind and given the extreme conditions of the terrain, the scientific objectives set for the expedition and the dogs were as follows:
– Record a maximum amount of physiological data for the dogs, including:
  • Effects of altitude on rest
  • The exaggerated effects of work in high altitudes
– Make a comparative study of the Working dog's diet in hypoxic high-altitude conditions
– List the specific pathological disorders encountered and deduce ways to prevent and/or treat them to be integrated into existing materials for search and rescue dog teams.

RESULTS

Intake of Food and Water

As a function of the slightly variable formats of the animals, daily water intake went from 1.5 liters at sea level to 7 or 8 liters during exertion in high altitude. There was no notable increase in volume or frequency of urination. Therefore, the daily hydrient requirement increased from approximately 60 ml per kg of body weight to 300 ml per kg of body weight. The group of Chilean dogs consumed slightly more water (by kg of body weight) than did the group of French dogs.

The following information was noted in regard to diet:
– Notable improvement of behavior for dogs receiving "experimental" food
– Preventive effectiveness of antioxidant supplements (vitamin E) and oxygen generating supplements (Omega 3 fatty acids)

Veterinary Medical Aspects

Among the pathological disorders encountered during the expedition, those linked to environmental conditions and terrain were predominant, whereas classic problems typical of "mountain sickness" in humans were less common.

Ocular problems (tearing, conjunctivitis) were comparable to those experienced by sled dogs in snow when there is bright sunshine. They appeared during the first days of the expedition because of very dry air and

---

Contents of a special veterinary bag for working with dogs in high altitudes

The following material should be added to the standard treatment and emergency kits:

- Protective booties (8 per dog)
- Anti-inflammatory and antiseptic cream (Algyval®)
- Products to treat stress-related diarrhea (Smectivet®, Imodium®)
- Artificial tears and anti-inflammatory collyrium
- Oxygen bottle with flexible mask
- Pre-cut survival blankets with hole for feet

---

because the high altitude makes the sun's rays even harsher. They can be prevented systematically with collyrium or artificial tears.

Foot abrasions (to the pads), are directly related to the volcanic soil and its high salt content. Treated with thick ointments, the abrasions will heal from the addition of hyperoxidated fatty acids (Algyval ND). They can be prevented with hyperoxidated creams applied three or four times per day and by using protective boots like those worn by sled dogs.

The myglobinuria encountered upon arrival in base camp can be attributed to trip conditions: The stress of the plane trip for all of the dogs from Santiago, Chile to Antofagasta added to some 12 hours in a 4X4, most of which was on unpaved roads. The extracellular dehydration caused by stress and the series of muscular micro-traumas explain this transient phenomena, which is not at all serious and which can be treated with a simple non-steroid anti-inflammatory.

When we examined the chronology of its appearance, the stress-related diarrhea experienced by 5 of the 10 dogs, was due to transportation and diet for those dogs that received standard food. At any rate, the most serious pathological problems encountered were all linked to extracellular dehydration, which led to bouts of heat stroke or to a need for intravenous infusion of liquids. Because of the ambient climate conditions, the altitude, and exertion, most of the dogs experienced an extracellular dehydration of 2-3% without the least clinical symptom, except for a slight hemoconcentration visible through hematocrit.

This is a classic phenomenon in sled dogs. In addition to water intake, maintaining electrolyte isotonicity is important, as are the consequences of an imbalance in metabolism and the phenomena of membrane polarity, for example. Any time an animal is dehydrated over a prolonged period of time (especially if the dehydration is caused by a stress-diarrhea-dehydration syndrome), electrolytes are lost which must be replaced. Given the changes this causes in hydro-electrolytes, the basic diet should be formulated with this information in mind. It is also recommended that you use electrolyte powders in a dog's drinking water. Several are available on the market. Simply pay attention to the isotonicity and the hypotonicity of the solution, since excess sodium can cause diarrhea in dogs.

Finally, also take into account the range of local daily temperatures, though this was not found to have caused any particular problems. Temperatures can easily exceed 30-35o C (85 to 95°F) and drop below 0°C (32°F) at night. Though dogs tolerate such ranges quite well, they are an additional stress factor that should be avoided for the dogs by setting up a place for them to sleep that is sheltered from the wind and potentially by having them wear suits or providing thermal survival blankets that have been pre-cut to a convenient size.

These summary of the pathological disorders encountered during the expedition leads us to suggest creating a special sort of veterinary "doctor's bag" used specifically for this type of operation. Finally, let us note that

Defense systems against free radicals

Type		Cofactor	Function
Enzymatic symptoms	Superoxide dismutase	Cu, Zn, Mn	Superoxide recycling
	Glutathion Peroxidase	Se	Peroxide recycling
	Catalase	Fe	Peroxide recycling
Metal Chelating Agents	Ferritin	-	Iron storage
	Siderophilin	-	Iron storage
Liposoluble Nutrients	Alpha-tocopherol	-	Destroys radicals
	Beta-carotene	-	Destroys radicals
Hydrosoluble Nutrients	Ascorbic acid	-	Destroys radicals
		-	Regenerates Vitamin E

though our results indicate a greater cellular damage and breakdown in dogs than in humans, the animals objectivize the pain and discomfort they experience much less than humans do. This is a very clear example of how important psychological perception is in a given situation, and how much it exacerbates physical problems in humans.

Exertion during situations of acute exposure to high-altitudes without acclimation is characterized in people and in dogs by an accumulation of physiological stress that is exacerbated by ambient hypoxia-mountain sickness, which leads to changes in cell structure and function that are primarily linked to the phenomena of membrane lipo-peroxidation and enlarging of free radicals. The scientific expedition in Licancabur with the search and rescue dogs in 1996 was the first of a series devoted to physiology in extreme environments and its consequences and prevention (especially nutritional). It allowed us:

– To better pinpoint the biological consequences of exertion in high altitudes without the dogs' having been prepared
– Note the need for using a complete dry food adapted to the conditions of intense stress (high energy density, enriched in certain fats and proteins, overall nutritional balance), in keeping with those already used for sled dogs
– To begin to quantify the phenomena of membrane peroxidation and the radicular changes caused, which may be partially prevented through an antioxidant supplement (5,000 mg of alphatocopherol for 30 kg (65 pounds) of body weight, daily in our case)
– To confirm information regarding dogs that had been heretofore only theory, regarding the perfect correlation between essential polyunsaturated fatty acids and their final concentration in the structure of the membrane, those of the omega 3 series improving tissue oxygenation in our case, and therefore overall energy for the animal (less easily fatigued upon exertion, better recuperation, better metabolic value of food)
– To define, through observation of specific pathological disorders encountered, the materials and medicinal elements that would allow us to maintain operating conditions for the animals so that they may continue to search for human victims and survivors.

Gum tissue exam

Time for capillaries to return to their color

Press on the tissue for a few seconds

Once you release, the color should return to normal in less than 2 seconds

BUYING A DOG

Each time you get a new dog, it should be examined completely in order to determine if it is capable of performing the required exercises. The help of a veterinarian can be extremely valuable for examining certain parts of the dog's body. Their expertise is essential.

A complete examination of a dog can be performed in one of two ways:

– from "the tip of the nose to the tip of the tail," including the legs
– examining each apparatus separately. By apparatus, we mean a group of organs working together toward the same purpose (for example, the digestive apparatus, which is made up of the mouth, the pharynx, the esophagus, the stomach, the intestines and related digestive glands). This is the method used at UMES, described below.

The veterinary terms used have been described and explained in the other chapters of the book.

Overall Exam

Before examining any particular aspect of a dog, the animal should be observed in its entirety:

– an examination from a distance allows you to appreciate its overall attitude (attentive, independent, despondent, happy, etc.), its conformation (balance, topline, stoutness, etc.). You should also measure the dog's size and appreciate its weight, especially if it is a puppy that is still growing.
– Its rectal temperature should be between 38 and 39° C (100 and 102°F). It varies in relation to the dog's overall state (the more excited the animal, the higher the temperature) and also in relation to its overall health (a dog with a rectal temperature higher than 39.5° C (103°F) is probably suffering from an infection).
– An examination of the dog's gums is a good way to check the repletion and quality of the blood. They should be pink. Capillary recoloration time (which is the amount of time gums take to return to their original color when you press on them for a few seconds) should be lower than 2 seconds (we also talk about capillary fill time).
– It is also necessary to check the dog's vaccination and worming calendar and other various certificates (tattooing, stud book, etc.) that are involved in purchasing a dog.

The examination of the animal apparatus by apparatus can be done in any order; the important thing is not to forget any.

Cardio-Vascular Apparatus Exam

Various elements should be examined:

– Heart rate should be taken with a stethoscope or by placing a hand behind the dog's left shoulder to feel the precordial beat. The heart rate varies depending on the size of the dog. For an animal at rest, it should be between:

– 100-200 beats per minute for a small dog
– 70-100 beats per minute for a medium-sized dog
– 60-70 beats per minute for a large dog

The femoral pulse is taken on the femoral artery on the inside of the thigh. It is important to note its nature (the pulse should be quite strong) and to check its coordination with the heart rate.

The heart rate should be regular, outside of the increase related to respiratory movement (perfectly physiological respiratory arrhythmia). Otherwise, additional examinations are necessary to check for blockages or extrasystoles.

Auscultation allows you to listen for heart sounds and to make sure there are no abnormal supplemental noises (murmurs, skips, etc.)

Palpating precordial beat by placing a hand behind the left elbow

Examination of the Respiratory Apparatus

Respiratory movements should be normal and regular. They can be appreciated by observing the rise and fall of the rib cage. Their frequency should be between 15 and 20 movements per minute.

An examination of the nose and sinuses allows you to make sure there is no drainage. Palpation of the trachea ensures that there is no collapse or triggerable cough. During auscultation, respiratory noises should not be overwhelmed by creaks, whistles, etc.

The femoral pulse is taken on the inside of the thigh

Examination of the Digestive Apparatus

Examination of the oral cavity allows you to check the quality of the animal's teeth (missing teeth, wear and tear of canines, etc.), to check for the presence of tartar (especially on the carnassials) and to check the quality of the gums and tongue (ulcers on the tongue, etc.).

Palpating the esophagus allows you to check its flexibility and to cause the animal to swallow, which should be done without pain.

Palpating the visceral organs allows you to pinpoint the entire digestive tract (stomach, small intestine, large intestine) as well as the liver, spleen, and pancreas. This should all be soft and painless.

Macroscopic examination (with the naked eye) of stools provides information on the overall function of the digestive tract.

The nose should be cool and moist with no cracks or discharge.

It is important to know what food the dog receives and if there are any recurrent digestive problems (stress-related diarrhea, constipation, etc.).

Examination of the Genital Apparatus

Palpating the male's testicles allows you to verify the number of testicles to detect the problem of monorchidism (a single testis has descended) or cryptorchidism (neither testis has descended) and to appreciate their conformation (symmetry, suppleness of the scrotum).

It is also important to check the mammary glands for any abnormal lumps. A rectal exam of the male allows you to check the condition of its prostate (size, shape, pain, etc.). The penis and the vulva should be free of any suspicious discharge, pustules, etc.

It is also imperative to check the entire heat calendar for females to make sure periods of heat appear regularly.

Examination of the Urinary Apparatus

Palpation of the kidneys through the abdomen allows you to appreciate their size, shape, etc. It is necessary to watch the dog urinate to check for urinary difficulties or incontinence. Macroscopic exam of the urine allows you to check its color, limpidity, amount, and odor.

The amount of liquid a dog consumes should be checked in comparison with the amount of urine per day.

Dermatological Examination

An overall examination of the coat allows you to detect dull patches, hair loss, etc.

A macroscopic search for external parasites and related signs should be performed (fleas/scratching, tics/abscesses, mange/pustules, etc.).

An examination of cutaneo-mucus junctures allows the discovery of ulcerations, which should particularly be checked on German Shepherds.

Examining the interdigital spaces and pads allows you to search for any foreign objects or change in the appearance of the skin.

Examining the ears is necessary to check for infection.

Examination of the Neuro-Locomotive Apparatus

Examination of Movement
Observing the dog as it moves (walking or trotting) allows you to study its walk: check for ataxia, paresis, hyper- or hypometria, etc.

Lifting the rib cage allows respiratory movements to be observed.

An ectropion or entropion will cause excessive tearing, among other things.

Stationary Examination

Examining different postures and reflexes of the dog allows you to check if the nervous system is functioning appropriately

– the overall attitude (apathetic, alert, animal leans to one side, etc.) will allow you to detect a disorder of the central nervous system.
– Studying the dog's proprioception and locomotion exercises (wheelbarrow, hemi-station, hemi-locomotion, etc.) allows you to pinpoint a vertebral problem.
– Reflexes of the patella, femur, and triceps help you to locate the problem and determine its nature.

Manipulating different bone segments allows you to pinpoint the location of a source of pain:
– hyperextension of the hips (one at a time, then together by pressing on the sacrum), before which we would search for pain, instability, cracking, etc.
– hyperflexion of the limbs, one at a time for a minute followed by the start of a trot will reveal limps.
– Examining the skeleton (by palpating the sub- and supra-lumbar, appreciating the cervical tonus, etc.).
– Palpation of the tendons and muscles, if possible after exertion, allows you to detect inflammation.

Complete examination of the skull and bone rays allows you to detect pain, malformations, etc.
Any abnormal exam should be confirmed by a veterinarian, who will perform additional exams if necessary.

Ophthalmologic Examination

– examination of the lids and conjunctiva allows you to detect conjunctivitis, entropions, extroprions, etc.
– fluorescin tests allow you to detect the presence of ulcers, keratitis, etc.
– examination of the anterior chamber can reveal discoloration, synechia, lenticular dysplasia, etc.)
– If possible, an examination of the posterior portion of the eye will allow you to visualize the choroid, the retina, etc.

Additional Examinations

Certain additional examinations may be useful to confirm or disprove clinical suspicions.

Radiography
– Radiography to detect hip or elbow dysplasia under general anesthesia (for dogs over 12 months of age)

A dog's movement should be observed from the front...

...the back

...and the side.

The hips should be manipulated as much as possible.

– Radiography of zones that are "at risk" for the breed (lumbar-sacral region for German Shepherds, cervical region in Dobermans, thoracic-lumbar region in Dachshunds, etc.).

Blood and Urine Tests
– blood count and analysis of lactates during a stress test for dogs that have difficulty maintain their level of performance during competition
- biochemistry and counts for specific disorders (diabetes, viral or bacterial infections, etc.)
– urinary bandage and urinary cyto-bacteriological exam if necessary.

Special Examinations
– Hearing Exam (for breeds at risk for deafness)
– Olfactory Exam (for search and rescue dogs)
– Electro-retinography (for breeds at risk for congenital retinal disorders)

This list is not exhaustive. It is up to the veterinarian to provide any additional examinations he deems necessary.

A well-organized and thorough approach to buying a dog should allow you to detect even minor problems. When acquiring an adult dog, there should be a two-week trial period.

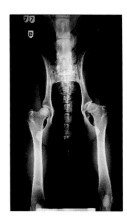

Hips radiography: severe arthrosis

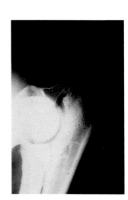

Radiography of the elbow, side view: non united anconeal process may lead to arthrosis

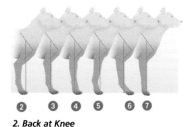

1. Normal Stance

Stances in

Dogs

2. Back at Knee
3. Down in Pastern
4. Knuckled Over
5. Receding Wrist
6. Long in Pastern
7. Upright Pastern

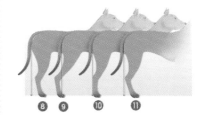

8. Camped Forward
9. Camped Out
10. Hyperextended Hock
11. Stands Under   udé

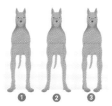

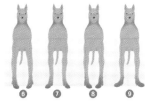

1. Normal
2. Turned Out
3. Pigeon-toed

4. Base Narrow in Front
5. Base Wide in Front

6. Spread Knees, Pigeon Toes
7. East-West Front
8. Pigeon-toed
9. Turned-out Feet

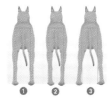
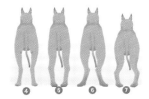

1. Normal Stance
2. Base Narrow in Rear
3. Base Wide in Rear

4. Turned-out Feet
5. Pigeon-toed
6. Cow-hocked
7. Barrel-hocked, Spread Hocks

MONITORING TRAINING AND MEDICAL SPORTS APTITUDE TESTS

Regular veterinary medical check-ups for Sporting and Working dogs have only just begun, and their effectiveness will only be real and complete once they are based on a battery of carefully chosen tests, since a single test will never be enough to provide an educated opinion, for example on the animal's training. The veterinarian should never forget that what happens in the field is far more telling than what happens in the laboratory.

Ideally, these tests should allow us to answer two main questions:
– Can the dog participate in competitions without risk of injury (qualitative performance)?
– Is it possible to predict a dog's performance in a particular competition (quantitative performance)?

Taking blood
during training

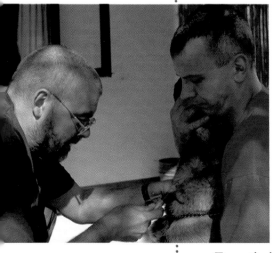

Studying the
oxygen consumption
of a dog during
a standardized
treadmill test

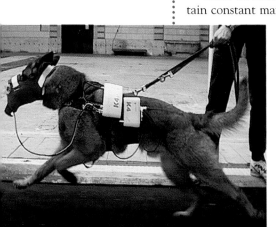

A list of questions owners would like answered is quite easy to draw up:

– Can training be intensified or should it be slowed down? Is there a risk of fatigue or overworking for the dog (quantitative problem)?
– Does training have an adverse effect on a given physical or physiological quality (energy or psychomotor), or on a psychological quality (qualitative problem)?
– Will training allow us to obtain the expected results when we need them?
– Should we more carefully adapt the dog's overall diet and nutritional supply?
– Is the dog's overall hygiene good?

As a result, the veterinarian's role in response to the owners' questions in this area should be:

– to establish that the physical qualities of the animal are appropriate for the sporting activity or work in question. The existence of a pedigree or any document of origin has absolutely nothing to do with the concept of a dog's physical aptitude.
– To monitor the evolution of these qualities as training progresses. An animal that does not progress despite a good training plan is surely suffering from an intrinsic problem (intercurrent problem) or an extrinsic problem (poorly devised diet, overall hygiene, etc.)
– To verify that training doesn't have any adverse effects on the body and possibly to suggest modifications to the training program based on repercussions observed (fatigue, overworking, etc.).

General Methodology

Once we address high-level Sporting or Working dogs that must maintain constant maximal operational effectiveness, it is necessary to incorporate regular physical and physiological aptitude check-ups for the animal. Most important is a regular check-up (every 4 to 6 weeks) that allows the veterinarian to examine the following structures at rest:

– all bone, digestive, muscular-tendinous, and ligamentary structures;
– the absence of behavioral symptoms of overworking or overtraining;
– a simple blood test that is both biochemical and especially hematologic, which allows him to diagnose an intercurrent infection, stress blood cell count, or chronic inflammatory problem early on.

It is a good idea beforehand to establish regular standardized tests with the same schedule:
- a test that always takes place at the same time, in the same place, under conditions that are as stable as possible (including the time of the last meal and last drinking);
- taking of simple physiological parameters before and after exertion and after a 30-minute period of recuperation (cardio-respiratory frequency, rectal temperature);
- blood test 30 minutes after the end of exertion, the data of which is compared to that obtained during rest by adding the energy parameters such as lactates and plasmatic free fatty acids, if possible.

Ideally, early on it is a good idea to list the factors involved in successfully performing a sport or a given activity, then determine the relative importance of each factor. This analytical methodology implies a scientific approach based on certain criteria and involves studying documents and observation charts. How many owners simply note each dog's performance in training on cards with their own knowledgeable impressions regularly?

In the last ten years, we have been able to use such an approach on some teams of sled dogs over several years. The results obtained on the evolution of their training programs was extremely rich.

Since success at sports is considered the optimal expression of physical functions, completed by the dog's unconscious desire to perform, it becomes the reflection of the interaction of psychological, physical, and physiological functions.

Many existing sports or types of work differ not only in their demands of locomotive and cardiac functions, but also fundamentally in the behavioral profile of the dogs in question. A dog is a dog, and several behavioral characteristics are common to all, but the good owner must be able to evaluate and compare elements as varied as: motivation, attitude, need to perform, resistance to a certain monotony, emotional stability, aggressiveness and tendency to fight, will, anxiety, vigilance, reflection, loyalty, sociability, etc.

The psychomotor aspect remains difficult to evaluate in a given dog even if we tend more and more to be aware of the importance of motricity and control by sensitive and sense organs in physical activities and canine sports. Coordination, balance, segmental and lateral independence, precision of controlled movements, and flexibility are all important elements that as of yet can only be appreciated empirically, by the expert's eye.

Development of Specific Tests

Though the entire body is used during exercise, certain systems especially limit its intensity or duration: neuro-muscular, cardio-vascular, respiratory, or endocrine systems. Their relative importance varies according to the type of physical activity performed. Defining the energy requirements of practicing a sport involves specifying which energy processes are used, when and how intense they are, even by which muscle or which type of muscle fibers. The best approach would then be both biomechanically physiological and energetically physiological. Where biomechanics are concerned, veterinary doctors are only beginning to imagine the study of specific movements by analyzing the animal on film or through involved and sophisticated exams such as electromyography.

In the field of sled dogs, we are beginning to use constraint gauges placed between the dog's harness and the pull line in order to best appreciate the evolution of the work of strict traction performed by the dog. The initiatives are good, but we need to recognize that the research has no means of really progressing in this specific field of knowledge of Sporting dogs, all the more so to help owners or veterinarians have simple, inexpensive testing methods!

Sports medicine monitoring of Sporting dog: breakdown of fixed and changing exams

Where energy is concerned however, we are being to better pinpoint the physiological and biological components of the different types of canine exertion, thanks to research programs developed in collaboration with dietary company research centers, such as Royal Canin.

The next stage now consists of defining simple, standardized tests for measuring:
– maximum alactic anaerobic power;
– maximum lactic anaerobic power;
– maximum aerobic (VO2max) power;

Here again we are making progress, but a bit more time is still needed for specialized centers (still quite few in number in veterinary universities) to put reliable and accessible tests on the market.

A dog's physical aptitude is based on two basic factors: energetic aptitude, especially strength and endurance of the canine "machine," and biomechanical aptitude, which consists of the qualities that allow energy potential to be expressed. Each of these groups of factors makes it difficult to express physical aptitude. A given individual does not present one, but several aptitudes and it is indispensable when this term is used to define the exercise to which it refers.

We can now answer the question, "Is this dog physically capable?". However, the question, "Can we predict or estimate its level of performance at a specific time?" remains unanswerable at present.

The future should certainly bring more satisfying information to dog owners, with the development of the concept of canine sporting medicine.

REGULATIONS

*S*port may be leisure, but it also often means competition. Competition has rules that vary from country to country but most importantly involves full respect for the animal, particularly by preventing and cracking down on any harmful practices like doping.

THE PROBLEM OF DOPING

Faced with the constant development of canine sports disciplines and the large stakes involved in some competitions, drug testing has become necessary to ensure that animals and sporting ethics are being respected. Greyhound races (in the United States, Australia, and Great Britain) and pulka and dog sled races are the firsts to have established international regulations.

Physical performance for any living creature is the result of two groups of factors:
– biological factors: the basis for the notion of physical ability (physiological potential to perform movement)
– environmental factors: the basis of constraints that hinder the restitution of mechanical energy outdoors.

Any attempt to improve performance must therefore involve changes to these two groups: limiting constraints and improving individual physical ability.
There are two ways of reaching this goal:
– biological preparation in the greatest sense of the word, the goal of which is to physiologically guide the animal to best express its genetic potential through gradual improvement of the quality of its functional structures, energy reserves, and energy efficiency through training, diet, warm-up, etc.
– doping, the goal of which is to artificially modify (often only temporarily) one or more of these factors.

Many different definitions of "doping" have been proposed since the beginning of the 20th century in medical and sports education conferences involving people and horses. Here we note two that seem to use the most appropriate:

– doping is the administration, in any form, to an individual in good health, of a product that is foreign to his body, or physiological products in abnormal quantities, with the singular goal of artificially increasing the individual's abilities for an unfair advantage in competition.
– doping is not the physiological preparation of the athlete (which itself is essential and must remain under medical surveillance). The following should be considered as doping: recourse to substances and methods intended to artificially increase performance in a competition, which goes against sporting ethics and the physical and psychological integrity of the athlete.

Doping is currently defined as the use of products banned in competition by the international authorities.

Whatever the case, the very difficulty that exists in defining the problem shows just how great the ethical (and media-enhanced) debate surrounding the issue is. In our view, the ethical debate on doping in Sporting dog competitions must first be settled before any technical considerations are even proposed.

Ethical Aspects

Here we are interested in the problem of doping in Sporting dogs. It is not our goal to lay forth the numerous debates and discussions of the different view points, decisions, legislations, or teams. This is why we find it important to prepare the reader for the officious and personal aspect of the following ideas and opinions.

CANINE SPORTS INVOLVED

Currently two canine sporting activities are directly affected by regular drug testing. Greyhound races and pulka and dog sled races are the only two objective performance disciplines (i.e., against the clock), as compared to subjective performance disciplines that are based on human judgment. Structurally speaking, these sports are also linked to structures that legally require the existence of regulations:

– Greyhound races where betting is allowed
– the pulka and dog sled race that is under the control of the ACFIS, via the IFSS, which means it is indirectly governed by the IOC.

POTENTIAL TYPES OF DOPING

Doping to Win
For a very long time, people have tried to artificially increase animals' performance in competition with others. So, even if doping in dogs is not as extreme as in humans or horses, it is nevertheless an issue.

However doping is defined, the principle remains the same: A dog must be able to pass a test (or attain a rank) by its own abilities, without its owner having resorted to medicinal methods or other tricks. Many Greyhound and sled dog races now have financial prizes. This being the case…it is far better to avoid the problem beforehand and establish testing of competitors.

Doping to Lose
Betting may lead the bad owner of a good dog to drug the animal with the goal of making it lose. Most people consider doping the consumption

or administration of stimulants, but giving a dog a drug to reduce its performance and thereby rig the game is also fraudulent.

Doping to Cause Another Dog to Lose

Now we have gone beyond simple fraud. The goal here is to administer a banned substance to a competitor (to improve or hinder its performance).

WHERE DOES DOPING START AND STOP?

Restrictive regulations or controlled medication?

This is also a real ethical debate that has affected many other sporting disciplines over the years. Before beginning any scientific, technical, or regulatory studies, we must first pinpoint the motives for establishing anti-doping regulations:

– compromising sporting ethics and encouraging deceit
– compromising the animal's health, in that all drugs have side effects
– compromising the most basic rules of animal protection, for example when drugs are used to mask pain
– compromising breeding and genetic selection, which begins to break down in dogs and the performance ratings are falsified

With these ideas in mind, all forms of regulations can be proposed, from the most drastic to the most lax, with the happy medium seeming fairly difficult to reach. If we take the example of horses, the Racing Code regulations refer to the "standard and normal food for animals." Does this mean that everything except grass, hay, and oats is a drug?

The definition provided by the French Equestrian Federation provides an element that we find much more constructive: protecting the animal's health.

Given this first realization, we should note that two main types of regulation are triggered: One is very restrictive (at the time of a test, the dog must be in top condition, and only compete if in good health, all possibilities of returning the animal to good health so it can compete are excluded). The other is based on controlled medication (a therapeutic agent, in normal dosage, used in a purely curative goal, and for which it has been proven that no repercussions on performance exist, may be used under strict control of a veterinarian).

While restrictive regulations may seem appropriate in short competitions like Greyhound racing, they are completely inadequate for sled dog races that can last from 2 to 21 days! It would be impossible to treat a minor cut! A specific approach to each discipline is therefore necessary.

In the Animal's Best Interest

As soon as you broach the subject of doping in canine sports, animal rights activists come knocking under the pretense of protecting the animals' rights, but who are really looking for public attention. These animal rights "advocates" clearly influence the general public, but their emergence should encourage people to use dogs responsibly. Let us remember that in legal terms, a "drug" is "an element or molecule used to reduce, relieve, or prevent illness or to alter the physiological state of a person or animal." This last notion includes elements aimed at improving performance, such as protective booties, or electrical stimulation, with large doses of vitamins and medicinal substances considered as doping agents.

At what point does a vitamin, an essential nutrient, become a drug or a doping agent? The answer depends on the intended use. This may seem surprising, but should really the user's actual intentions be the deciding factor? These aspects are instead decided by the authorities in the public's best interest.

Certain people think that linguistic communication is the very basis of our concept of "interest" and also that this concept is limited to humans. Other believe that other species of animals have means of visually and vocally communicating with others in their species. Many animal observers, ourselves included, think that animals show their interest by their behavior. This manifestation of one's "own best interest" is the key to innate, natural, or moral rights. Therein lies the question of natural rights, where undeniably most communities have admitted the legal rights and protection of animals. Should we consider the dog's best interest as an individual or as a species when we set up regulations involving a given substance? The image of animal rights advocates as a group of terrorists should be avoided by those who are involved in using animals responsibly. By the same token, those who use animals owe it to themselves to incorporate all of the viewpoints possible with regard to animal rights and their protection in our community. Such an understanding is essential for effectively showing user responsibility so that Sporting and Working dogs can be fully accepted by the community.

Races have long involved betting. The need for honesty

in the game, in the way those involved think about the game, and in the way the game is perceived is understood and admitted. This was the initial reason for establishing drug testing, prohibiting the use of stimulants and depressives, then later, substances not naturally found in the body that affect speed, effort, courage, etc.

Official chemists controlled the testing such that any molecule suspected of existing was effectively prohibited, despite any biological significance, which all led to an absurd medical situation. The regulations were also geared toward positive lists, and banned drugs, even if the strict nature of the lists did not take into account the various uses of many drugs and the limits of science. At the same time, the drug testing programs became more expensive for the canine disciplines involved.

It is clear to everyone now that we still do not know exactly what is or is not a doping agent for dogs. At the very least, the list is far from complete, because science certainly does not have all the answers as to what a dog's best interests really are.

Position and Role of the Veterinarian

The question to be asked at this point is what should the veterinarian's role be in drug testing Sporting dogs. We shall come back to the international structures and methods already in existence for pulka and dog sledding, the only discipline in which things seem very clear on an international level today.

In the are of leisure sports, and also in competition, veterinarians should not be seen as the enemy in charge of enforcing legislation. Where doping is concerned, the veterinarian's primary role should be informative and preventive. He should participate by providing scientific and technical information in creating the texts. He should be considered as a tool in the actual taking of a sample.

Simply put, we think that dog handlers have a right to speak their piece regarding drug testing regulations and that for their opinions to be respected within and outside the realm of competition, their opinions should be explained, argued, and perceived as support, not as the canine equivalent of hazing.

Physiopathological Aspects

Pharmacological Data

Kinetics and the pharmacological or toxic effects of drugs in dogs are important to know in order to understand the methods for drug testing and its regulations. It is certainly not our intention here to provide an exhaustive pharmacological study of the problem.

Absorption, distribution, biotransformation, and elimination of each molecule for the target species must be understood because they have a considerable effect on drug testing practices (pharmacokinetics allows us to appreciate the nature and value of samples to be performed). Variations in the evolution of the banned substance, when influenced by different factors in the organism, can also affect the results of the test.

In the same way, the half-life must allow the persistence of a substance to be measured. We also use elimination time (the time in which it is possible to detect products in body fluids). Tobin prefers to speak of Detection Time, the evaluation of which allows us to propose times to use between the end of a treatment and a test.

Though clearly coded and available with regard to doping in horses, this information has not yet been adapted for dogs.

APPLICATIONS TO TESTING METHODS

The samples taken during a drug test must:
– pose no danger to the animal
– be easy to perform
– respect specific pharmacokinetic information

Saliva

Performed on horses in the past, this test has been abandoned in that species because of amounts collected were too small. This type of sample does not seem very realistic in dogs following exertion, which is why we have not considered it.

Blood

In our opinion, blood samples have all of the advantages (heparin tubes). It should nonetheless be noted that it takes a while to convince the competitors to submit to the blood test. Some believe that taking blood from the animal will compromise its performance the following day, which could easily cause an antibrachial hematoma (which is why the sample must be taken aseptically from the jugular, calmly and without the slightest error). In sledding competitions in Europe, blood tests are required and no longer pose a problem at all.

Urine

The urine sample must come from natural urination, without using a probe or administering a diuretic. In calm situations, racing Greyhounds urinate frequently after exertion and taking a sample therefore seems easy enough to accomplish, using a chemically cleaned container. This is not the case for sled dogs, who are more or less dehydrated after long periods of exertion and who therefore experience temporary post-exertion anuria. In this case, taking a sample requires much more patience and know-how. In very long courses, when samples are taken at checkpoints, a plastic bag is placed around the penis or vulva and held in place with clips attached to the dog's fur. Clearly this is not the most graceful of testing methods—by any stretch of the imagination, but at least it's fairly easy to perform on males!

THE RELATIONSHIP BETWEEN PHARMACOKINETICS AND TEST RESULTS

Many authors have shown several pharmacokinetic elements that can influence the reliability of test results obtained.

Means of Administration
For different means of administration of the same drug, the blood concentration evolution curves differ as a function of time:

Galenic Form
Certain pharmaceutical forms may slow down the absorption phase of a drug because of their excipients and may be detected longer in biological fluids.

Individual
Variations in individual response to the administration of a drug must be considered.

Other factors involving the animal, the drug molecule, or the means of administration can influence the metabolic transformation of the product and, as a result, its detection time.

HARMFUL CONSEQUENCES OF DOPING AGENTS

Artificial administration that shunts natural barriers regulating the transfer between the internal and external systems, and the problem of accidental simultaneous administration of foreign bodies, bacteria, toxic elements, etc. rapidly increases the concentration of the product administered inside the system, even if it is a natural product that already exists in the organism, this increase is necessarily associated with a natural reaction of feedback that tends to reduce natural cellular mechanisms for producing the substance or to accelerate the mechanisms for its breakdown or elimination. Moreover, when a neuro-endocrine substance is found in an abnormally high quantity inside the system, it acts on the corresponding target organs to modify or replace the normal command as well as the regulatory cycles. The normal operation of this regulated system is then suddenly altered in the absence of structural and functional adaptation of these organs to the order sent.

Doping agents can therefore have considerable harmful effects, even if it is difficult to talk about actual toxicity.

Using Blood as a Doping Agent
We have not yet discussed this type of doping practiced by some col-

leagues. It consists of blood or globule transfusions or even intramuscular globule injections. A blood sample is taken out of season, then only the red globules are frozen and conserved to later be reinjected into the animal just prior to a difficult competition.

The increased concentration of hemoglobin linked to exposure in high altitudes and the increase in plasma volume linked to training are generally accompanied by an increase in maximum oxygen consumption. This positive correlation between hemoglobin and maximum oxygen consumption, sometimes associated with increased cardiac activity, leads a certain number of authors to imagine that the essential factor of this max VO2 increase was the available hemoglobin supply and therefore to imagine globule transfusions as a way to improve the athlete's endurance. In fact, it now appears that the transfusion is insufficient to compensate or overcompensate the initial sample taken, taking into account the length of physiological restoration which is often too brief. Nonetheless, regardless of the results obtained, and without even considering the ethical aspect, quantitative overcompensation after depletion poses several problems:

- decrease in energy potential for several weeks with the direct consequences of either corresponding decrease in intensity and duration or usual training or maintaining them, which then necessarily leads to a relative increase in the training load in relation to individual physiological potential.

- Increased volume following the transfusion is soon compensated by certain regulation phenomena: decrease in ADH (Anti-diuretic hormone) as liquid spaces return to equilibrium and an increase in urination; an increase in the blood viscosity and peripheral resistance; compensatory decrease in heart rate, even an overall flow, especially in the peripheries.

- Finally, it is not certain whether the undeniable quantitative increase in the overall capacity for oxygen transport is able to improve its local functional availability and its supply by unit of time, given the compensating physiological adaptations.

Anabolics

Anabolics of course have hormonal effects that must be considered: drop in fertility for males and females, development of masculine characteristics, etc. In addition to these "traditional" effects, using repeated high doses of anabolic steroids causes premature hardening of connective cartilage in young animals who are given the drugs in order to artificially increase muscle mass.

These hormones, which intervene in protein synthesis and tissue growth, normally act in synergy and the extra-physiological administration of certain molecules lead to inadequate and unbalanced development of the animal's biomechanics: for example, greater muscle development than corresponding tendon development frequently causes chronic tendinitis and ruptured tendons during activity. Such a disorder, often encountered with the use of anabolic steroids, is also promoted by the related hydro-electrolyte effects (hydrosodic retention, high blood pressure, edematous process…all unfavorable factors for normal metabolism and muscular-tendinous oxygenation). These molecules also have a dangerous effect on plasmatic lipoproteins.

Stimulants and Tranquilizers

This group contains all substances with a neuro-endocrine effect intended to reinforce motor commands, awareness, aggression, motivation or to reduce the effects of stress or even pain.

In the first case, the consequences of this type of drug use alter the animal's perception of balance, distances, and precision movements. In addition to decreasing performance (sometimes quite noticeably), this can also lead to more traumatic accidents from unusual movements (poor perception and adaptation to an irregularity in the track).

In the second case, the decrease of subjective sensations linked to the activity and to the decrease of subconscious information from the different areas of regulation can cause the development of forces and strength that exceed the limits of physiological adaptability with a major locomotive or cardio-vascular structural breakdown (the case with adrenergic drug use: catecholamines, amphetamines, caffeine, etc.).

Certain tranquilizers (diazepam, acepromazine) increase CPK (Creatine Phosphokinase) levels in the blood, suggesting that muscle cells have been affected. Respiratory depression is also sometimes observed.

Bioenergetic Doping

The goal of bioenergetic doping is to quantitatively increase overall energy requirements and qualitatively increase their availability by increasing the carrying capacity for the whole energy chain. Many substances have been used this way to encourage captation of substrata or their use (catecholamines). The risks run are the same as those previously described.

Moreover, the administration of substances via an extra-physiological transcutaneous path can suddenly alter physiological conditions in the way the organism functions. The result may be a deficient functioning of the energy exchange mechanisms with the external system modifying the physiological conditions of the internal system for a while (risks: tissue damage and muscular-tendinous injury during exertion).

Anti-Inflammatories

Using non-steroid anti-inflammatories as doping agents is dangerous because they are administered essentially for their antalgic effect. To go beyond pain—which exists for a reason: to warn us of an injury—amounts to forcing the dog to dangerously and uncontrollably exert itself.

Moreover, we have already encountered a case of ulcers from the repeated distribution of phenylbutazone, a problem which is documented in horses.

Beta-Blocking Substances

The very principle of beta-blocking methods implies that they are "blocking substances": reduced effects of stress (artificial changes to the neuro-endocrine command system), immediate improvement of performance. In fact, like many other substances that alter the characteristics of the biological regulatory system, their metabolic and cardio-vascular effects are dangerous for maintaining the level of performance in a healthy subject. At the cellular level of a muscle, the beta 2 impediment that hinders glycogenolysis and beta 1 impediment, that hinders lipolysis, thereby reduce the availability of intracellular energy substrata. The beta 2 blockage slows the elimination of lactates, for which we know the osmotic power of water retention. This local metabolic gene can be reinforced by an external energy supply that is also reduced: decrease in the carrying capacities of the cardio-vascular system by the sudden rise in flow and the perfusion pressure through beta 1 (cardiac) blockage with a decrease in glucose in the blood supply from the liver (beta 1) and fatty acids from the adipose tissue (beta 2).

Clearly, drugs can cause more effects than just those intended by the people who use them. A knowledge of harmful side effects often convinces dog owners to avoid this type of practice.

Note: Involuntary Doping

A Sporting dog may undergo drug testing and come up positive without the owner's being responsible. The National Greyhound Association, which brings together 140,000 competing Greyhounds finds itself right in the middle of this problem. In the United States, bets placed during Greyhound races reached $3,203,321,724 in 1988! Many dogs showed levels of procaine during drug testing, though the honesty of their owners and trainers was hard to question The investigation led by the National Greyhound Association found the culprit to be the dogs' food supply.

Indeed, the dogs need a high-protein diet and, as a result, each received 600-750 grams of raw red meat per day (the total consumption in the US is 50-70 tons per day). The primary source of this meat, for cost reasons, is leftovers from human consumption (known for the "4Ds": animals that are diseased, dying, disabled, or dead). It turned out that, depending on the state, 50 to 90% of these meats were contaminated by the procaine from the shots given earlier to the animals in penicillin-procaine injections for therapeutic reasons…generally not deemed successful. The residual procaine was then absorbed by the Greyhound, then eliminated in a concentrated form in the urine. Thanks to this discovery, a simple color-reaction test for detecting residual procaine in meat is not available to trainers and owners.

Such problems must also be taken into account since it is not impossible to imagine the appearance of seemingly harmless nutritional supplements on the market…but very effective in performance obtained! The good faith of users should also be taken into consideration.

From the sample to the analysis: working towards a standardized procedure

Everybody should be concerned by the war against drugs, even in dogs: practicing veterinarians, owners, trainers, racing veterinarians. To really be effective, this action must take place on two levels:
  – serious education (prevention)
  – effective control (dissuasion)

But, as France's Jean Pierre Soisson said several years ago when he was Minister of Youth and Sports, "Prevention before repression."

We should mention that currently, there is only one specific regulation regarding Sporting dogs on the international level: the International Federation of Sled Dog Sport, applied in Europe and in France during official pulka and dog sled competitions. As co-creators and organizers since 1985, we have based our approach on personal experience without attempting to avoid criticism in the least!

THE OPTIMAL CONTROL "THEORY"

For an athlete (and Sporting dog owners are considered as athletes) to accept regulations and control without discussion, the control must respond to the following rules:

Be serious
In the field, controls must be done systematically, seriously, and without giving in to even the slightest criticism. Regulatory documentation should always be read with the greatest attention by the competitors or national team managers… and the veterinarian in charge of the testing must follow the documentation exactly.

Be infallible
Accredited anti-drug test labs must be completely effective. These labs must be tested and must all reach the same levels of performance in the testing. It is therefore always best to regularly check the effectiveness of a given accredited center of expertise by testing its abilities with "anonymous" samples, which we do for each series of tests using different molecules.

Be fast

In the Olympic Games in Seoul, Korea, all of the tests were performed within 60 minutes to 10 hours. We should mention that for dogs, a delay of a few days is still necessary (generally 3 or 4). Official ranking and prizes in the area of dog sledding are only awarded after the results from the lab have been obtained.

Be Effective:

The lab must be able to go back in time to unmask anabolic treatment. Until 1976, the search for anabolics was ineffective if the drugs had been stopped 3 weeks prior to competition. Certain equipment now allows us to detect the use of anabolic steroids 6 to 8 months after the last administration.

Be Complete:

Often even today (for reasons of cost), expertise on the samples taken only involves testing for very specific products based on the sporting discipline in question. For dogs, it therefore seems indispensable to use these accredited laboratories working in the field of horses to develop the most complete screening possible.

Support a Crackdown on the Problem

With all of the reservations already expressed toward regulation that is too drastic and definitive, we think that once it has been implemented, any disregard for such regulation should be grounds for punishment especially since the animal has been endangered. Since we have been in charge of drug testing, in only one instance has an animal tested positive for drugs (phenylbutazone), which resulted in the removal of the animal's titles (it had just won the European Championship), and its removal by the governing national authority from all "human" sporting disciplines for 5 years! And we haven't had any cases since…

Respecting the chain of evidence: samples are coded and stored under lock and key.

ESTABLISHING A TESTING PROGRAM

Well-designed anti-drug testing should incorporate the following three stages:
– a "chain of evidence" that includes collecting and identifying samples
– a laboratory in which to analyze the samples and search for approximately 200 drugs
– examination of the results obtained by an official commission that must verify any positive results, provide the dog's owner with means of recourse, and determine the punishment to apply.

The Chain of Evidence

Officials at canine sporting events should designate a

person to oversee the taking of samples and provide a team to help in testing procedures. Ideally, this team would be independent of the veterinarians working at the event.

The Head Judge or Race Marshal is responsible for providing the person in charge of the tests (in a random drawing of the participants or based on their rank) with the list of dogs that must be tested (by blood or urine). Then, generally in the hour following the end of a competition, he will:
– verify the identity of the dog presented for testing (which would have also been done by the judges prior to the competition)

Necessary documents

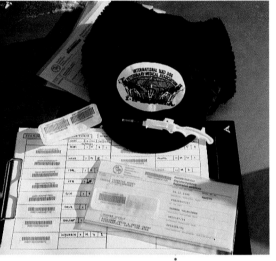

– divide the sample into two separate samples that are sealed and identified by code only, in the presence of two witnesses(the owner or musher and a handler or judge).

At this stage, it is important to note that the dog owner or his representative can choose from among a group of sampling tools (urine containers, needles, and syringes) so that no claims may be made that potentially positive results were due to the tools used.

In general, laboratories specialized in this type of testing provide the organization with the necessary tools:
– plastic containers or pre-wrapped syringes
– self-adhesive seals that ensure the samples are not tampered with on their way to the laboratory
– bar codes labels to stick on the samples, insuring totally anonymous identification
– NCR forms for the "chain of confidence" (only the person in charge of the event keeps the bar code / dog corresponding document)
– A cooler with a lock in which to safely transport the samples to the lab

It is clearly essential to ensure the individual identification of each dog prior to participation in the event and it should be noted that the use of identification transponders (electronic chips implanted under the dog's skin) have made the identification process much more reliable in drug testing.

The Testing Laboratory

It is not our goal to elaborate on all of the different techniques used by the testing laboratory. Let it suffice to say that they are complicated (thin layer chromatography, E.L.I.S.A. immunology tests, gaseous chromatography, spectrometry of mass, etc.), and also expensive: Depending on the country, the analysis of a single sample can vary from $3,000 to $6,000.

Final Results

Given the results, and based on the regulations of the sport in question, a positive finding can mean:

– that the participant can request a second opinion on the sample (which has been sealed and conserved by the testing laboratory) in an accredited laboratory of his choice and at his expense;

– that upon close examination of the file by the competency commission (a dog that tests positive for theobromine may well have received a chocolate treat, which can make it appear it has been administered drugs!)

– a punishment all the more serious because the obvious will to administer drugs to the dog is established and recognized.

Examples of Anti-Drug Regulations

The existing regulations refer to lists of banned products, such as the list used by the International Federation for Sled Dog Sport (IFSS), which prohibits:

– analgesic substances
– steroid or non-steroid anti-inflammatory substances
– anti-prostaglandins
– central nervous system stimulants
– cough medicine
– sedatives and anesthetics
– diuretics
– anabolic steroids
– muscle relaxants
– antihistamine substances

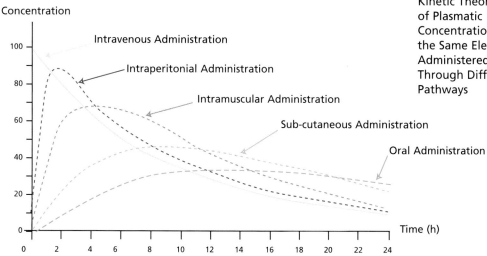

Kinetic Theory of Plasmatic Concentrations of the Same Element Administered Through Different Pathways

– anticholinergic substances
– blood injections

Regardless of the regulations, it is important that all owners realize the danger of using these substances in Sporting dogs. Doping has been part of canine sports for a relatively short period of time. A lot of people talk about it, but few really know the signs or consequences of doping—or realize what it represents in the field. We must now establish an open and dynamic dialogue with dog owners that can evolve as doping evolves. The way in which drugs are used in competition today will likely change over time.

Finally, we must not overlook the material aspect of the issue: The budget needed for testing in the 1990 IFSS World Championships and in the 1990 Alpirod (to only mention dog sledding) was approximately $17,000, which is a lot for any organization. This is also the price of the respect for the animal and sporting ethics.

Clearance Time in Dogs for the Primary Categories of Medicine

Molecules	Clearance Time (Hours)	Molecules	Clearance Time (Hours)
Non-steroid Anti-inflammatories		**Tranquilizers/Anesthetics/Muscle Relaxants**	
Acetaminophen	48	Diazepram	48
Aspirin	72	Methocarbamol	72
Ibuprofen	48		
Ketoprofen	>96	**Opiates**	
		Butorphanol	72
Cortico-steroids			
Dexamethasone	48	**Anti-diarrhea Medications**	
Fludrocortisone	72	Kaopectate	24
Methylprednisolone	>96	Loperamide	96
Prednisolone	48	Diphenoxalate	72
Prednisone	48		
Hydrocortisone	72	**Vermifuges**	
		Fenbendazole	72
Bronchio-dilators/Anti-cough /Anti-histamine		Ivermectine	72
Aminophylline	96	Mebendazole	72
Clenbuterol	48	Metronidazole	96
Ephedrin	72		
Pseudo-ephedrin	72	**Antibiotics**	
Pyrilamin	72	Amoxycillin	72
Theophylline	72	Ampicillin	72
Local Anesthetics		**Sulfamides**	
Bupivicaine	72	Sulfachlorpyridazine	72
Lidocaine	48	Sulfadimethoxine	120
Mepivacaine	72	Sulfamethzaine	72
Procaine	48	Sulfamethoxazole	120
		Trimethroprim	72

Proposed framework of reference for the development and approval of a potential ergogenic aide for exertion. Nutritional, physiological, and mechanical support is encouraged, but all forms of pharmacological support is prohibited, clearly to the detriment of responsible use of medicinal products.

Ergogenic Aide	Effective
Increases quantity, control, and effectiveness of the work produced	Continually improves performance

Harmless	Approval
Harmless for animal, entourage, and environment	Government Users General Public

Different Types of Doping Products

Substances That Allow Initial Performance Level to be Restored
– Non-steroid anti-inflammatories
– Corticoids
– Local anesthetics
– Fluids and electrolytes

Substances Used to Win
– Short-term effect: fast-action stimulants, amphetamines, cocaine, narcotics
– Chronic effect: anabolic steroids, low doses of tranquilizers or anti-depressants

Substances Accidentally Present in Food
– Procaine in meat (residue from penicillin-procaine injections)
– Caffeine
– Theobromine in chocolate
– Consumption of plants

Masking Substances
– Administration of dipyrone or thiamin to interfere with analytical detection methods

Diluting Substances
– Diuretics

Substances Used to Lose
– Nervous system depressants

INTERNATIONAL HEALTH LEGISLATION

At a time when international competitions are becoming more and more prevalent in the world of canine sporting events, causing dogs to be more frequently transported from one country to another, it seems to be a good idea to provide a brief overview of current international health legislation. Clearly, such information is constantly changing alongside changes in national regulations, and what is applicable when this book is printed will likely have been changed a few months or years later. For this reason, readers should be aware that they can always refer to the appropriate department of the international organization in charge of managing animal-related health problems:

> *Office International des Epizooties (O.I.E.)*
> *Département de l'Information et du Commerce*
> *International*
> *(Department of Information and International Trade)*
> *12 rue Prony*
> *75017 Paris, France*
> *Phone: 33.1.44.15.18.88*
> *Fax: 33.1.42.67.09.87*
> *Website: www.oie.int/home.htm*

National health regulations regarding dogs usually deal primarily with rabies, which is fatal for humans and may be carried by dogs. For this reason, we refer readers wishing to find information specific to certain countries to the various charts in the appendix.

While certain countries continue to impose long quarantine periods for importing dogs (in some cases these rules are politically based and have nothing to do with actual biological risks), two European countries have recently decided to do away with them: Norway and Sweden. For these two countries, the required procedure for temporarily importing a dog (for competition) or definitively importing a dog (for sale or transfer) is as follows:

1) an import permit is required and may be obtained from, completed, and returned to the following addresses:

Statens Karantenestasjon Foor Dyr
Verkseier Furulunds Vei 44
0688 Olso, Norway
Phone: 47.22.30.25.90
Fax: 47.22.30.17.43

Statens Jurdbruksverk
Smittskyddsenheten
55182 Jönköping, Sweden
Phone: 46.36.15.50.00
Fax: 46.36.15.50.05

All requests for permits must be accompanied by the appropriate payment (500 NOK or 400 SEK per dog)

2) The dog must be clearly identified with an indelible mark. The identification number must be on the veterinary certificates. The required identification system is currently electronic marking (an electronic chip is implanted under the dog's skin) and care must be taken to make sure the system used meets current ISO standards

3) The dog must be accompanied by a certificate proving that it has been appropriately vaccinated against rabies and a document stating that its rabies immunity has been tested in an authorized laboratory. This document shall specify the date and place the test was taken, as well as the dog's level of circulating rabies antibodies (at least 0.5 International Units per milliliter).

- for an initial rabies vaccination of a 3-month old puppy, the rabies immunity evaluation test must be done between the ages of 4 and 11 months.

- For an adult animal having booster shots, the rabies immunity evaluation must be performed between 1 and 11 months after the previous vaccination.

Official Laboratories performing this test are as follows:

C.N.E.V.A.
Domaine Pixecourt
BP 9
54220 Malzeville, France

Veterinaerinstituttet
Avdelning for Virologi
Postboks 8156 Dep.
0033 Oslo, Norway

Statens Veterinarmedicinska Anstalt
Virologista Advelningen
Box 585
74123 Uppsama, Sweden

Statens Veterinarmedicinska Anstalt
BP 368
00101 Helsinki, Finland

4) The dog must be accompanied by a certificate of vaccination against leptospirosis, specifying the type of vaccine used and the date of vaccination, which must have taken place at least 1 month earlier and less than 12 months prior to the date of entering the country's borders.

5) The dog must be accompanied by a certificate of vaccination against distemper, specifying the type of vaccine and the date of vaccination, which must have taken place at least 1 month earlier and less than 24 months prior to the date of entering the country's borders.

6) The dog must be accompanied by a certificate stating it has been wormed and specifying the type of vermifuge used and the date of treatment.

7) The dog must be accompanied by a certificate of good health, drawn up by an official veterinarian from the country of origin during the 10 days prior to entering the new country's borders, specifying that the animal is clinically healthy and does not appear to be carrying any contagious diseases. This certificate must also specify that the dog was treated with a specific vermifuge for flatworms (tape worms).

For other countries where the legislation is more simple, we refer the reader to the charts below.

Countries or territories in which it is prohibited to import dogs:

Cypress
Iceland
Jamaica
New Caledonia
New Zealand
Papua
French Polynesia
Yemen

Countries with Significant Quarantine Times

Country	Length of Quarantine
Korea	10 days
China	-
Mauritius	-
Ireland	6 months
Japan	14 days
Malaysia	30 days
Malta	6 months
Oman	6 months
Panama	40 days
The Seychelles	6 months
Singapore	30 days
Taiwan	49-120 days
Tanzania	-
United Kingdom	6 months (to be abolished in 2000)

Health Formalities Required to Import Dogs

Country	Anti-Rabies Certificate	Good Health Certificate	Other
South Africa	2 months < . < 3 years	Yes	Transit certificate
Argentina	Controlled by the consulate	Controlled by the consulate	-
Australia	Dogs from countries affected by rabies are prohibited from entering country		-
Brazil	Yes	Yes, legalized by originating authorities	-
Bulgaria	1 month < . < 1 year	< 5 days	-
Canada	Yes	Yes	Health exam by customs officials
USA	30 days < . < 1 year	Yes	Health exam by customs officials
Hungary	Yes	Yes	Vaccine: Distemper
India	Yes	< 7 days	-
Israel	Yes	Yes	-
Japan	Yes	Yes	Quarantine: 14 days
Mexico	Controlled by the consulate	Controlled by the consulate	-
Poland	Yes	Yes	-
Romania	Yes	Yes	Vaccine: Rabies, 14 days prior to entry
Czech Republic	Yes	< 48 hours	-
Russia	Yes	Yes	Documents translated into Russian and controlled by the consulate
Venezuela	Yes	Controlled by the consulate	Vaccine: distemper
Belgium	Yes	Yes	-
Netherlands	Yes	Yes	-
Luxembourg	Yes	Yes	-
France	< 1 year	Yes	-
Finland	Yes	Yes	Vaccines: distemper, hepatitis, parvovirus high-recommended
ly			
Switzerland	Yes	Yes	Vaccines: leptospirosis, hepatitis, parvovirus, highly recommended
Austria	Yes	Yes	
Denmark	Yes	Yes	
Greece	Yes	Yes	Vaccines: distemper, parvovirus
Germany	Yes	< 20 days	Certificate of vermifugation
Portugal	Yes	Yes	-
Italy	Yes	<10 days	-
Spain	Yes	Yes	-

VETERINARIANS AND CANINE SPORTS COMPETITION

Sporting dog trainers are competitors, often athletes themselves, and always sports enthusiasts. They make up 20 to 30 percent of the membership of simple dog obedience clubs and virtually 100 percent of the membership of organizations devoted to a particular sport. Sporting dogs are athletes who require a specific way of life and must be monitored biologically and medically like elite human athletes.

Complete vet team on a big sled dog race

For utility dogs, the most important notions are operational performance and optimal physical performance on an ongoing basis. Here again, veterinarians who have worked to acquire and develop specific skills and knowledge are an important part of the final result.

With the growth of various sporting dog disciplines and the many uses of dogs as professional assistants to humans, veterinarians must respond increasingly to the very specialized and specific needs of trainers. Still too often informal, these needs involve a number of areas:

– general biological training of the owner/competitor;

– advice on breeding, especially in terms of improving performance;

– prevention of disorders related to physical effort, as well as breeding and group living;

– a good knowledge of organizations and regulations and a contribution to their development;

– an effective presence on the site of competition;
– implementation, understanding, and application of anti-doping regulations.

Still, the true function of veterinarians in a particular canine sport is often poorly defined and depends more on the degree of interest in that sporting discipline than on a true definition of responsibilities. Based on enthusiasm as well as logic (both technical and financial), this function must be better defined in each discipline so that the roles of veterinarians can be better delineated and made official.

The purpose of this chapter is simply to provide a basis for reflection. The potential roles of veterinarians in the world of canine sports are discussed below in no particular order.

Veterinarians giving advice on optimizing canine performance

Obviously, the systematic effort to improve performance by breeders, handlers, competitors, and trainers has increased the incidence of disorders specific to the group involved, since intense performance most often means increased fragility.

Each sporting and working dog has a genetically determined psychological performance limit. The goal of a good training plan, as discussed in the specific chapters, is therefore to attain this limit and maintain the animal there. The veterinarian's advice must fit into this notion of an "overall training plan" and must include:

– support for optimal genetic selection;
– regular monitoring of the dog's general condition (kennel hygiene and design, preventive treatment programs that interfere the least possible with training and competition, regular biochemical and hematological tests);
– participation in developing training plans (still too often, the physical training of sporting dogs is nothing but the product of vague empiricism aimed only at accruing miles on the track);
– nutritional advice, both in finding the food most adapted to the type of effort and size of the dog and in using nutritional supplements, many of which are nothing but a waste of money,
– early detection of cumulative stress that is too great for the dog and can lead to psychological demotivation and later true illness.

Veterinarians training trainers

Given the principle that "we use well only what we understand well," we believe that biological and veterinary information must be as extensive as possible. In the manner of pulka and dog sled racing and annual American and Australian conferences on the Greyhound, each discipline could have veterinary commissions to provide basic training to trainers who are members. This type of activity would foster a true exchange between veterinarians and trainers that would prove very beneficial to the veterinarians themselves.

Veterinarians on site during competition

The veterinarian must work round the clock under any conditions

We believe that one or more veterinarians should be present on site for the duration of each canine sports competition. No country is anywhere near such a state of affairs.

In this regard, sled dog racing is certainly a good example. In this sport, teams of specialized veterinarians are assembled for each event.

Completely independent, they are present on site twenty-four hours a day and are an integral part of the overall setting of this sport. Their presence is even more important, since the possibility of medical or surgical emergencies is compounded by regulations (drug tests, if any) and communication (interface with certain animal protection groups and the media). On-site veterinarians must be fully knowledgeable about the sporting discipline involved. This generally makes them even more enthusiastic about the competition, which leads them to increase their skills and knowledge.

The still limited function of on-site veterinarians in canine sports competition is now and must concretely become more important and better acknowledged by organizers. This will benefit all those involved, starting with the dogs, but will be possible only if veterinarians do their best to respond to trainers' needs and respect their skills and knowledge.

SPORTING DOGS ON THE INTERNET

Thanks to the Internet revolution of the late twentieth centu-
ry, trainers of sporting and utility dogs now have access to spe-
cialized, constantly changing data banks. We therefore
thought it would be helpful to provide readers of this work a
list—though obviously not exhaustive—of useful sites that
anyone can " surf " for hours on end to glean useful informa-
tion from all over the world.

International canine sporting organizations

All Sports and Purposes
> Workingdogs.com
> Crealink.net/sports-canins/
> dspace.dial.pipex.com/willchapman/dogslinks.htm
> dspace.dial.pipex.com/willchapman/c4bsport.htm
> webusers.anet-stl.com/~dvgamer/links.html
> www.dogpatch.org

International Kennel Club Federation
> www.fci.be/

International Rescue Dog Organization
> webnz.com/lynx_downunder/iro/irointro.html

Search and Rescue Association
> www.sara.org

International Ring Sport
> members.aol.com/malndobe/frring.htm

International Agility Link
> www.dogpatch.org/agility/IAL/ial.html

International Greyhound Research Database
> www.agcouncil.com

International Assistance Dog Organizations
> - International Association of Assistance Dog Partners
> www. ismi.net/iaadp/index.html
> - PAWS
> www.ismi.net/paws

International Federation of Sled Dog Sport
> www.sleddog.worldsport.com

Providing Responsible Information on a Dog's Environment (PRIDE)
www.ptialaska.net/~pride1/
International Sled Dog Racing Association (ISDRA)
www.isdra.org
European Sled Dog Racing Association (ESDRA)
www.wvnet.at/KUNDEN/ESDRA
Protection Dogs
- World Protection Dog Association
www.wpda.com
List of International Clubs
workingdogs.com/doc0007.htm#club
International Glossary
www.ecn.purdue.edu/~laird/dogs/glossary

Canine sports

Detection and Utility Dogs
dspace.dial.pipex.com/willchapman/c4bworki.htm
dspace.dial.pipex.com/willchapman/c4brescu.htm
Police Dogs
www.policek9.com
Herding Dogs
crealinks.net/bearded
Sled Dogs
www.sleddog.org
www.worldsport.com/sports/sleddog/home.html
Noatak.com
- Alaskan Sled Dog and Racing Association
www.corecom.net/~whiteepp/asdra.htm
- British Musher's Association
www.webheads.co.uk/sleddog/index.htm
- German Sled Dog Sport
www.dssv.org
- Sled Dog Races
www.iditarod.org
www.yukonquest.org
www.scandream.org
www.wyomingstagestop.org
www.finnmarkslopet.no
www.beargrease.com
www.race2sky.com
Flyball
muskie.fishnet.com/~flyball/

Agility
>www.dogpatch.org/agility/l
>www.agilty.net
>www.agility.be/
>www.usdaa.com (United States Dog Agility Association)
>dspace.dial.pipex.com/willchapman/c4bagili.htm

Frisbee Disc Dogs
>www.discdog.com/

Schutzhund
>webusers.anet-stl.com/~dvgamer/links.html

Ring, "Mondioring"
>crealinks.net/ring
>www.datacomm.ch/rene_sagarra/

Greyhounds
>nga.jc.net

Rescue Dogs
>www.workingdogs.com/doc0008.htm
>world.conk.com/world/sar_ring/
>www.wtp.net/ASDK9SAR/page7.html

Veterinary medicine

>www.vetmed.ufl.edu/
>www.vet-alfort.fr/
>vet.cabweb.org

Canine Sports Medicine
>www.concentric.net/~Dovervet/csmu/

Magazines

>www.cyberpet.com/cyberdog/products/pubmag/dgsptmag.htm
>(Dog Sports Magazine)
>www.polarnet.com/users/mushing/default.htm (Mushing)

The exciting world of racing Greyhoun

>ISDVMA - International Sled Dog Veterinary Medical
>Association
>PO Box 543, Sylvania, OH 43560 USA. tel. 419-531-
>5589, fax 419-531-5404

Transportation (regulations)

>www.lattmag.com/iataanim.htm

Royal Canin

>royal-canin.com

ROYAL CANIN

OVERVIEW OF THE BREEDING AND SPORTS MEDICINE UNIT (UMES)

WHAT IS THE UMES?

The Breeding and Sports Medicine Unit was established in 1996 at the initiative of Dr. Dominique Grandjean as part of the National Veterinary School in Alfort.

Its mission is to act as a scientific and technical link between dog professionals and veterinarians, thereby serving as a "technical institute" devoted to the dog.

Thus, besides being a development structure for the technical/financial approach to dog breeding, basic research, specialized clinics, field work, and the study and implementation of assisted canine reproduction, the UMES is also a privileged center for specific education available not only to veterinary students and practitioners, but also to breeders, breed organizations, and other dog professionals (with topic nights, seminars, etc.).

COMPONENTS OF THE UMES

Medicine and finance of dog breeding

This entity was created with the objective of improving the technical/financial management and sanitary conditions of dog breeding.

The UMES regularly helps resolve breeding and group pathology problems, thanks to consultations conducted either long-distance or on site through direct cooperation with the UMES.

Research Center for Assisted Canine Reproduction (CERCA)

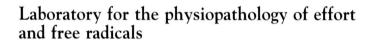

CERCA's aim is to improve canine reproduction by examining males, monitoring bitches from the first heat to the end of gestation (hormone doses, ultrasound scanning, etc.), and using artificial insemination. CERCA is equipped to harvest, preserve, and use sperm from purebred dogs. Research is conducted on semen preservation, insemination techniques, egg maturation, and fertilization. A specialized clinic is open to all purebred dogs.

Laboratory for the physiopathology of effort and free radicals

The central theme of this laboratory is "oxidative cell stress," one of the manifestations of which is the destruction of cell membranes by "free radicals."

Research is focused on protecting cell membranes by supplementing the dog's ration. In this vein, scientific field trips are regularly conducted in hostile environmental conditions (sled dog races, dogs working at high-altitudes).

Sports medicine

A recent development, canine sports and utility medicine is fashioned after human and equine sports medicine. Within this framework, three mornings of consultations are dedicated to diseases specific to canine athletes and to preparing dogs for effort (training and feeding plans, exertion tests on a treadmill, etc.).

Physiotherapy and physical rehabilitation

Since the practice of canine sports is sometimes synonymous with traumatic disease, the UMES also has a physical rehabilitation clinic. This clinic uses techniques derived from human physical therapy, including electrotherapy, ultrasound, pulsed short-wave therapy, and hydrotherapy. The aim of these various methods is rapid rehabilitation after an injury, bone surgery, or extensive neurological surgery.

UMES contact information

Breeding and Sports Medicine Unit
Alfort National Veterinary School
7, avenue du Général de Gaulle
94704 MAISONS-ALFORT Cedex
Telephone: (33) 01 43 96 71 76
Fax: (33) 01 43 96 70 80
e-mail: bacque@vet-alfort.fr
website: www.vet-alfort.fr/

UMES contact information

Name	Telephone	e-mail
Dominique GRANDJEAN	(33) 01 43 96 71 03	grandjean@vet-alfort.fr
Nathalie MOQUET	(33) 01 43 96 70 31	moquet@vet-alfort.fr
Sandrine PAWLOWIEZ	(33) 01 43 96 70 56	pawlo@vet-alfort.fr
Anne-Karen TOURTEBATTE	(33) 01 43 96 70 56	umes@vet-alfort.fr
Boris JEAN	(33) 01 43 96 70 31	bjean@vet-alfort.fr
Hélène BACQUE	(33) 01 43 96 71 76	bacque@vet-alfort.fr

PHOTO CREDITS (pages)